RICHARD E. HILDENBRAND
8934 PINEY BRANCH RD
SILVER SPRING, MD. 20903

Statistical Power Analysis
for the Behavioral Sciences

Statistical Power Analysis
for the Behavioral Sciences

JACOB COHEN

DEPARTMENT OF PSYCHOLOGY
NEW YORK UNIVERSITY
NEW YORK, NEW YORK

1969

ACADEMIC PRESS   New York San Francisco London
A Subsidiary of Harcourt Brace Jovanovich, Publishers

ACADEMIC PRESS, INC.
111 Fifth Avenue, New York, New York 10003

United Kingdom Edition published by
ACADEMIC PRESS, INC. (LONDON) LTD.
24/28 Oval Road, London NW1

LIBRARY OF CONGRESS CATALOG CARD NUMBER: 79-84152

PRINTED IN THE UNITED STATES OF AMERICA

to Marcia and Aviva

Preface

During my first dozen years of teaching and consulting on applied statistics with behavioral scientists, I became increasingly impressed with the importance of statistical power analysis, an importance which was increased an order of magnitude by its neglect in our textbooks and curricula. The case for its importance is easily made: What behavioral scientist would view with equanimity the question of the probability that his investigation would lead to statistically significant results, i.e., its power? And it was clear to me that most behavioral scientists not only could not answer this and related questions, but were even unaware that such questions were answerable. Casual observation suggested this deficit in training, and a review of a volume of the *Journal of Abnormal and Social Psychology* (JASP) (Cohen, 1962), supported by a small grant from the National Institute of Mental Health (M-5174A), demonstrated the neglect of power issues and suggested its seriousness.

The reason for this neglect in the applied statistics textbooks became quickly apparent when I began the JASP review. The necessary materials for power analysis were quite inaccessible, in two senses: they were scattered over the periodical and hardcover literature, and, more important, their use assumed a degree of mathematical sophistication well beyond that of most behavioral scientists.

For the purpose of the review, I prepared some sketchy power look-up tables, which proved to be very easily used by the students in my courses at New York University and by my research consultees. This generated the idea for this book. A five-year NIMH grant provided the support for the program of research, system building, computation, and writing of which the present volume is the chief product.

The primary audience for which this book is intended is the behavioral or biosocial scientist who uses statistical inference. The terms "behavioral" and "biosocial" science have no sharply defined reference, but are here intended in the widest sense and to include the academic sciences of psychology, sociology, branches of biology, political science and anthropology, economics, and also various "applied" research fields: clinical psychology and psychiatry, industrial psychology, education, social and welfare work, and market, political polling, and advertising research. The illustrative problems, which make up a large portion of this book, have been drawn from behavioral or biosocial science, so defined.

Since statistical inference is a logical-mathematical discipline whose applications are not restricted to behavioral science, this book will also be useful in other fields of application, e.g., agronomy and industrial engineering.

The amount of statistical background assumed in the reader is quite modest: one or two semesters of applied statistics. Indeed, all that I really assume is that the reader knows how to proceed to perform a test of statistical significance. Thus, the level of treatment is quite elementary, a fact which has occasioned some criticism from my colleagues. I have learned repeatedly, however, that the *typical* behavioral scientist approaches applied statistics with considerable uncertainty (if not actual nervousness), and requires a verbal-intuitive exposition, rich in redundancy and with many concrete illustrations. This I have sought to supply. Another feature of the present treatment which should prove welcome to the reader is the minimization of required computation. The extensiveness of the tables is a direct consequence of the fact that most uses will require no computation at all, the necessary answers being obtained directly by looking up the appropriate table.

The sophisticated applied statistician will find the exposition unnecessarily prolix and the examples repetitious. He will, however, find the tables useful. He may also find interesting the systematic treatment of population effect size, and particularly the proposed conventions or operational definitions of "small," "medium," and "large" effect sizes defined across all the statistical tests. Whatever originality this work contains falls primarily in this area.

This book is designed primarily as a handbook. When so used, the reader is advised to read Chapter 1 and then the chapter which treats the specific statistical test in which he is interested. I also suggest that he read all the relevant illustrative examples, since they are frequently used to carry along the general exposition.

The book may also be used as a supplementary textbook in intermediate level courses in applied statistics in behavioral/biosocial science. I have been using it in this way. With relatively little guidance, students at this level quickly learn both the concepts and the use of the tables. I assign the first chapter early in the semester and the others in tandem with their regular textbook's treatment of the various statistical tests. Thus, each statistical test or research design is presented in close conjunction with power-analytic considerations. This has proved most salutary, particularly in the attention which must then be given to anticipated population effect sizes.

Pride of place, in acknowledgment, must go to my students and consultees, from whom I have learned much. I am most grateful to the memory of the late Gordon Ierardi, without whose encouragement this work would not have been undertaken. Patricia Waly and Jack Huber read and constructively criticized portions of the manuscript. I owe an unpayable debt of gratitude to Joseph L. Fleiss for a thorough technical critique. Since I did not follow all his advice, the remaining errors can safely be assumed to be mine. I cannot sufficiently thank Catherine Henderson, who typed much of the text and all the tables, and Martha Plimpton, who typed the rest.

As already noted, the program which culminated in this book was supported by the National Institute of Mental Health of the Public Health Service under grant number MH-06137, which is duly acknowledged. I am also most indebted to Abacus Associates, a subsidiary of American Bioculture, Inc., for a most generous programming and computing grant which I could draw upon freely.

New York
June, 1969   JACOB COHEN

Contents

1

The Concepts of Power Analysis

The power of a statistical test is the probability that it will yield statistically significant results. Since statistical significance is so earnestly sought and devoutly wished for by behavioral scientists, one would think that the *a priori* probability of its accomplishment would be routinely determined and well understood. Quite surprisingly, this is not the case. Instead, if we take as evidence the research literature, we find that statistical power is only infrequently understood and almost never determined. The immediate reason for this is not hard to discern—the applied statistics textbooks aimed at behavioral scientists typically do little more than mention it.

The purpose of this book is to provide a self-contained treatment of statistical power analysis from an "applied" viewpoint. The purpose of this chapter is to present the basic conceptual framework of statistical hypothesis testing, giving emphasis to power, followed by the framework within which this book is organized.

1.1 GENERAL INTRODUCTION

When the behavioral scientist has occasion to don the mantle of the applied statistician, the probability is high that it will be for the purpose of testing one or more null hypotheses, i.e., "the hypothesis that the phenomenon to be demonstrated is in fact absent [Fisher, 1949, p. 13]." Not that he hopes to "prove" this hypothesis. On the contrary, he typically hopes to "reject" this hypothesis and thus "prove" that the phenomenon in question is in fact present.

Let us acknowledge at the outset the necessarily probabilistic character of statistical inference, and dispense with the mocking quotation marks

1

about words like *reject* and *prove*. This may be done by requiring that an investigator set certain appropriate probability standards for research results which provide a basis for rejection of the null hypothesis and hence for the proof of the existence of the phenomenon under test. Results from a random sample drawn from a population will only approximate the characteristics of the population. Therefore, even if the null hypothesis is, in fact, true, a given sample result is not expected to mirror this fact exactly. Before sample data are gathered, therefore, the investigator working in the Fisherian framework selects some prudently small value **a** (say .01 or .05), so that he *may* eventually be able to say about his sample data, "*If the null hypothesis is true*, the probability of the obtained sample result is no more than **a**," i.e. a statistically significant result. *If* he can make this statement, since **a** is small, he is said to have rejected the null hypothesis "with an **a** significance criterion" or "at the **a** significance level." If, on the other hand, he finds the probability to be greater than **a**, he cannot make the above statement and he has failed to reject the null hypothesis, or, equivalently finds it "tenable," or "accepts" it, all at the **a** significance level.

We have thus isolated one element of this form of statistical inference, the standard of proof that the phenomenon exists, or, equivalently, the standard of disproof of the null hypothesis that states that the phenomenon does not exist.

Another component of the significance criterion concerns the exact definition of the nature of the phenomenon's existence. This depends on the details of how the phenomenon is manifested and statistically tested, e.g., the directionality/nondirectionality ("one tailed"/"two tailed") of the statement of the alternative to the null hypothesis.[1] When, for example, the investigator is working in a context of comparing some parameter (e.g., mean, proportion, correlation coefficient) for two populations A and B, he can define the existence of the phenomenon in two different ways:

1. The phenomenon is taken to exist if the parameters of A and B differ. No direction of the difference, such as A larger than B, is specified, so that departures in either direction from the null hypothesis constitute evidence against it. Because either tail of the sampling distribution of differences may contribute to **a**, this is usually called a two-tailed or two-sided test.

2. The phenomenon is taken to exist only if the parameters of A and B differ in a direction specified in advance, e.g., A larger than B. In this

---

[1] Some statistical tests, particularly those involving comparisons of more than two populations, are naturally nondirectional. In what immediately follows, we consider those tests which contrast two populations, wherein the experimenter ordinarily explicitly chooses between a directional and nondirectional statement of his alternate hypothesis. See below, Chapters 7 and 8.

circumstance, departures from the null hypothesis only in the direction specified constitute evidence against it. Because only one tail of the sampling distribution of differences may contribute to **a**, this is usually called a one-tailed or one-sided test.

It is convenient to conceive of the significance criterion as embodying both the probability of falsely rejecting the null hypothesis, **a**, and the "sidedness" of the definition of the existence of the phenomenon (when relevant). Thus, the significance criterion on a two-tailed test of the null hypothesis at the .05 significance level, which will be symbolized as $a_2 = .05$, says two things: (*a*) that the phenomenon whose existence is at issue is understood to be any difference between the two populations' parameter values, and (*b*) that the standard of proof is a sample result that would occur less than 5% of the time if the null hypothesis is true. Similarly, a prior specification defining the phenomenon under study as that for which the parameter value for A is larger than that of B (i.e., one tailed) and the probability of falsely rejecting the null is set at .10 would be symbolized as a significance criterion of $a_1 = .10$. The combination of the probability and the sidedness of the test into a single entity, the significance criterion, is convenient because this combination defines in advance the "critical region," i.e., the range of values of the outcome which leads to rejection of the null hypothesis and, perforce, the range of values which leads to its nonrejection. Thus, when an investigator plans a statistical test at some given significance criterion, say $a_1 = .10$, he has effected a specific division of all the possible results of his study into those which will lead him to conclude that the phenomenon exists (with risk **a** no greater than .10 and a one-sided definition of the phenomenon) and those which will not make possible that conclusion.[2]

The above review of the logic of simple statistical inference reduces to a null hypothesis and a significance criterion which defines the circumstances which will lead to its rejection or nonrejection. Observe that the significance criterion embodies the risk of mistakenly rejecting a null hypothesis. The entire discussion above is conditional on the truth of the null hypothesis.

But what if, indeed, the phenomenon *does* exist and the null hypothesis is *false*? This is the usual expectation of the investigator, who has stated the null hypothesis for tactical purposes so that he may reject it and conclude that the phenomenon exists. But, of course, the fact that the phenomenon exists in the population far from guarantees a statistically significant result,

---

[2] The author has elsewhere expressed serious reservations about the use of directional tests in psychological research in all but relatively limited circumstances (Cohen, 1965). The bases for these reservations would extend to other regions of behavioral science. These tests are however of undoubted statistical validity and in common use, so he has made full provision for them in this work.

i.e., one which warrants the conclusion that it exists, for this conclusion depends upon meeting the agreed-upon standard of proof (i.e., significance criterion). It is at this point that the concept of statistical power must be considered.

The power of a statistical test of a null hypothesis is the probability that it will lead to the rejection of the null hypothesis, i.e., the probability that it will result in the conclusion that the phenomenon exists. Given the characteristics of a specific statistical test of the null hypothesis and the state of affairs in the population, the power of the test can be determined. It clearly represents a vital piece of information about a statistical test applied to research data (cf. Cohen, 1962). For example, the discovery, during the planning phase of an investigation, that the power of the eventual statistical test is low should lead to a revision in the plans. As another example, consider a completed experiment which led to nonrejection of the null hypothesis. An analysis which finds that the power was low should lead one to regard the negative results as ambiguous, since failure to reject the null hypothesis cannot have much substantive meaning when, even though the phenomenon exists (to some given degree), the *a priori* probability of rejecting the null hypothesis was low. A detailed consideration of the use of power analysis in planning investigations and assessing completed investigations is reserved for later sections.

The power of a statistical test depends upon three parameters: the significance criterion, the reliability of the sample results, and the "effect size," that is, the *degree* to which the phenomenon exists.

1.2   Significance Criterion

The role of this parameter in testing null hypotheses has already been given some consideration. As noted above, the significance criterion represents the standard of proof that the phenomenon exists, or the maximum risk of mistakenly rejecting the null hypothesis. As used here, it directly implies the "critical region of rejection" of the null hypothesis, since it embodies both the probability of a class of results given that the null hypothesis is true (**a**), as well as the definition of the phenomenon's existence with regard to directionality.

The significance level, **a**, has been variously called the error of the first kind, the Type I error, and the alpha error. Since it is the rate of rejecting a true null hypothesis, it is taken as a relatively small value. It follows then that the smaller the value, the more rigorous the standard of null hypothesis rejection or, equivalently, of proof of the phenomenon's existence. Assume that a phenomenon exists in the population to some given degree. Other things equal, the more stringent the standard for proof, i.e., the lower the value of **a**, the poorer the chances are that the sample will provide results which meet this standard, i.e., the lower the power. Concretely, if an investigator is prepared to run only a 1 % risk of false rejection of the null hypothesis, the probability of his data meeting this standard is lower than would be the case were he prepared to use the less stringent standard of a 10 % risk of false rejection.

The practice of taking **a** very small ("the smaller the better") then results in power values being relatively small. However, the complement of the power (1 − power), here symbolized as **b**, is also error, called Type II or beta error, since it represents the "error" rate of failing to reject a false null hypothesis. Thus it is seen that statistical inference can be viewed as weighing, in a manner relevant to the substantive issues of an investigation, these two kinds of errors. An investigator can set the risk of false null hypothesis rejection at a vanishingly small level, say **a** = .001, but in so doing, he may reduce the power of his test to .10 (hence beta error probability, **b**, is 1 − .10 = .90). Two comments may be made here:

1. The general neglect of issues of statistical power in behavioral science may well result, in such instances, in the investigator's failing to realize that the **a** = .001 value leads in his situation to power = .10, **b** = .90 (Cohen, 1962). Presumably, although not necessarily, such a realization would lead to a revision of experimental plans, including possibly an upward revision of the **a** level to increase power.

2. If the investigator proceeds as originally planned, he implies a conception of the relative seriousness of Type I to Type II error (risk of false null rejection to risk of false null acceptance) of **b/a** = .90/.001 = 900 to 1, i.e., he implicitly believes that mistakenly rejecting the null hypothesis under the assumed conditions is 900 times more serious than mistakenly accepting it. In another situation, with **a** = .05, power = .80, and hence **b** = 1 − .80 = .20, the relative seriousness of Type I to Type II error is **b/a** = .20/.05 = 4 to 1; thus mistaken rejection of the null hypothesis is considered four times as serious as mistaken acceptance.

The directionality of the significance criterion (left unspecified in the above examples) also bears on the power of a statistical test. When the null hypothesis can be rejected in *either* direction so that the critical significance region is in *both* tails of the sampling distribution of the test statistic (e.g., a **t** ratio), the resulting test will have less power than a test at the same **a** level which is directional, *provided that* the sample result is in the direction predicted. Since directional tests cannot, by definition, lead to rejecting the null hypothesis in the direction *opposite* to that predicted, these tests have almost no power to detect such effects. When the experimental results are in the predicted direction, all other things equal, a test at level a_1 will have power equal for all practical purposes to a test at $2a_2$.

Concretely, if an experiment is performed to detect a difference between the means of populations A and B, say m_A and m_B, in *either* direction at the $a_2 = .05$ significance criterion, under given conditions, the test will have a certain power. If, instead, an anticipation of m_A greater than m_B leads to a test at $a_1 = .05$, this test will have power approximately equal to a two-tailed test with $a_2 = .10$, hence greater power than the test at $a_2 = .05$, provided that in fact m_A is greater than m_B. If m_B is greater than m_A, the test at $a_1 = .05$ has virtually no power. The temptation to perform directional tests because of their greater power at the same **a** level should be tempered by the realization that they preclude finding results opposite to those anticipated. There are occasional circumstances where the nature of the decision is such that the investigator does not need to know about effects in the opposite direction. For example, he will take a certain course of action if m_A is greater than m_B and not otherwise. If otherwise, he does not need to distinguish between their equality and m_B greater than m_A. In such infrequent instances, one-tailed tests are appropriate (Cohen, 1965, pp. 106–111).

In the tables in this book, provision is made for tests at the .01, .05, and .10 significance levels. Where a statistical test may ordinarily be performed either nondirectionally or directionally, both a_2 and a_1 tables are provided. Since power for $a_1 = .05$ is virtually identical with power for $a_2 = .10$, a single power table suffices. Similarly, tables for $a_1 = .01$ provide values for $a_2 = .02$, and tables for $a_1 = .10$ values for $a_2 = .20$; also, tables for $a_2 = .01$ provide values for $a_1 = .005$, tables at $a_2 = .05$ provide values for $a_1 = .025$.

1.3   RELIABILITY OF SAMPLE RESULTS AND SAMPLE SIZE

The reliability (or precision) of a sample value is the closeness with which it can be expected to approximate the relevant population value. It is necessarily an estimated value in practice, since the population value is generally unknown. Depending upon the statistic in question, and the specific statistical model on which the test is based, reliability may or may not be directly dependent upon the unit of measurement, the population value, and the shape of the population distribution. However, it is *always* dependent upon the size of the sample.

For example, one conventional means for assessing the reliability of a statistic is the standard error (SE) of the statistic. If we consider the arithmetic mean of a variable X ($\overline{X}$), its reliability may be estimated by the standard error of the mean,

$$SE_{\overline{X}} = \sqrt{\frac{s^2}{n}},$$

where s^2 is the usual unbiased estimate (from the random sample) of the population variance of **X**, and **n** is the number of independent units in (i.e., the size of) the sample.

Concretely, if a sample of **n** = 49 cases yields a variance estimate for IQ of 196, then the standard error of the mean is given by

$$SE_{\overline{\textbf{x}}} = \sqrt{\frac{\textbf{s}^2}{\textbf{n}}} = \sqrt{\frac{196}{49}} = 2.$$

Thus, sample means based on 49 cases can be expected to have variability as measured by their own standard deviation of 2 IQ units. Clearly the greater the degree to which means of different samples vary among themselves, the less any of them can be relied upon, i.e., the less the reliability of the mean of the sample in hand. Note that in this instance reliability depends upon the unit of measurement (IQ) and sample size, but not on the value of the population mean or (to any material degree) on the shape of the IQ distribution.

On the other hand, consider the sampling reliability of a product moment coefficient of correlation, **r**. Its standard error is

$$SE_r = \frac{1 - \textbf{r}_p^{\,2}}{\sqrt{\textbf{n} - 1}},$$

where
    $\textbf{r}_p$ = the population value of **r** and
    n = the number of paired observations in the sample.

Note that the reliability of the sample **r** depends upon the magnitude of the (generally unknown) population $\textbf{r}_p$ value and **n**, but not on the units in which the correlated variables are measured.

Not all statistical tests involve the explicit definition of a standard error of a sample value, but all do involve the more general conception of sample reliability. Moreover, and most important, whatever else sample reliability may be dependent upon, it *always* depends upon the size of the sample.

The nature of the dependence of reliability upon **n** is obvious from the illustrative formulas, and, indeed, intuitively. The larger the sample size, other things being equal, the smaller the error and the greater the reliability or precision of the results. The further relationship with power is also intuitively evident: the greater the precision of the sample results, other things being equal, the greater the probability of detecting a nonnull state of affairs, i.e., the more clearly the phenomenon under test can manifest itself against the background of (experimentally irrelevant) variability. Thus, we can directly formulate the relationship between sample size and power. As is intuitively obvious, increases in sample size increase statistical power, the probability of detecting the phenomenon under test.

Focusing on sample size as an invariant factor in power should not make the researcher lose sight of the fact that other research elements potentially under his control also effect power. Random measurement error, be it due to psychometric unreliability, observational carelessness, dirty testtubes, or any other source, because it increases the variability of the observations beyond their necessary "true" variability, also reduces the precision of sample results and thus reduces power. In general, *anything* which reduces the variability of observations by the exclusion of sources of variability which are irrelevant to the assessment of the phenomenon under study will serve to increase power. Experimental design is an area of inquiry wholly devoted to the removal of irrelevant sources of variability for the increase of precision and therefore for the increase of the statistical power of tests of null hypotheses (cf. Cox, 1958).

In this book, provision is made for the accomplishment of power analyses for the statistical tests associated with the most frequently utilized experimental designs and their accompanying null hypotheses. Issues such as the effects of a given level of random measurement error on power are not explicitly provided for. Sample size, the invariant feature of sample precision, is, however, a factor in all the power tables. It is used in both of the major kinds of analysis tables herein provided; in the power tables, sample size is one of the elements used to determine the power of the test, and in the sample size tables, it is the dependent variable of the function of the desired level of power (in both instances under given conditions of significance criterion and effect size).

1.4   THE EFFECT SIZE

To this point, the phenomenon in the population under statistical test was considered as either absent (null hypothesis true) or present (null hypothesis false). The absence of the phenomenon implies some specific value for a population parameter. For example, in a study to determine whether there is a sex difference in incidence of paranoid schizophrenia, the investigator may draw a sample of patients bearing that diagnosis from the relevant population and determine the proportion of males. The null hypothesis being tested is that the population proportion of males is .50, a specific value.[3,4] Equivalently, we might say that the size of the "effect" of sex on the presence of

[3] The assumption is made here that .50 is the proportion of males in the population of interest.

[4] For the sake of simplicity, the null hypothesis is treated in this section for the nondirectional form of the significance criterion. For example, a directional (one-tailed) test here that the male proportion is greater than .50 implies a null hypothesis that it is equal to *or less than* .50. The reader may supply his own necessary qualifications of the null hypothesis for the directional case in each illustration.

the diagnosis is zero. In another study concerned with the IQs of children born in multiple births, the null hypothesis might be that the multiple birth population in question has a mean IQ of 100 (i.e., the general population mean), again a specific value, or that the size of effect of being part of a multiple birth on IQ is zero. As yet another example of a one-sample test, in a study of the construct validity of a neurophysiological measure of intro-version–extroversion, its product moment **r** with an accepted questionnaire measure for a sample of college students is determined. The null hypothesis here is that the population **r** is zero, or that the effect size of one on the other is zero.

In circumstances where two populations are being compared, the null hypothesis usually takes the form "the difference in the value of the rele-vant parameters is zero," a specific value. Thus, in a consumer survey research to determine whether preference for a particular brand A over its chief competitor B is related to the income level of the consumer, the null hypothesis might be: The difference in median family income of brand A and brand B users is zero, or, equivalently, that the size of the effect of income on brand preference is zero. Or, in a personnel selection study to determine which of two screening tests, A or B, is a better predictor of performance ratings (C), the null hypothesis might take the form: The difference between population product moment **r**'s of A with C and B with C is zero.

Statistical tests involving more than two samples test null hypotheses that imply the constancy of a parameter over the populations involved. The literal statement of the null hypothesis depends upon the specific test involved. For example, the **F** test of the analysis of variance for $k \geq 2$ means has as its null hypothesis the proposition that the variance of a set of population means is zero, a condition that can only obtain when they are equal. Simi-larly, a test of whether a set of $k \geq 2$ population proportions are equal can be performed by means of the chi-square statistic. The null hypothesis here is that the variance of the population proportions equals zero (an exact value), a condition which can only obtain when they are all equal. In both of these instances we can think of the null hypothesis as the circumstance in which differences in the "independent" variable, the **k** populations, have no effect (have an effect size of zero) on the means or proportions of the dependent variable.

Thus, we see that the absence of the phenomenon under study is expressed by a null hypothesis which specifies an exact value for a population para-meter, one which is appropriate to the way the phenomenon under study is manifested. Without intending any necessary implication of causality, it is convenient to use the phrase "effect size" to mean "the *degree* to which the phenomenon is present in the population," or "the degree to which the null hypothesis is false." Whatever the manner of representation of a phenomenon in a particular research in the present treatment, the null hypothesis always means that the effect size is zero.

By the above route, it can now readily be made clear that when the null hypothesis is false, it is false to some specific degree, i.e., *the effect size* (ES) *is some specific nonzero value in the population.* The larger this value, the greater the *degree* to which the phenomenon under study is manifested. Thus, in terms of the previous illustrations:

1.   If the percentage of males in the population of psychiatric patients bearing a diagnosis of paranoid schizophrenia is 52%, and the effect is measured as a departure from the hypothesized 50%, the ES is 2%; if it is 60%, the ES is 10%, a larger ES.

2.   If children of multiple births have a population mean IQ of 96, the ES is 4 IQ units (or − 4, depending on directionality of significance criterion); if it is 92, the ES is 8 (or − 8) IQ units, i.e., a larger ES.

3.   If the population product moment **r** between neurophysiological and questionnaire measures of introversion–extroversion is .30, the ES is .30; if the **r** is .60, so is the ES, a larger value and a larger departure from the null hypothesis, which here is **r** = 0.

4.   If the population of consumers preferring brand A has a median annual income $700 higher than that of brand B, the ES is $700. If the population median difference and hence the ES is $1000, the effect of income on brand preference would be larger.

Thus, whether measured in one unit or another, whether expressed as a difference between two population parameters or the departure of a population parameter from a constant or in any other suitable way, the ES can itself be treated as a parameter which takes the value zero when the null hypothesis is true and *any other specific nonzero value* when the null hypothesis is false, and in this way the ES serves as an index of degree of departure from the null hypothesis.

The reasons that the above dicussion has proceeded in such redundant detail are twofold. On the one hand, ES is in practice a most important determinant of power or required sample size or both, and on the other hand, it is the least familiar of the concepts surrounding statistical inference among practicing behavior scientists. The reason for the latter, in turn, can be found in the difference in null hypothesis testing between the procedures of Fisher (1949) and those of Neyman and Pearson (1928, 1933).

The Fisherian formulation posits the null hypothesis as described above, i.e., the ES is zero, to which the "alternative" hypothesis is that the ES is *not* zero, i.e., *any* nonzero value. Without further specification, although null hypotheses may be tested and thereupon either rejected or not rejected, no basis for statistical power analysis exists. By contrast, the Neyman-Pearson formulation posits an *exact* alternative for the ES, i.e., the *exact* size of the effect the experiment is designed to detect. With an exact alternative hypothesis or specific nonzero ES to be detected, given the other elements in statistical inference, statistical power analysis may proceed.

Thus, in the previous illustrations, the statements about possible population ES values (e.g., "if the population product moment **r** between neurophysiological and questionnaire measures of introversion–extroversion is .30, the ES is .30") are statements of alternative hypotheses.

The relationship between ES and power should also be intuitively evident. The larger the ES posited, other things (significance criterion, sample size) being equal, the greater the power of the test. Similarly, the relationship between ES and necessary sample size: the larger the ES posited, other things (significance criterion, desired power) being equal, the smaller the sample size necessary to detect it.

To this point, the ES has been considered quite abstractly as a parameter which can take on varying values (including zero in the null case). In any given statistical test, it must be indexed or measured in some defined unit appropriate to the data, test, and statistical model employed. In the previous illustrations, ES was variously expressed as a departure in percent from 50, a departure in IQ units from 100, a product moment **r**, a difference between two medians in dollars, etc. It is clearly desirable to reduce this diversity of units as far as possible, consistent with present usage by behavioural scientists. From one point of view, a universal ES index, applicable to all the various research issues and statistical models used in their appraisal, would be the ideal. Apart from some formidable mathematical-statistical problems in the way, even if such an ideal could be achieved, the result would express ES in terms so unfamiliar to the researcher in behavioral science as to be self-defeating.

However, some generalization is obviously necessary. One cannot prepare a set of power tables for each new measurement unit with which one works. That is, the researcher who plans a test for a difference in mean IQs must use the same power tables as another who plans a test for a difference in mean weights, just as they will use the same tables of **t** when the research is performed. **t** is a "pure" (dimensionless) number, one free of raw unit, as are also, for example, correlation coefficients or proportions of variance. Thus, as will be seen in Chapter 2, the ES index for differences between population means is standardized by division by the common within-population standard deviation (σ), i.e., the ES here is not the difference between mean "raw" scores, but the difference between mean "**z**" standard scores (Guilford, 1965), or the mean difference expressed in within-population σ units. In the **F** test for **k** ≥ 2 population means, the ES also uses such standardized means; in testing "main effects" in the analysis of variance the ES is *their* standard deviation, σ_m, the standard deviation of standardized means (Chapter 8).

Each test for which power tables are provided thus has a metric-free ES index appropriate to it. A higher order of generalization is frequently possible. Specifically, several ES indices can be translated into the proportion of variance (PV) accounted for in the dependent variable. Where this is possible, it is discussed in the introductory material for the test. Also, each ES index chosen usually relates to yet other commonly used indices (correlation coefficients, noncentrality parameters), and these are also described in the same place.

The behavior scientist who comes to statistical power analysis may find himself grappling with the problem of what ES to posit as an alternate to the null hypothesis, or, more simply, how to answer the questions "How large an effect do I expect exists in the population?" He may initially find it difficult to answer the question even in general terms, i.e., "small" or "large," let alone in terms of the specific ES index demanded. Being forced to think in more exact terms than demanded by the Fisherian alternative (ES is any nonzero value) is likely to prove salutary. He can call upon theory for some help in answering the question and on his critical assessment of prior research in the area for further help. When these are supplemented with the understanding of the ES index provided in the introductory material to the relevant chapter, he can decide upon the ES value to adopt as an alternative to the null.

When the above has not provided sufficient guidance, the reader has an additional recourse. For each statistical test's ES index, the author proposes, *as a convention*, ES values to serve as operational definitions of the qualitative adjectives "small," "medium," and "large." This is an operation fraught with many dangers: The definitions are arbitrary, such qualitative concepts as "large" are sometimes understood as absolute, sometimes as relative; and thus they run a risk of being misunderstood.

In justification, several arguments may be offered. It must first be said that all conventions are arbitrary. One can only demand of them that they not be unreasonable. Also, all conventions may be misused and their conventional status thus abused. For example, the .05 significance criterion, although unofficial, has come to serve as a convention for a (minimum) basis for rejecting the null hypothesis in most areas of behavioral and biological science. Unfortunately, its status as only a convention is frequently ignored; there are many published instances where a researcher, in an effort at rectitude, fails to report that a much desired null rejection would be possible at the .06 level but instead treats the problem no differently than he would have had it been at the .50 level! Still, it is convenient that "significance" without further specification can be taken to mean "significance at no more than the .05 level."

Although arbitrary, the proposed conventions will be found to be reasonable by reasonable men. An effort was made in selecting these operational criteria to use levels of ES which accord with a subjective average of effect sizes such as are encountered in behavioral science. "Small" effect sizes must not be so small that seeking them amidst the inevitable operation of measurement and experimental bias and lack of fidelity is a bootless task, yet not so large as to make them fairly perceptible to the naked observational eye. Many effects sought in personality, social, and clinical-psychological research are likely to be small effects as here defined, both because of the validity attenuation of the measures employed and the subtlety of the issues frequently involved. In contrast, large effects must not be defined as so large that their quest by statistical methods is wholly a labor of supererogation, or to use Tukey's delightful term "statistical sanctification." That is, the difference in size between apples and pineapples is of an order which hardly requires an approach via statistical analysis. On the other side, it cannot be defined so as to encroach on a reasonable range of values called medium. Large effects are frequently at issue in such fields as sociology, economics, and experimental and physiological psychology, fields characterized by the study of potent variables or the presence of good experimental control or both.

Since effects are appraised against a background of random variation, the control of various sources of variation through the use of improved research designs serves to increase effect sizes as they are defined here. A simple example of this is a study of sex difference in some defined ability. Assume that a difference of 4 score points exists between male and female population means, where each population has a standard deviation of 16. A research plan which randomly samples the two populations (simple randomized design or comparison between two independent means) is operating with an ES of $4/16 = .25$. Another research plan might proceed by comparing means of males and their sisters (comparison of two dependent means). Now, these populations can also be assumed to have a mean difference of 4 score points, but because of the removal of the variation between families afforded by this design (or equivalently when allowance is made for the brother–sister correlation in the ability), the *effective* standard deviation will be reduced to the fraction $\sqrt{1-r}$ of 16, say to 12 (when r between siblings $= .44$), and the actual ES operating in the situation is $4/12 = .33$, a larger value than for the simple randomized design. Thus, *operative* effect sizes may be increased not only by improvement in measurement and experimental technique, but also by improved experimental designs.

Each of the Chapters 2–8 will present in some detail the ES index appropriate to the test to which the chapter is devoted. Each will be translated into alternative forms, the operational definitions of "small," "medium," and "large" will be presented, and examples drawn from various fields will illustrate the test. This should serve to clarify the ES index involved and make the methods and tables useful in research planning and appraisal.

1.5   TYPES OF POWER ANALYSIS

Four parameters of statistical inference have been described: power, significance criterion (**a**), sample size (**n**), and effect size (ES). They are so related that any one of them is a function of the other three, which means that when any three of them are fixed, the fourth is completely determined. This relationship makes formally possible four types of power analysis; in each, one of these parameters is determined as a function of the other three (Cohen, 1965, pp. 97–101).

1.5.1   POWER AS A FUNCTION OF **a**, ES, AND **n**. The preceding material has been largely oriented toward the type of analysis in which, given the specification of **a**, ES, and **n**, power is determined. For example, an investigator plans a test of the significance of a product moment **r** at $a_2 = .05$ using **n** = 30 cases. The ES he wishes to detect is a population **r** of .40. Given these specifications, he finds (by the methods of Section 3.3 in Chapter 3) that power equals .61. He may then decide to change his specifications to increase power.

Such analyses are usefully performed as part of research planning. They can also be performed on completed studies to determine the power which a given statistical test had, as in the power survey of the studies in a volume of the *Journal of Abnormal and Social Psychology* (Cohen, 1962). In each of Chapters 2–8, the power tables (numbered B.3.A, where B is the chapter number and A indexes the significance criterion) are designed for this type of analysis. The sections designated B.3 discuss and illustrate the use of these tables.

1.5.2   **n** AS A FUNCTION OF ES, **a**, AND POWER. When an investigator anticipates a certain ES, sets a significance criterion **a**, and then specifies the amount of power he desires, the **n** which is necessary to meet these specifications can be determined. This (second) type of power analysis must be at the core of any rational basis for deciding on the sample size to be used in an investigation (Cohen, 1965, pp. 97–99). For example, an investigator wishes to have power equal to .80 to detect a population **r** of .40 (the ES) at $a_2 = .05$. By the methods described in Section 3.4 in Chapter 3, he finds that he must have **n** = 46 cases to meet these specifications. (A discussion of the basis for specifying desired power and the use of power = .80 as a convention will be found in Section 2.4 of Chapter 2.)

This major type of power analysis is discussed and illustrated in the Sections B.4 (where B indexes the chapter numbers 2–8). Each of these sections contain sample size tables (numbered B.4.A) from which, given **a**, the ES, and desired power, the **n** is determined.

1.5.3 ES AS A FUNCTION OF **a, n**, AND POWER. A third type of power analysis is of less general utility than the first two, but may nevertheless be quite useful in special circumstances. Here, one finds the ES which one can expect to detect for given **a, n**, and with specified power. For example, an investigator may pose the question, "For a significance test of a product moment **r** at $a_2 = .05$ with a sample of **n** = 30, what must the population **r** (the ES) be if power is to be .80, i.e., what is the *detectable* ES for these specifications?" The answer, obtainable by backward interpolation (in Table 3.3.5) is that the population **r** must be approximately .48. Were his **n** equal to 46, the detectable ES would be **r** = .40.

This form of power analysis may be conventionalized for use in comparisons of research results as in literature surveys (Cohen, 1965, p. 100). One can define, as a convention, a comparative detectable effect size (CDES) as that ES detectable at $a_2 = .05$ with power = .50 for the **n** used in the statistical test. So defined, the CDES is an inverse measure of the sensitivity of the test, expressed in the appropriate ES unit.

This type of power analysis is not discussed in detail in the ensuing chapters. However, when the reader has become familiar with the use of the tables, he will find that it can be accomplished for all of the statistical tests discussed by backward interpolation in the power tables, or when it proves more convenient, in the sample size tables.

1.5.4 **a** AS A FUNCTION OF **n**, POWER, AND ES. The last type of power analysis answers the question, "What significance level must I use to detect a given ES with specified probability (power) for a fixed given **n**?" Consider an investigator whose anticipated ES is a population **r** of .30, who wishes power to be .75, and who has an **n** of 50, which he cannot increase. These specifications determine the significance criterion he must use, which can be found (by rough interpolation between subtables in Table 3.4.1) to be about $a_1 = .08$, or $a_2 = .15$).

This type of analysis is very uncommon, at least partly because of the strength of the significance criterion convention, which makes investigators loath to consider "large" values of **a**. We have seen that this frequently means tolerating (usually without knowing it) large values of **b**, i.e., low power. When power issues are brought into consideration, some circumstances may dictate unconventionally large **a** criteria (Cohen, 1965, p. 99ff).

This type of power analysis is not, as such, further discussed in Chapters

2–8, although it is indirectly considered in some of the examples. When the reader has become familiar with the tables, it can be accomplished for all the statistical tests discussed in this book by interpolation between subtables of the sample size tables (B.4.A), or when more convenient, between power tables (B.3.A), within the range provided for **a**, i.e., a_2: .01–.20, and a_1: .005–.10.

In summary, four types of power analysis have been described. This book is designed primarily to facilitate two of these, the solutions for power and for sample size. It is also possible, but with less ease, to accomplish the other two, solution for ES and for **a**, by means of backward interpolation in the tables.

1.6   SIGNIFICANCE TESTING

Although the major thrust of this work is power analysis, a simple relationship between power and significance made it relatively simple in the computation of the power tables to provide an aid to significance testing which users of this handbook may find convenient. Generally, we can define the effect size *in the sample* (ES_S) using sample statistics in the same way as we define it for the population, and a statistically significant ES_S is one which exceeds an appropriate criterion value. For most of the power tables, these criterion values for significance of the sample ES (for the given **a** significance criterion and **n**) are provided in the second column of the power tables under the symbol for the ES for that test with subscript c (for criterion), e.g., d_c for the **t** test on means.

1.7   PLAN OF CHAPTERS 2—8

Each of the succeeding chapters presents a different statistical test. They are similarly organized, as follows:

Section 1. The test is introduced and its uses described.

Section 2. The ES index is described and discussed in detail.

Section 3. The characteristics of the power tables and the method of their use are described and illustrated with examples.

Section 4. The characteristics of the sample size tables and the method of their use are described and illustrated with examples.

Section 5. The use of the power tables for significance tests is described and illustrated with examples.

2

The t Test for Means

2.1 INTRODUCTION AND USE

The arithmetic mean is by far the most frequently used measure of location by behavioral scientists, and hypotheses about means the most frequently tested. The tables have been designed to render very simple the procedure for power analysis in the case where two samples, each of n cases, have been randomly and independently drawn from normal populations, and the investigator wishes to test the null hypothesis that their respective population means are equal, $H_0: m_A - m_B = 0$ (Hays, 1963, pp. 319–321; McNemar, 1962, p. 102f), referred to below as Case 0. The test is the t test for independent means. The tables can also be used to analyze power for (a) the t test on means of two independent samples when $n_A \neq n_B$ (Case 1), (b) an approximate t test on the means of independent samples when $\sigma_A \neq \sigma_B$ (Case 2), (c) a one-sample t test of the null hypothesis that a population mean equals some specified value, $H_0: m = c$ (Case 3) (Hays, 1963, p. 311; McNemar, 1962, p. 101), and (d) the t test on the means of dependent samples i.e., paired values (Case 4) (Hays, 1963, pp. 333–335; Edwards, 1960, p. 101ff). These latter four applications will be discussed below, following consideration of the (Case 0) t test for independent means drawn from equally varying populations and based on equal size samples. Finally, the tables can also be used for significance testing, as detailed in Section 2.5.

In the formal development of the t distribution for the difference between two independent means, the assumption is made that the populations sampled are normally distributed and that they are of homogeneous (i.e., equal) variance. Moderate departures from these assumptions, however, have generally negligible effects on the validity of both Type I and Type II error calculations. This is particularly true for nondirectional tests and as sample

17

sizes increase above 20 or 30 cases. The only noteworthy exception to the above is under the condition of substantially unequal variances together with substantially unequal sample sizes (whether small or large). Summaries of the evidence in regard to the "robustness" of the **t** (and **F**) test is provided by Scheffé (1959, Chapter 10), and in less technical terms, by Cohen (1965, pp. 114–116). See also Boneau (1960, 1962).

2.2   THE EFFECT SIZE INDEX: **d**

As noted above (Section 1.4), we need a "pure" number, one free of our original measurement unit, with which to index what can be alternately called the degree of departure from the null hypothesis or the alternate hypothesis, or the ES (effect size) we wish to detect. This is accomplished by standardizing the raw effect size as expressed in the measurement unit of the dependent variable by dividing it by the (common) standard deviation of the measures in their respective populations, the latter also in the original measurement unit. For the two independent samples case, this is simply

(2.2.1)
$$\mathbf{d} = \frac{\mathbf{m_A} - \mathbf{m_B}}{\sigma}$$

for the directional (one-tailed) case or

(2.2.2)
$$\mathbf{d} = \frac{|\mathbf{m_A} - \mathbf{m_B}|}{\sigma}$$

for the nondirectional (two-tailed) case,

where $\mathbf{d}$ = ES index for **t** tests of means in standard unit,

$\mathbf{m_A}, \mathbf{m_B}$ = population means expressed in raw (original measurement) unit, and

σ = the standard deviation of either population (since they are assumed equal).

The use of **d** is not only a necessity demanded by the practical requirements of table making, but proves salutary in those areas of the behavioral sciences where raw units are used which are quite arbitrary or lack meaning outside the investigation in which they are used or both. Consider, for example, the question whether religious groups A and B differ in their favorableness toward the United Nations. The latter may well be indexed by an *ad hoc* attitude scale which yields a score expressed in points, such that the more points the more favorable the attitude. The absolute size of a point is a consequence of arbitrariness in the decisions made by the investigator, and/or in the scale construction method, and/or in the writing or selection of the items. If the A population has a mean of 280 and the B population a mean of 270, the question "How large is the effect?" can only be answered with "ten points," a generally unsatisfactory answer in the absence of a basis for answering the necessarily following question, "Well, how large is a point?"

d provides an answer to such questions by expressing score distances in units of variability. If in the above situation, the common within-population standard deviation is $\sigma = 100$ scale points,

$$\mathbf{d} = \frac{\mathbf{m}_A - \mathbf{m}_B}{\sigma} = \frac{280 - 270}{100} = \frac{10}{100} = .1,$$

i.e., the means differ by a tenth of a standard deviation. Since both numerator and denominator are expressed in scale units, these "cancel out," and **d** is a pure number (here a ratio), freed of dependence upon any specific unit of measurement.

On the other hand, consider the circumstance when $\sigma = 5$ rather than 100. Now,

$$\mathbf{d} = \frac{10}{5} = 2.0,$$

i.e., the means differ by two standard deviations. This is obviously a much larger difference than is $\mathbf{d} = .1$.

But *how* large are each of these differences, and how *much* larger is the second than the first? There are various ways the values of **d** may be understood.

2.2.1   **d** AS PERCENT NONOVERLAP: THE **U** MEASURES. If we maintain the assumption that the populations being compared are normal and with equal variability, and conceive them further as equally numerous, it is possible to define measures of nonoverlap (**U**) associated with **d** which are intuitively compelling and meaningful. As examples:

1.   When $\mathbf{d} = 0$, and therefore either population distribution is perfectly superimposed on the other, there is 100% overlap or 0% nonoverlap, hence $\mathbf{U}_1 = 0$. In such a circumstance, the highest 50% of population B exceeds the lowest 50% of population A. We designate as $\mathbf{U}_2$ (50% in this example), a second percentage measure of nonoverlap, the percentage in the B population that exceeds the same percentage in the A population. Finally, as third measure of nonoverlap, $\mathbf{U}_3$, we take the percentage of the A population which the upper half of the cases of the B population exceeds. When $\mathbf{d} = 0, \mathbf{U}_3 = 50.0\%$.

2.   When $\mathbf{d} = .1$ as in the above example, the distribution of the population with the larger mean, B, is almost superimposed on A, but with some slight excess, i.e., some nonoverlap. $\mathbf{U}_1$ here equals 7.7%, that is, 7.7% of the area covered by both populations combined is not overlapped. For $\mathbf{U}_2$,

the value is 52.0%, i.e., the highest 52.0% of the B population exceeds the lowest 52.0% of the A population. For U_3, the value is 54.0%, i.e., the upper 50% of population B exceeds 54.0% of the values in the A population.

3.   When we posited the smaller σ ($= 5$), we found $d = 2.0$. U_1 then equals 81.1%, the amount of combined area not shared by the two population distributions. In this case, the highest 84.1% of the B population exceeds the lowest 84.1% of the A population, thus $U_2 = 84.1\%$. Finally, the upper half of the B population exceeds 97.7% of the A population, so that $U_3 = 97.7\%$.

Table 2.2.1

Equivalents of d

d	U_1	U_2	U_3	r	r^2
0	0.0%	50.0%	50.0%	.000	.000
.1	7.7	52.0	54.0	.050	.002
.2	14.7	54.0	57.9	.100	.010
.3	21.3	56.0	61.8	.148	.022
.4	27.4	57.9	65.5	.196	.038
.5	33.0	59.9	69.1	.243	.059
.6	38.2	61.8	72.6	.287	.083
.7	43.0	63.7	75.8	.330	.109
.8	47.4	65.5	78.8	.371	.138
.9	51.6	67.4	81.6	.410	.168
1.0	55.4	69.1	84.1	.447	.200
1.1	58.9	70.9	86.4	.482	.232
1.2	62.2	72.6	88.5	.514	.265
1.3	65.3	74.2	90.3	.545	.297
1.4	68.1	75.8	91.9	.573	.329
1.5	70.7	77.3	93.3	.600	.360
1.6	73.1	78.8	94.5	.625	.390
1.7	75.4	80.2	95.5	.648	.419
1.8	77.4	81.6	96.4	.669	.448
1.9	79.4	82.9	97.1	.689	.474
2.0	81.1	84.1	97.7	.707	.500
2.2	84.3	86.4	98.6	.740	.548
2.4	87.0	88.5	99.2	.768	.590
2.6	89.3	90.3	99.5	.793	.628
2.8	91.2	91.9	99.7	.814	.662
3.0	92.8	93.3	99.9	.832	.692
3.2	94.2	94.5	99.9	.848	.719
3.4	95.3	95.5	*	.862	.743
3.6	96.3	96.4	*	.874	.764
3.8	97.0	97.1	*	.885	.783
4.0	97.7	97.7	*	.894	.800

* Greater than 99.95

The reader is free to use whichever of these **U** measures he finds most meaningful to him in the context of his application. They are simply related to **d** and each other through the cumulative normal distribution. If **d** is taken as a deviate in the unit normal curve and **P** as the percentage of the area (population of cases) falling below a given normal deviate, then

(2.2.3) $\mathbf{U}_3 = \mathbf{P}_d,$

(2.2.4) $\mathbf{U}_2 = \mathbf{P}_{d/2}$

(2.2.5) $\mathbf{U}_1 = \dfrac{2\mathbf{P}_{d/2} - 1}{\mathbf{P}_{d/2}} = \dfrac{2\mathbf{U}_2 - 1}{\mathbf{U}_2}.$

Table 2.2.1 presents $\mathbf{U}_1$, $\mathbf{U}_2$, and $\mathbf{U}_3$ for values of **d** = .1 (.1) 2.0 (.2) 4.0. Its use will be illustrated after we have considered two other bases for the understanding of **d**.

2.2.2 **d** IN TERMS OF CORRELATION AND PROPORTION OF VARIANCE. Membership in the A or in the B population may be considered to be a simple dichotomy or a two point scale. Scoring it, for example, 0 for membership in A and 1 for membership in B (the values assigned are immaterial), one can express the relationship between population membership and any other variable as a Pearson product-moment correlation coefficient (**r**). Each member in the two populations may be characterized by a pair of variables, the "score" on population membership (**X**) and the value of the other variable (**Y**), and the **r** between **X** and **Y** can then be found by any of the usual computing formulas for **r** (Hays, 1963, p. 505ff; McNemar, 1962, p. 112), or more readily as the point biserial **r** (McNemar, 1962, p. 192). Investigators may prefer to think of effect sizes for mean differences in terms of **r**'s, rather than **d**'s, and they are related by

(2.2.6) $\mathbf{r} = \dfrac{\mathbf{d}}{\sqrt{\mathbf{d}^2 + 4}}.$

Formula (2.2.6) is appropriately used when the A and B populations are such that they can be conceived as equally numerous. This will usually be the case when A and B represent some experimental manipulation (e.g., the presence or absence of a stimulus, or two different sets of instructions), or some abstract property (e.g., high versus low anxiety level, or native versus foreign speaker), as well as when the dichotomy represents real and equally numerous populations, as is the case (at least approximately) with males and females. The case of equally numerous populations is the usual one. This is the case assumed for the values of **r** given in Table 2.2.1.

When, however, the populations are concrete and unequal collections of cases, the inequality should figure in the assessment of the degree of relationship (e.g., finally diagnosed schizophrenics versus others on a diagnostic psychological test). The more general formula for **r** should then be used:

$$(2.2.7) \qquad\qquad \mathbf{r} = \frac{\mathbf{d}}{\sqrt{\mathbf{d}^2 + (1/\mathbf{pq})}},$$

where **p** = proportion of A's in combined A and B populations, and

q = 1 − **p** (i.e., proportion of B's).

[The reader will note that when **p** = **q** = .5, formula (2.2.7) reduces to formula (2.2.6).]

Once a difference between population means of A and B can be expressed as **r**, it can also and usually most usefully be expressed as $\mathbf{r}^2$, the proportion of the total variance (PV) of **Y** in the combined A and B populations associated with or accounted for by population membership (**X** = 0 or 1).

Table 2.2.1 present values of both **r** and $\mathbf{r}^2$ equivalent to **d** for the case where equally numerous populations are assumed. If the means of two equally numerous populations on a variable **Y** differ by **d** = 1.0, then population membership relates to **Y** with an **r** = .447, and an $\mathbf{r}^2$ = .200 of the combined population variance in **Y** is associated with A versus B membership (**X**).

2.2.3   "SMALL," "MEDIUM," AND "LARGE" **d** VALUES. When working with a variable **Y** which has been well studied, the selection of an effect size expressed in **d** offers no particular difficulty. On the one hand, estimates of the within-population σ are readily at hand and the number of raw points difference between A and B population means to be detected (or to serve as an alternate hypothesis to the null) arise naturally out of the content of the inquiry. Thus, a psychologist studying the effects of treatment in phenylpyruvic mental deficiency will likely have an estimate of the σ of IQ in such a population (e.g., σ = 12.5) and be able to posit an interest in detecting a mean difference between treated and untreated cases of, say, 10 IQ points. Thus, he goes directly to **d** = 10/12.5 = .8. Similarly, an anthropologist studying social class differences in height in a preliterate culture would have an estimated σ of height, for example, 2.5 in., and would posit the mean difference he was seeking to detect between two social class populations, say 2 in. He, too, could then find his difference expressed as **d** = 2/2.5, which (also) equals .8.

But consider now the frequently arising circumstance where the variable **Y** is a new measure for which previously collected data or experience are sparse or even nonexistent. Take, for example, an especially constructed test of learning ability appropriate for use with phenylpyruvic mental deficients. The investigator may well be satisfied with the relevance of the test to his purpose, yet may have no idea of either what the σ is or how many points of difference on **Y** between means of treated and untreated populations he can expect. Thus, he has neither the numerator $(\mathbf{m_A} - \mathbf{m_B})$ nor the denominator (σ) needed to compute **d**.

It is precisely at this point in the apparent dilemma that the utility of the **d** concept comes to the fore. It is not necessary to compute **d** from a posited difference between means and an estimated standard deviation; one can posit **d** *directly*. Thus, if the investigator thinks that the effect of his treatment method on learning ability in phenylpyruvia is small, he might posit a **d** value such as .2 or .3. If he anticipates it to be large, he might posit **d** as .8 or 1.0. If he expects it to be medium (or simply seeks to straddle the fence on the issue), he might select some such value as **d** = .5.

The terms "small," "medium," and "large" are relative, not only to each other, but to the area of behavioral science or even more particularly to the specific content and research method being employed in any given investigation (see above, Section 1.4). In the face of this relativity, there is a certain risk inherent in offering conventional operational definitions for these terms for use in power analysis in as diverse a field of inquiry as behavioral science. This risk is nevertheless accepted in the belief that more is to be gained than lost by supplying a common conventional frame of reference which is recommended for use only when no better basis for estimating the ES index is available.

SMALL EFFECT SIZE: **d** = .2. In new areas of research inquiry, effect sizes are likely to be small (when they are not zero!). This is because the phenomena under study are typically not under good experimental or measurement control or both. When phenomena are studied which cannot be brought into the laboratory, the influence of uncontrollable extraneous variables ("noise") makes the size of the effect small relative to these (makes the "signal" difficult to detect).

The implication of **d** = .2 as the operational definition of a small difference between means can be seen in Table 2.2.1. When **d** = .2, normally distributed populations of equal size and variability have only 14.7% of their combined area which is not overlapped $(\mathbf{U_1})$. If B is the population with the larger mean and A the other, the highest 54% of the B population exceeds the lowest 54% of the A population $(\mathbf{U_2})$. Our third measure of nonoverlap $(\mathbf{U_3})$ indicates that 57.9% of the A population is exceeded by the mean (or equivalently the upper half) of the B population.

From the point of view of correlation and maintaining the idea of equally numerous populations, **d** = .2 means that the (point biserial) **r** between population membership (A vs. B) and the dependent variable **Y** is .100, and $\mathbf{r^2}$ is accordingly .010. The latter can be interpreted as meaning that population membership accounts for 1% of the variance of **Y** in the combined A and B populations.

The above sounds indeed small. Yet it is the order of magnitude of the difference in mean IQ between twins and nontwins, the latter being the larger (Husén, 1959). It is also approximately the size of the difference in mean height between 15- and 16-year-old girls (i.e., .5 in. where the σ is about 2.1). Other examples of small effect sizes are adult sex differences on the Information and Picture Completion Subtests of the Wechsler Adult Intelligence Scale, favoring men, while a difference favoring women on the Digit Symbol Test which is twice as large (Wechsler, 1958, p. 147).

MEDIUM EFFECT SIZE: $d = .5$.   A medium effect size is conceived as one large enough to be visible to the naked eye. That is, in the course of normal experience, one would become aware of an average difference in intelligence between clerical and semiskilled workers or between members of professional and managerial occupational groups (Super, 1949, p. 98).

In terms of measures of nonoverlap (Table 2.2.1), a $d = .5$ indicates that 33.0% ($=U_1$) of the combined area covered by two normal equal-sized equally varying populations is not overlapped; that (where $m_B > m_A$) 59.9% ($=U_2$) of the B population exceeds 59.9% of the A population; finally, that the upper half of the B population exceeds 69.1% ($=U_3$) of the A population.

In terms of correlation, $d = .5$ means a point biserial **r** between population membership (A vs. B) and a dependent variable **Y** of .243. Thus, .059 ($=r^2$) of the **Y** variance is "accounted for" by population membership.

Expressed in the above terms, the reader may feel the effect size designated medium to be small. That is, an amount not quite equal to 6% of variance may well not seem large enough to be called medium. But $d = .5$ is the magnitude of the difference in height between 14- and 18-year-old girls (about 1 in. where $\sigma = 2$). As noted above, it represents the difference in mean IQ between clerical and semiskilled workers and between professionals and managers (about 8 points where $\sigma = 15$). It is also the difference in means on the World War II General Classification Test for enlisted men who had been teachers versus those who had been general clerks (Harrell and Harrell, 1945, pp. 231–232). Depending on his frame of reference, the reader may consider such differences either small or large. We are thus reminded of the arbitrariness of this assignment of quantitative operational definitions to qualitative adjectives.

LARGE EFFECT SIZE: $d = .8$.   When our two populations are so separated as to make $d = .8$, almost half ($U_1 = 47.4\%$) of their areas are not overlapped. $U_2 = 65.5\%$, i.e., the highest 65.5% of the B population exceeds the lowest 65.5% of the A population. As a third measure, the mean or upper half of the B population exceeds the lower 78.8% ($=U_3$) of the A population.

The point biserial **r** here equals .371, and r^2 thus equals .138.

Behavioral scientists who work with correlation coefficients (such as, for example, educational psychologists) do not ordinarily consider an **r** of .371 as large. Nor, in that frame of reference, does the writer. Note however that it is the .8 separation between means which is being designated as large, not the implied point biserial **r**. Such a separation, for example, is represented by the mean IQ difference estimated between holders of the Ph.D. degree and typical college freshmen, or between college graduates and persons with only a 50–50 chance of passing in an academic high school curriculum (Cronbach, 1960, p. 174). These seem like grossly perceptible and therefore large differences, as does the mean difference in height between 13- and 18-year-old girls, which is of the same size (**d** = .8).

2.3 POWER TABLES

The power tables are used when, in addition to the significance criterion and ES, the sample size is also specified; the tables then yield power values. Their major use will then be *post hoc*, i.e., to find the power of a test after the experiment has been performed. They can, of course, also be used in experimental planning by varying **n** (or ES or **a** or all these) to see the consequences to power of such alternatives.

2.3.1 CASE 0: $\sigma_A = \sigma_B$, $n_A = n_B$. The power tables are designed to yield power values for the **t** test for the difference between the means of two independent samples of equal size drawn from normal populations having equal variances (Case 0). They are described for such use below, and in a later section for other conditions (Cases 1–4). Tables list values for **a**, **d**, and **n**:

1. Significance Criterion, **a**. There are tables for the following values of **a**: $a_1 = .01$, $a_1 = .05$, $a_1 = .10$; $a_2 = .01$, $a_2 = .05$, $a_2 = .10$, where the subscripts refer to one- and two-tailed tests. Since power at a_1 is to an adequate approximation equal to power at $a_2 = 2a_1$ for power greater than (say) .10, one can also use the tables for power at $a_2 = .02$ (from the table for $a_1 = .01$), $a_2 = .20$ (from $a_1 = .10$), $a_1 = .005$ (from $a_2 = .01$), and $a_1 = .025$ (from $a_2 = .05$).

2. Effect Size, ES. It will be recalled that in formula (2.2.1) the index **d** was defined for one-tailed tests as

$$d = \frac{m_B - m_A}{\sigma},$$

where the alternate hypothesis specifies that $m_B > m_A$, and σ is the common within-population standard deviation (i.e., $\sigma_A = \sigma_B = \sigma$).

Table 2.3.1

Power of t test of $m_1 = m_2$ at $a_1 = .01$

		.10	.20	.30	.40	.50	.60	.70	.80	1.00	1.20	1.40
n	d_c											
8	1.31	02	03	04	05	08	12	14	19	30	43	57
9	1.22	02	03	04	06	09	13	16	22	35	49	63
10	1.14	02	03	04	07	10	14	18	25	40	55	70
11	1.08	02	03	05	07	11	15	21	28	45	61	76
12	1.02	02	03	05	08	12	17	23	31	49	66	81
13	.98	02	03	05	08	13	19	26	34	53	71	85
14	.94	02	03	06	09	14	20	28	38	57	75	88
15	.90	02	04	06	10	15	22	31	41	61	79	90
16	.87	02	04	06	10	16	24	34	44	64	82	92
17	.84	02	04	07	11	18	26	36	47	68	85	94
18	.81	02	04	07	12	19	27	38	49	71	87	95
19	.79	02	04	07	13	20	29	40	51	74	89	96
20	.77	02	04	08	13	21	30	42	54	76	91	97
21	.75	02	05	08	14	22	32	44	56	79	93	98
22	.73	02	05	08	15	23	34	46	59	81	94	98
23	.71	02	05	09	15	24	36	48	61	83	95	99
24	.70	02	05	09	16	25	37	50	64	85	95	99
25	.68	02	05	10	17	27	39	53	66	87	96	99
26	.67	02	05	10	17	28	41	55	68	89	97	99
27	.65	02	05	10	18	29	42	57	70	90	97	*
28	.64	02	05	11	19	30	44	59	72	91	98	
29	.63	02	06	11	19	31	46	60	74	92	98	
30	.62	03	06	11	20	32	48	62	75	93	99	
31	.61	03	06	12	21	34	50	64	77	94	99	
32	.60	03	06	12	22	35	51	66	79	94	99	
33	.59	03	06	13	22	36	52	67	80	95	99	
34	.58	03	06	13	23	37	53	69	81	95	99	
35	.57	03	07	13	24	38	55	70	83	96	*	
36	.56	03	07	14	25	40	56	72	84	96		
37	.55	03	07	14	26	41	58	73	85	97		
38	.55	03	07	15	26	42	60	75	86	97		
39	.54	03	07	15	27	43	61	76	87	98		
40	.53	03	07	15	28	45	62	78	88	98		
42	.52	03	08	16	30	47	64	80	90	98		
44	.51	03	08	17	31	49	67	82	91	99		
46	.49	03	08	18	33	51	69	83	93	99		
48	.48	03	08	19	34	53	71	85	94	99		

Table 2.3.1 *(continued)*

n	d_c	.10	.20	.30	.40	.50	.60	.70	.80	1.00	1.20	1.40
						d						
50	.47	03	09	20	36	55	73	87	95	99	*	*
52	.46	03	09	21	37	57	75	88	95	*		
54	.45	04	10	21	39	59	77	90	96			
56	.45	05	10	22	40	61	79	91	97			
58	.44	05	10	23	41	62	81	92	97			
60	.43	05	11	24	43	64	82	93	98			
64	.42	05	11	26	46	68	85	94	98			
68	.40	05	12	27	49	71	87	96	99			
72	.39	05	12	29	52	74	89	97	99			
76	.38	05	13	31	55	76	91	97	99			
80	.37	05	14	33	57	78	92	98	*			
84	.36	06	15	34	60	81	94	99				
88	.35	06	16	36	62	83	95	99				
92	.35	06	16	38	64	85	96	99				
96	.34	06	17	39	66	86	96	99				
100	.33	06	18	41	69	88	97	*				
120	.30	07	21	49	77	93	99					
140	.28	07	25	57	84	96	*					
160	.26	07	29	63	89	98						
180	.25	08	33	69	93	99						
200	.23	09	37	75	95	*						
250	.21	11	46	84	98							
300	.19	13	55	91	99							
350	.18	16	61	95	*							
400	.16	18	69	97								
450	.16	20	75	98								
500	.15	22	80	99								
600	.13	27	87	*								
700	.12	32	92									
800	.12	37	95									
900	.11	42	97									
1000	.10	46	98									

* Power values below this point are greater than .995.

Table 2.3.2

Power of t test of $m_1 = m_2$ at $a_1 = .05$

							d					
n	d_c	.10	.20	.30	.40	.50	.60	.70	.80	1.00	1.20	1.40
8	.88	07	10	13	19	25	31	38	46	61	74	85
9	.82	07	11	15	20	27	34	41	50	66	79	88
10	.78	08	11	16	22	29	36	45	53	70	83	91
11	.74	08	12	17	23	31	39	48	57	74	86	94
12	.70	08	12	18	25	33	41	51	60	77	89	96
13	.67	08	13	18	26	34	44	54	63	80	91	97
14	.64	08	13	19	27	36	46	57	66	83	93	98
15	.62	08	13	20	28	38	48	59	69	85	94	98
16	.60	09	14	21	30	40	51	62	72	87	95	99
17	.58	09	14	22	31	42	53	64	74	89	96	99
18	.56	09	15	22	32	43	55	66	76	90	97	99
19	.55	09	15	23	33	45	57	68	78	92	98	*
20	.53	09	15	24	34	46	59	70	80	93	98	
21	.52	09	16	25	36	48	60	72	82	94	99	
22	.51	09	16	26	37	50	62	74	83	95	99	
23	.50	10	16	26	38	51	64	76	85	96	99	
24	.48	10	17	27	39	53	66	77	86	96	99	
25	.47	10	17	28	40	54	67	79	88	97	99	
26	.46	10	18	28	41	55	69	80	89	97	*	
27	.46	10	18	29	42	57	70	82	90	98		
28	.45	10	18	30	43	58	72	83	90	98		
29	.44	10	19	30	44	59	73	84	91	98		
30	.43	10	19	31	46	61	74	85	92	99		
31	.42	10	19	32	47	62	76	86	93	99		
32	.42	11	20	33	48	63	77	87	93	99		
33	.41	11	20	33	49	64	78	88	94	99		
34	.40	11	20	34	50	66	79	89	95	99		
35	.40	11	21	34	50	67	80	89	95	99		
36	.39	11	21	35	51	68	81	90	96	99		
37	.39	11	21	36	52	69	82	91	96	*		
38	.38	11	22	36	53	70	83	91	96			
39	.38	11	22	37	54	71	84	92	97			
40	.37	11	22	38	55	72	84	93	97			
42	.36	12	23	39	57	74	86	94	98			
44	.35	12	24	40	59	75	87	95	98			
46	.35	12	24	41	60	77	89	95	99			
48	.34	12	25	43	62	79	90	96	99			

Table 2.3.2 *(continued)*

n	d_c	.10	.20	.30	.40	.50	.60	.70	.80	1.00	1.20	1.40
						d						
50	.33	12	26	44	63	80	91	97	99	*	*	*
52	.33	13	26	45	65	81	92	97	99			
54	.32	13	27	46	66	83	93	98	99			
56	.31	13	28	47	68	84	93	98	99			
58	.31	13	28	49	69	85	94	98	*			
60	.30	13	29	50	70	86	95	98				
64	.29	14	30	52	73	88	96	99				
68	.28	14	31	54	75	90	97	99				
72	.28	15	33	56	77	91	97	99				
76	.27	15	34	58	79	92	98	*				
80	.26	15	35	60	81	93	98					
84	.26	16	36	61	82	94	99					
88	.25	16	37	63	84	95	99					
92	.24	17	38	65	85	96	99					
96	.24	17	40	66	87	96	99					
100	.23	17	41	68	88	97	*					
120	.21	19	46	75	93	99						
140	.20	21	51	80	95	99						
160	.18	23	56	85	97	*						
180	.17	24	60	88	98							
200	.16	26	64	91	99							
250	.15	30	72	96	*							
300	.13	34	79	98								
350	.12	37	84	99								
400	.12	41	88	*								
450	.11	44	91									
500	.10	47	93									
600	.10	53	97									
700	.09	59	98									
800	.08	64	99									
900	.08	68	*									
1000	.07	72										

* Power values below this point are greater than .995.

Table 2.3.3

Power of t test of $m_1 = m_2$ at $a_1 = .10$

		d										
n	d_c	.10	.20	.30	.40	.50	.60	.70	.80	1.00	1.20	1.40
8	.67	13	18	24	30	37	44	53	60	74	85	92
9	.63	14	19	25	32	39	47	56	64	78	88	94
10	.59	14	19	26	34	42	50	59	67	81	91	96
11	.57	14	20	27	35	44	53	62	70	84	93	97
12	.54	15	21	28	37	46	56	65	73	87	94	98
13	.52	15	21	29	38	48	58	68	76	89	96	99
14	.50	15	22	30	40	50	61	70	79	90	97	99
15	.48	15	23	31	42	52	63	72	81	92	97	99
16	.46	16	23	32	43	54	65	75	83	93	98	*
17	.45	16	24	33	44	56	67	76	84	94	98	
18	.44	16	24	34	46	58	69	78	86	95	99	
19	.42	16	25	35	47	59	70	80	87	96	99	
20	.41	16	25	36	48	61	72	82	89	97	99	
21	.40	17	26	37	50	62	74	83	90	97	99	
22	.39	17	26	38	51	64	75	84	91	98	*	
23	.38	17	27	39	52	65	77	86	92	98		
24	.38	17	27	40	53	67	78	87	93	98		
25	.37	17	28	41	55	68	79	88	94	99		
26	.36	18	28	41	56	69	80	89	94	99		
27	.35	18	29	42	57	70	82	90	95	99		
28	.35	18	29	43	58	72	83	91	95	99		
29	.34	18	30	44	59	73	84	91	96	99		
30	.33	18	30	45	60	74	85	92	96	99		
31	.33	19	31	45	61	75	86	93	97	*		
32	.32	19	31	46	62	76	86	93	97			
33	.32	19	32	47	63	77	87	94	97			
34	.31	19	32	48	64	78	88	94	98			
35	.31	19	33	48	65	79	89	95	98			
36	.30	19	33	49	66	80	89	95	98			
37	.30	20	33	50	66	80	90	96	98			
38	.30	20	34	51	67	81	91	96	99			
39	.29	20	34	51	68	82	91	96	99			
40	.29	20	35	52	69	83	92	97	99			
42	.28	20	35	53	70	84	93	97	99			
44	.28	21	36	55	72	85	94	98	99			
46	.27	21	37	56	73	86	94	98	99			
48	.26	21	38	57	75	88	95	98	*			

Table 2.3.3 *(continued)*

n	d_c	.10	.20	.30	.40	.50	.60	.70	.80	1.00	1.20	1.40
50	.26	22	39	58	76	89	96	99	*	*	*	*
52	.25	22	39	59	77	90	96	99				
54	.25	22	40	61	78	90	97	99				
56	.24	22	41	62	80	91	97	99				
58	.24	23	42	63	81	92	97	99				
60	.24	23	42	64	82	93	98	99				
64	.23	24	44	66	83	94	98	*				
68	.22	24	45	68	85	95	99					
72	.21	25	47	70	87	96	99					
76	.21	25	48	71	88	96	99					
80	.20	26	49	73	89	97	99					
84	.20	26	51	74	90	97	*					
88	.19	27	52	76	91	98						
92	.19	27	53	77	92	98						
96	.19	28	54	79	93	99						
100	.18	29	55	80	94	99						
120	.17	31	60	85	96	*						
140	.15	33	65	89	98							
160	.14	35	69	92	99							
180	.14	37	73	94	99							
200	.13	39	76	96	*							
250	.11	44	83	98								
300	.10	48	88	99								
350	.10	52	91	*								
400	.09	55	94									
450	.09	59	96									
500	.08	62	97									
600	.07	67	99									
700	.07	72	99									
800	.06	76	*									
900	.06	80										
1000	.06	83										

* Power values below this point are greater than .995.

Table 2.3.4

Power of t test of $m_1 = m_2$ at $a_2 = .01$

n	d_c	.10	.20	.30	.40	.50	.60	.70	.80	1.00	1.20	1.40
						d						
8	1.49	01	02	02	03	05	07	09	12	21	33	46
9	1.38	01	02	02	04	05	08	11	15	25	39	54
10	1.28	01	02	03	04	06	09	12	17	29	45	61
11	1.21	01	02	03	04	07	10	14	20	33	50	67
12	1.15	01	02	03	05	07	11	16	22	38	55	72
13	1.10	01	02	03	05	08	12	18	25	42	61	77
14	1.05	01	02	03	06	09	14	20	27	46	65	81
15	1.01	01	02	04	06	10	15	22	30	50	70	85
16	.97	01	02	04	07	11	16	24	33	54	73	88
17	.94	01	02	04	07	12	18	26	35	57	77	90
18	.91	01	02	04	08	12	19	28	38	61	80	92
19	.88	01	02	05	08	13	21	30	41	64	83	94
20	.86	01	02	05	09	14	22	32	44	67	85	95
21	.83	01	03	05	09	15	24	34	46	70	87	96
22	.81	01	03	05	10	16	25	36	49	73	89	97
23	.79	01	03	06	10	17	27	38	51	75	91	98
24	.78	01	03	06	11	18	28	40	54	78	92	98
25	.76	01	03	06	11	19	30	42	56	80	93	99
26	.74	01	03	06	12	20	31	44	58	82	95	99
27	.73	01	03	07	12	21	33	46	60	84	95	99
28	.71	02	03	07	13	22	34	48	63	85	96	99
29	.70	02	03	07	14	23	36	50	65	87	97	*
30	.69	02	03	07	14	24	37	52	66	88	97	
31	.68	02	04	08	15	25	39	54	68	89	98	
32	.66	02	04	08	15	26	40	56	70	91	98	
33	.65	02	04	08	16	27	42	57	72	92	98	
34	.64	02	04	08	17	28	43	59	74	92	99	
35	.63	02	04	09	17	30	45	61	75	93	99	
36	.62	02	04	09	18	31	46	62	77	94	99	
37	.62	02	04	09	18	32	48	64	78	95	99	
38	.61	02	04	10	19	33	49	66	80	95	99	
39	.60	02	04	10	20	34	50	67	81	96	*	
40	.59	02	04	10	20	35	52	68	82	96		
42	.58	02	05	11	22	37	55	71	84	97		
44	.56	02	05	12	23	39	57	74	86	98		
46	.55	02	05	12	24	41	60	76	88	98		
48	.54	02	05	13	26	43	62	78	90	99		

Table 2.3.4 *(continued)*

n	d_c	.10	.20	.30	.40	.50	.60	.70	.80	1.00	1.20	1.40
50	.53	02	06	14	27	45	64	81	91	99	*	*
52	.51	02	06	14	28	47	67	82	92	99		
54	.50	02	06	15	30	49	69	84	93	99		
56	.50	02	06	16	31	51	71	86	94	*		
58	.49	02	06	16	32	53	73	87	95			
60	.48	02	07	17	34	55	75	88	96			
64	.46	02	07	18	36	58	78	91	97			
68	.45	02	08	20	39	62	81	93	98			
72	.44	02	08	21	42	65	84	94	98			
76	.42	03	09	23	44	68	86	95	99			
80	.41	03	09	24	47	71	88	96	99			
84	.40	03	10	26	50	74	90	97	99			
88	.39	03	10	27	52	76	91	98	*			
92	.38	03	11	29	54	78	93	98				
96	.38	03	11	30	57	80	94	99				
100	.37	03	12	32	59	82	95	99				
120	.34	04	15	39	69	90	98	*				
140	.31	04	18	47	77	94	99					
160	.29	05	21	54	84	97	*					
180	.27	05	25	60	88	98						
200	.26	06	29	66	92	99						
250	.23	07	36	78	97	*						
300	.21	09	45	86	99							
350	.20	10	53	92	*							
400	.18	12	60	95								
450	.17	14	66	97								
500	.16	16	72	98								
600	.15	20	81	*								
700	.14	24	88									
800	.13	28	92									
900	.12	33	95									
1000	.12	37	97									

* Power values below this point are greater than .995.

Table 2.3.5

Power of t test of $m_1 = m_2$ at $a_2 = .05$

							d					
n	d_c	.10	.20	.30	.40	.50	.60	.70	.80	1.00	1.20	1.40
8	1.07	05	07	09	11	15	20	25	31	46	60	73
9	1.00	05	07	09	12	16	22	28	35	51	65	79
10	.94	06	07	10	13	18	24	31	39	56	71	84
11	.89	06	07	10	14	20	26	34	43	61	76	87
12	.85	06	08	11	15	21	28	37	46	65	80	90
13	.81	06	08	11	16	23	31	40	50	69	83	93
14	.78	06	08	12	17	25	33	43	53	72	86	94
15	.75	06	08	12	18	26	35	45	56	75	88	96
16	.72	06	08	13	19	28	37	48	59	78	90	97
17	.70	06	09	13	20	29	39	51	62	80	92	98
18	.68	06	09	14	21	31	41	53	64	83	94	98
19	.66	06	09	15	22	32	43	55	67	85	95	99
20	.64	06	09	15	23	33	45	58	69	87	96	99
21	.62	06	10	16	24	35	47	60	71	88	97	99
22	.61	06	10	16	25	36	49	62	73	90	97	99
23	.59	06	10	17	26	38	51	64	75	91	98	*
24	.58	06	10	17	27	39	53	66	77	92	98	
25	.57	06	11	18	28	41	55	68	79	93	99	
26	.56	06	11	19	29	42	56	69	80	94	99	
27	.55	06	11	19	30	43	58	71	82	95	99	
28	.54	07	11	20	31	45	59	73	83	96	99	
29	.53	07	12	20	32	46	61	74	85	96	99	
30	.52	07	12	21	33	47	63	76	86	97	*	
31	.51	07	12	21	34	49	64	77	87	97		
32	.50	07	12	22	35	50	65	78	88	98		
33	.49	07	13	22	36	51	67	80	89	98		
34	.48	07	13	23	37	53	68	81	90	98		
35	.48	07	13	23	38	54	70	82	91	98		
36	.47	07	13	24	39	55	71	83	92	99		
37	.46	07	14	25	39	56	72	84	92	99		
38	.46	07	14	25	40	57	73	85	93	99		
39	.45	07	14	26	41	58	74	86	94	99		
40	.45	07	14	26	42	60	75	87	94	99		
42	.43	07	15	27	44	62	77	89	95	99		
44	.42	07	15	28	46	64	79	90	96	*		
46	.41	08	16	30	48	66	81	91	97			
48	.41	08	16	31	49	68	83	92	97			

Table 2.3.5 *(continued)*

n	d_c	.10	.20	.30	.40	.50	.60	.70	.80	1.00	1.20	1.40
50	.40	08	17	32	50	70	84	93	98	*	*	*
52	.39	08	17	34	51	71	86	94	98			
54	.38	08	18	34	53	73	87	95	98			
56	.37	08	18	35	55	74	88	96	99			
58	.37	08	19	36	57	76	89	96	99			
60	.36	08	19	37	58	77	90	97	99			
64	.35	09	20	39	61	80	92	98	99			
68	.34	09	21	41	64	82	93	98	*			
72	.33	09	22	43	66	85	94	99				
76	.32	09	23	45	69	86	95	99				
80	.31	10	24	47	71	88	96	99				
84	.30	10	25	49	73	90	97	99				
88	.30	10	26	51	75	91	98	*				
92	.29	10	27	52	77	92	98					
96	.29	11	28	54	79	93	99					
100	.28	11	29	56	80	94	99					
120	.26	12	34	64	87	97	*					
140	.24	13	38	71	92	99						
160	.22	14	43	76	95	99						
180	.21	16	47	81	97	*						
200	.20	17	51	85	98							
250	.18	20	61	92	99							
300	.16	23	69	96	*							
350	.15	26	75	98								
400	.14	29	81	99								
450	.13	32	85	99								
500	.12	35	88	*								
600	.11	41	93									
700	.10	46	96									
800	.10	52	98									
900	.09	56	99									
1000	.09	61	99									

* Power values below this point are greater than .995.

Table 2.3.6

Power of t test of $m_1 = m_2$ at $a_2 = .10$

n	d_c	.10	.20	.30	.40	.50	.60	.70	.80	1.00	1.20	1.40
8	.88	11	12	15	20	25	31	38	46	61	74	85
9	.82	11	13	16	21	27	34	42	50	66	79	89
10	.78	11	13	17	22	29	37	45	53	70	83	92
11	.74	11	13	18	24	31	39	48	57	74	86	94
12	.70	11	14	19	25	33	42	51	60	77	89	96
13	.67	11	14	19	26	34	44	54	63	80	91	97
14	.64	11	14	20	27	36	46	57	66	83	93	98
15	.62	11	15	21	29	38	49	59	69	85	94	98
16	.60	11	15	21	30	40	51	62	72	87	95	99
17	.58	11	15	22	31	42	53	64	74	89	96	99
18	.56	11	16	23	32	43	55	66	76	90	97	99
19	.55	11	16	24	33	45	57	68	78	92	98	*
20	.53	12	16	24	35	47	59	70	80	93	98	
21	.52	12	17	25	36	48	61	72	82	94	99	
22	.51	12	17	26	37	50	62	74	83	95	99	
23	.50	12	17	26	38	51	64	76	85	96	99	
24	.48	12	18	27	39	53	66	77	86	96	99	
25	.47	12	18	28	40	54	67	79	88	97	99	
26	.46	12	18	29	41	55	69	80	89	97	*	
27	.46	12	19	29	42	57	70	82	90	98		
28	.45	12	19	30	44	58	72	83	90	98		
29	.44	12	19	31	45	59	73	84	91	98		
30	.43	12	20	31	46	61	74	85	92	99		
31	.42	13	20	32	47	62	76	86	93	99		
32	.42	13	20	33	48	63	77	87	93	99		
33	.41	13	21	33	49	64	78	88	94	99		
34	.40	13	21	34	50	66	79	89	95	99		
35	.40	13	21	35	51	67	80	89	95	99		
36	.39	13	22	35	52	68	81	90	96	99		
37	.39	13	22	36	52	69	82	91	96	*		
38	.38	13	22	37	53	70	83	91	96			
39	.38	13	23	37	54	71	84	92	97			
40	.37	13	23	38	55	72	84	93	97			
42	.36	13	24	39	57	74	86	94	98			
44	.35	14	24	40	58	75	87	95	98			
46	.35	14	25	41	60	77	89	95	99			
48	.34	14	25	43	62	79	90	96	99			

Table 2.3.6 *(continued)*

n	d_c	.10	.20	.30	.40	.50	.60	.70	.80	1.00	1.20	1.40
50	.33	14	26	44	63	80	91	97	99	*	*	*
52	.33	14	27	45	65	81	92	97	99			
54	.32	14	27	46	66	83	93	98	99			
56	.31	15	28	47	68	84	93	98	99			
58	.31	15	29	49	69	85	94	98	*			
60	.30	15	29	50	70	86	95	98				
64	.29	15	30	52	73	88	96	99				
68	.28	16	32	54	75	90	97	99				
72	.28	16	33	56	77	91	97	99				
76	.27	16	34	58	79	92	98	*				
80	.26	17	35	60	81	93	98					
84	.26	17	36	61	82	94	98					
88	.25	17	37	63	84	95	99					
92	.24	18	39	65	85	96	99					
96	.24	18	40	66	87	96	99					
100	.23	18	41	68	88	97	99					
120	.21	20	46	75	93	99	*					
140	.20	22	51	80	95	99						
160	.18	23	56	85	97	*						
180	.17	25	60	88	98							
200	.16	26	64	91	99							
250	.15	30	72	96	*							
300	.13	34	79	98								
350	.12	37	84	99								
400	.12	41	88	*								
450	.11	44	91									
500	.10	47	93									
600	.10	53	97									
700	.09	59	98									
800	.08	64	99									
900	.08	68	*									
1000	.07	72										

* Power values below this point are greater than .995.

For two-tailed tests [formula (2.2.2)],

$$d = \frac{|m_A - m_B|}{\sigma},$$

where the alternate hypothesis specifies only that $m_A \neq m_B$.
Provision is made for $d = .10 \,(.10)\, .80 \,(.20)\, 1.40$. Conventional definitions of ES have been offered above, as follows:

> small: $d = .20$,
> medium: $d = .50$,
> large: $d = .80$.

3. Sample Size, **n**. This is the size of *each* of the two samples being compared. Provision is made for $n = 8 \,(1)\, 40 \,(2)\, 60 \,(4)\, 100 \,(20)\, 200 \,(50)$ $500 \,(100)\, 1000$.

The values in the body of the table are the power of the test times 100, i.e., the percentage of tests carried out under the given conditions which will result in the rejection of the null hypothesis. The values are rounded to the *nearest* unit, and they are generally accurate to within ± 1 as tabled (i.e., to within .01).

Illustrative Examples

2.1 An experimental psychologist designs a study to appraise the effect of opportunity to explore a maze without reward on subsequent maze learning in rats. Random samples of 30 cases each are drawn from the available supply and assigned to an experimental (E) group which is given an exploratory period and a control (C) group, which is not. Following this, the 60 rats are tested and the number of trials needed to reach a criterion of two successive errorless runs is determined. The (nondirectional) null hypothesis is $|m_E - m_C| = 0$. He anticipates that the ES would be such that the highest 60% of one population would exceed the lowest 60% of the other, i.e., $U_2 \cong 60\%$ (Section 2.2). Referring to Table 2.2.1, he finds that $U_2 = 59.9\%$ is equivalent to our conventional definition of a medium effect: $d = .50$. That is, the alternative hypothesis is that the population means differ by half a within-population standard deviation. The significance criterion is $a_2 = .05$. What is the power of the test? Summarizing the specifications,

$$a_2 = .05, \qquad d = .50, \qquad n_E = n_C = n = 30.$$

In Table 2.3.5 (for $a_2 = .05$), for column $d = .50$ and row $n = 30$ power equals .47. Thus, for the given sample sizes and using the $a_2 = .05$ significance criterion, the investigator does not quite have a fifty–fifty chance of detecting $d = .50$.

The choice of d need not have proceeded by asserting the expectation that the ES was "medium" and using the conventional $d = .5$ value. Experience with the subjects and the maze in question or reference to the literature may have provided the experimenter with an estimate of the within-population standard deviation of trials scores, σ (say 2.8), and theory or intuition may have suggested a specific value for the experimental effect, $|m_C - m_E|$ ($= 2$ trials, let us say). He would then use the explicit formula (2.2.2),

$$d = \frac{|m_1 - m_2|}{\sigma} = \frac{2}{2.8} = .71.$$

In this case, in Table 2.3.5 with $n = 30$ as before but now with $d = .70$, power is found to be .76 (or by linear interpolation for $d = .71$, power $= .77$).

It can also be argued that, given a theory, the psychologist would probably predict the direction of the difference, say $m_C > m_E$ (i.e., the animals profit from their exploratory experience) and that therefore a directional test should be used. In this case, Table 2.3.2 for $a_1 = .05$ would be used, with the results

for "medium" $d = .50$: $n = 30$,   power $= .61$,
for explicit d (from (2.2.1)) $= .71$: $n = 30$,   power $= .86$.

As described above (Chapter 1, Section 1.2), power is greater for directional tests than nondirectional tests, other things equal, provided that the experimental results are in the anticipated direction. The experimenter is in an embarrassing position when he obtains large experimental effects in the unanticipated direction (Cohen, 1965, pp. 106–111).

This example was chosen, in part, to point out that the frequently selected sample size of 30 does not provide adequate power at the conventional $a_2 = .05$ against a medium ES, which is frequently as large as can reasonably be expected. Only when a large ($d = .80$) ES can be anticipated, for $n = 30$ at $a_2 = .05$, is power as high as most investigators would wish, in this instance .86 (from Table 2.3.5). When a small ($d = .20$) ES is anticipated, for $n = 30$, $a_2 = .05$, power is only .12 (Table 2.3.5)—probably not worth the effort involved in performing the experiment.

2.2 A psychiatric investigator, in pursuing certain endocrinological factors implicated in schizophrenia, performs an experiment in which urine samples of 500 schizophrenics and 500 comparable normals are analyzed for a certain relevant metabolic product which is approximately normally distributed with homogeneous variability. Since the implicated endocrinological factor is only indirectly related to the metabolic product in the urine and perhaps for other reasons, he anticipates only a small ES, specifically that $d = .20$. He selects the conservative significance criterion of $a_2 = .01$. What is the power of his t test? Summarizing the specifications:

$$a_2 = .01, \qquad d = .20, \qquad n_S = n_N = 500.$$

In Table 2.3.4 (for $a_2 = .01$), for column $d = .20$, row $n = 500$, power $= .72$.

Were he to be satisfied with the less stringent $a_2 = .05$ significance criterion, he would find (from Table 2.3.5) power equal to .88. Note that rather large samples are required to detect small effects (at least as we have conventionally defined them). Ordinarily, the investigator seeking to detect a small effect will hardly be able to afford the luxury of a stringent significance criterion such as $a = .01$. He may well want to consider increasing his Type I (a) error risk to perhaps .10 in order to keep the magnitude of his Type II (b) error risk from becoming so large as to make the experiment uninformative in the likely event of a nonsignificant difference. Naturally, the increase in a is made before, not after, the data are collected.

2.3.2   CASE 1: $n_A \neq n_B$, $\sigma_A = \sigma_B$. The power tables will yield useful approximate values when, from the two normal equally varying populations, samples of different sizes are drawn. In such cases, compute the harmonic mean of n_A and n_B,

$$(2.3.1) \qquad\qquad n' = \frac{2n_A\, n_B}{n_A + n_B}$$

and in the n column of the table, find n'.

Power values found under these conditions will be underestimates.[1] However, within the values for n available in the table when n_A/n_B is between .5 and 2.0, the true value will generally be within .01 of the tabled value. Further, once n' is large (say greater than 25), even far greater discrepancies between n_A and n_B will result in trivially small underestimates.[2]

The fact that n_A is not equal to n_B will *not* effect the validity of the interpretation of d in terms of the U and r measures of Section 2.2, provided we continue to conceive of the *populations* as equally numerous, although the *samples* are of unequal n.

---

[1] This is because the table is treating the t test for n as based on $df = 2n' - 2$, when there are actually $df = n_A + n_B - 2$, a larger value.

[2] This is because of the speed with which the t distribution with $df > 50$ approaches that with $df = \infty$, i.e., the normal distribution.

Illustrative Example

   2.3 In a psychological service center, cases are assigned by an essentially random process to different psychotherapeutic techniques, a "standard"
technique (A) and one featuring some innovation (B). After a period of
time, 90 cases have been treated by Method A and 60 cases by Method B.
The investigator wishes to determine whether the new method (B) is better
than the old (A), using final staff conference consensus ratings of improvement as the criterion. He posits an ES such that, with the B population
higher, about 40% ($=\mathbf{U}_1$) of the area covered by both population distributions would not overlap (see Chapter 2, Section 2.2). From Table 2.2.1,
he finds that $\mathbf{U}_1 = 38.2\%$ is equivalent to $\mathbf{d} = .6$. The statement of the problem
implies a directional test, since, presumably he is indifferent to the possibility
that B is worse than A. (Recall that the null hypothesis here is $\mathbf{m}_A \leqq \mathbf{m}_B$,
thus that B worse than A is indistinguishable from B = A.) Accordingly,
he uses a one-tailed test, with, say the $\mathbf{a}_1 = .05$ significance criterion. Thus,
his specifications are

$$\mathbf{a}_1 = .05, \qquad \mathbf{d} = .6\ (\mathbf{U}_1 = 38.2\%), \qquad \mathbf{n}_A = 90 \neq 60 = \mathbf{n}_B$$

   With unequal $\mathbf{n}$, he finds [from (2.3.1)]

$$\mathbf{n}' = \frac{2\mathbf{n}_A\ \mathbf{n}_B}{\mathbf{n}_A + \mathbf{n}_B} = \frac{2(90)\ (60)}{90 + 60} = \frac{10800}{150} = 72.$$

   (Note that $\mathbf{n}'$, the harmonic mean, is smaller than the arithmetic mean,
which is $(90 + 60)/2 = 75$.)
   In Table 2.3.2 (for $\mathbf{a}_1 = .05$), column $\mathbf{d} = .6$, row $\mathbf{n} = 72$, he finds power
equal to .97 (a trivially small underestimate).
   Note that had he performed a *non*directional test which would have
permitted the conclusion that B was worse than A, his power (Table 2.3.5
for $\mathbf{a}_2 = .05$) would have been .94. Power is less, but at this level not much
less; he might consider the possibility of reaching the conclusion that B is
worse than A worth the small loss of power.

   2.3.3.   CASE 2: $\sigma_A \neq \sigma_B$, $\mathbf{n}_A = \mathbf{n}_B$. For normal populations of unequal
variance, the formula for $\mathbf{t}$ does not follow the tabled values for $\mathbf{t}$, that is,
this condition constitutes a "failure of the assumptions" (or more properly
conditions) under which $\mathbf{t}$ is generated. However, there is ample evidence
for the robustness of the $\mathbf{t}$ test despite moderate failure of this assumption
provided that sample sizes are about equal (Scheffé, 1959; Cohen, 1965).
Approximations to the true power values which are adequate for most
purposes are available by using the tables in the ordinary way.
   It should be kept in mind that when $\sigma_A \neq \sigma_B$, the definition of $\mathbf{d}$ will be

slightly modified. Since there is no longer a common within-population σ, **d** is defined as above (formulas (2.2.1) and (2.2.2)), but instead of σ in the denominator, the formula requires the root mean square of σ_A and σ_B, that is, the square root of the mean of the two variances:

$$(2.3.2) \qquad\qquad \sigma' = \sqrt{\frac{\sigma_A{}^2 + \sigma_B{}^2}{2}}.$$

The unequal variability need not affect the conception of **d** developed in Section 2.2. Given that there is a difference between σ_A and σ_B, we merely are using a kind of average within-population standard deviation to standardize the difference between means. It is not the arithmetic mean of σ_A and σ_B, but, as noted, the root mean square. (However, unless σ_A and σ_B differ markedly, σ' will not differ greatly from the arithmetic mean of σ_A and σ_B.)

In interpreting **d** for this case, the **U** (percent nonoverlap) measures can no longer be generally defined and the Table 2.2.1 **U** columns will not obtain. However, interpreting **d** in terms of **r** and **r**^{2} proceeds completely unaffected by $\sigma_A \neq \sigma_B$, and the conventional definitions of small, medium, and large **d** can also continue to be used.

Note that if $\sigma_A \neq \sigma_B$ and it is also the case that $n_A \neq n_B$, the nominal values for **t** and power at a given significance criterion, **a**, may differ greatly from the true values (Scheffé, 1959; Cohen, 1965, p. 115). Under these conditions ($\sigma_A \neq \sigma_B$ and $n_A \neq n_B$, simultaneously), the values in Tables 2.3 may be greatly in error.

Illustrative Example

2.4 A labor economist plans a sample survey of men and women workers in a given occupation to determine whether their mean weekly wages differ. He proceeds to do a **t** test,[3] using random samples of 100 cases in each group and a nondirectional significance criterion of $a_2 = .01$. He deems it quite possible that the wage variability differs between the two populations, i.e., $\sigma_A \neq \sigma_B$. He may arrive at the ES = **d** he is interested in detecting in any of the following ways:

1. Explicit **d**. He may plan for allowing that the difference between means, $|m_A - m_B|$, is $2.00 a week, and that the "average" variability of the two populations is $4.00. Note that this value is not the standard deviation of either the population of men workers or that of women workers,

---

[3] Departure from normality of the population distributions should not materially affect the validity of the **t** test and power estimate for samples of this size.

but the root mean square of their respective population standard deviations, σ' (formula (2.3.2)). He then finds **d** by formula (2.2.2), at \$2.00/\$4.00 = .5.

2. Direct Use of **d**. From the experience with the **d** concept, he may directly posit **d** = .5, or arrive at that value as a convention. Although the unit he is using is σ' and not σ, this need not substantially alter his conception of **d**.

3. Correlation and Proportion of Variance. If he finds it conceptually convenient to work in correlational terms, he may conceive of the ES he seeks to detect as a degree of (point biserial) correlation between sex and weekly wage as **r** $\cong$ .25, or as the amount of wage variance associated with sex as $\mathbf{r}^2 \cong .06$. In Table 2.2.1, he finds that **r** = .243 and $\mathbf{r}^2 = .059$ are equivalent to **d** = .5. The fact that $\sigma_A \neq \sigma_B$ does not at all affect the validity of the correlational interpretation of a mean difference. Note, however, that under these conditions the **U** measures no longer apply.

Thus, by any of the above routes, we have the specifications:

$$\mathbf{a}_2 = .01, \qquad \mathbf{d} = .5, \qquad \mathbf{n}_A = \mathbf{n}_B = 100.$$

In Table 2.3.4, for column **d** = .5, row **n** = 100, he finds power equal to .82. If he is prepared to work with the less stringent $\mathbf{a}_2 = .05$, he would find from Table 2.3.5 power equal to .94. On the other hand, if he is prepared to restrict his test to detecting a wage difference favoring men workers and not the opposite, he would use the $\mathbf{a}_1 = .01$ level and from Table 2.3.1 find power = .88.

2.3.4 CASE 3: ONE SAMPLE OF **n** OBSERVATIONS. Up to this point we have considered the most frequent application of the **t** test, i.e., to cases involving the difference between two sample means where we test the hypothesis that two population means are equal or, equivalently, that their difference is zero. The **t** test can also be used with a single sample of observations to test the hypothesis that the population mean equals some specified value, $\mathbf{H}_0 : \mathbf{m} = \mathbf{c}$. The value specified is relevant to some theory under consideration. As an example, consider an anthropological field study of a preliterate group in which a random sample of **n** children is tested by means of a "culture-fair" intelligence test which yields an IQ whose mean, as standardized in Western culture, is 100. The null hypothesis then is that the population mean for the preliterate children is 100. As another example, consider an attitude scale so constructed that a neutral position is represented by a value of 6 (as in Thurstone equal-appearing interval scaling). For a single sample of **n** subjects, one can test the null hypothesis that the population from whence they are drawn is, on the average, neutral, i.e., $\mathbf{H}_0 : \mathbf{m} = 6$. Rejection with a sample mean greater than 6 yields the conclusion that the population is on the average "favorable" toward the social object, and with less than 6 that the population is on the average "unfavorable."

For the one-sample case (Case 3), we define

(2.3.3) $$\mathbf{d}_3' = \frac{\mathbf{m} - \mathbf{c}}{\sigma}$$

as the ES index. Conceptually there has been no change: $\mathbf{d}_3'$ is the difference between the (alternate) population mean (**m**) and the mean specified by the null hypothesis (**c**), standardized by the population standard deviation (σ). Since **c** is conceived as the mean of a normal population whose standard deviation is also σ, i.e., the population specified by the null hypothesis, the interpretation of $\mathbf{d}_3'$ proceeds exactly as described in Section 2.2 with regard to Table 2.2.1 and the operational definition of small, medium, and large effects.

However, the tables cannot be used as for the Case 0 two-sample test for two reasons:

1.   In the statistical test for Case 0, there are two sample means, each of **n** cases, each contributing sampling error to the observed sample difference between means, while in the one-sample test, there is only one sample mean based on **n** cases, the value **c** being a hypothetical population parameter and thus without sampling error.

2.   The power tables were computed on the basis that **n** is the size of each of two samples and that therefore the **t** test would be based on $2(\mathbf{n} - 1)$ degrees of freedom. In the one-sample case, **t** is perforce based on only $\mathbf{n} - 1$ degrees of freedom.

Thus, if one simply used the power tables directly for $\mathbf{d}_3'$ and **n** for the one-sample case, one would be presuming (*a*) twice as much sampling error with consequently less power and (*b*) twice the number of degrees of freedom with consequently more power than the values on which the tables' preparation was predicated. These are not, however, equal influences; unless the sample size is small (say less than 25 or 30), the effect of the underestimation of the degrees of freedom is negligible. On the other hand, the doubling of the sampling error would have a substantial effect for all values of **n**. However, the latter is readily compensated for. For the one-sample case, use the power tables with **n** and

(2.3.4) $$\mathbf{d} = \mathbf{d}_3'\sqrt{2}.$$

Multiplying $\mathbf{d}_3'$ by $\sqrt{2}$ (approximately 1.4) compensates for the tables' assumption of double the error variance. Another problem resulting from the use of **n** is that the tabled value for power presumes that the degrees of freedom are $2(n - 1)$, when actually there are only $n - 1$ degrees of freedom. Since t approximates the limiting normal distribution fairly well even when its degrees of freedom are as few as 25 or 30, power values based on double the actual degrees of freedom will not be materially overestimated except in small samples.

Seeking values for $d = d_3'\sqrt{2}$ raises the troublesome problem of numbers intermediate between the ones tabled. However, linear interpolation between power values will, except in rare instances, provide approximate power values which will differ from the true ones by no more than one or two units.

The value of d_3' (*not* d) may be arrived at (or interpreted) through the equivalences with the U and r statistics (Section 2.2 and Table 2.2.1). It requires the further conceptualization that c [the "null" value of the population mean, formula (2.3.3)] is the mean of a normal population whose σ and size are equal to that of the population being sampled.

In summary, for Case 3, one defines d_3' as above and interprets it exactly as described in Section 2.2, but values for power are sought in the power tables by means of $d = d_3'\sqrt{2}$. The resulting value is, except for very small samples, a very slight overestimate.

Illustrative Example

2.5 It can be taken as known because of extensive record keeping over a long period, that under standard conditions a given strain of laboratory rats has a mean weight gain of 70 grams from birth to 90 days. To test the implications of a developmental theory, an experiment is performed in which a sample of 60 animals is reared from birth in total darkness. The investigator is interested in whether, under these experimental conditions, the mean weight gain of a population of animals departs from the standard population mean of 70 in either direction, even slightly. Thus, the null hypothesis he tests is $H_0: m = c = 70$. The investigator accepts $d_3' = .20$ [formula (2.3.3)] as a conventional operational definition of a slight departure. He uses the relatively lenient significance criterion of $a_2 = .10$.

In order to allow for the fact that we have only one sample mean contributing to error, rather than the two which the construction of the tables presumes, the tables must be considered not for d_3', but using formula (2.3.4), for $d = d_3'\sqrt{2} = .20 \ (1.4) = .28$. Thus, the specifications for estimating power are

$$a_2 = .10, \qquad d = .28, \qquad n = 60.$$

In Table 2.3.6. (for $a_2 = .10$), for row $b = 60$, he finds power in columns $d = .20$ and $d = .30$ to be .29 and .50, respectively. Linear interpolation between these values yields approximate power at $d = .28$ of $.8(.50 - .29)$ $+ .29 = .46$.

2.3.5   CASE 4: ONE SAMPLE OF **n** DIFFERENCES BETWEEN PAIRED OBSERVATIONS. Although the general one-sample case as described in Case 3 above does not occur with much frequency in behavioral science applications, a special form of it appears quite frequently. Data are frequently gathered in **X**, **Y** pairs which are matched in some relevant way so that there are **n** pairs of **X**, **Y** observations. The **t** test of the $m_X - m_Y$ difference proceeds with the paired differences, $X - Y = Z$. Since $m_X - m_Y = m_{(X-Y)} = m_Z$, the null hypothesis that $m_X - m_Y = 0$, or equivalently that $m_X = m_Y$, is identical to the null hypothesis that $m_Z = 0$. This in turn means that the one-sample formula for d_3' (2.3.3) has $c = 0$ and becomes

$$(2.3.5) \qquad\qquad d_Z' = \frac{m_Z}{\sigma_Z}.$$

The **Z** subscript is used to emphasize the fact that our raw score unit is no longer **X** or **Y**, but **Z**. If the investigator is content to work with σ_Z as the standardizing unit, he can proceed to do so as described for Case 3, using d_Z', and looking in the power tables for $d = d_Z'\sqrt{2}$ [formula (2.3.4) for **Z**].

Note, however, that the **t** test predicated here is the one described in textbooks as being for matched, dependent, or *correlated* means. If one were to compute the product moment **r** between the **X** and **Y** values for each pair in the population, the result would in general be a nonzero value. Indeed, since matching is an experimental design technique used to remove irrelevant sources of variance (see above, section 1.3), in practice such an **r** will be positive and material, say at least greater than $+ .30$. In contrast, with independent samples such as have been described in previous sections of this chapter, the random pairing of **X** and **Y** values implied would perforce yield a population **r** of zero.

Now, the σ_Z of the denominator in formula (2.3.4), and hence the unit in which the ES index d_Z' for the difference in matched pairs is expressed, is given by

$$(2.3.6) \qquad\qquad \sigma_Z = \sigma_{X-Y} = \sqrt{\sigma_X^2 + \sigma_Y^2 - 2r\sigma_X\sigma_Y}.$$

Note that as **r** (the population between **X** and **Y** as paired) increases, σ_Z decreases. In the case of matched pairs here being considered, on the assumption of equal variance, i.e., $\sigma_X^2 = \sigma_Y^2 = \sigma^2$,

$$(2.3.7) \qquad\qquad \sigma_Z = \sigma_{X-Y} = \sqrt{2\sigma^2 - 2r\sigma^2} = \sigma\sqrt{2(1 - r)}.$$

Thus, the relative size of the standardizing unit for the d_Z' of Case 4 (dependent) to the **d** of Case 0 (independent) is $\sigma\sqrt{2(1-r)}/\sigma = \sqrt{2(1-r)}$. In other words, a given difference between population means for matched (dependent) samples is standardized by a value which is $\sqrt{2(1-r)}$ as large as would be the case were they independent. Alternatively (and equivalently), the d_z' value used as an ES index for means from matched samples, when expressed in the *same* terms as for independent samples, namely σ, the common within-population standard deviation, is $1/\sqrt{2(1-r)}$ larger than the **d** value for the same raw score difference in independent samples.

Although one can treat the matched pairs in Case 3 form, the standardizing unit, σ_z, will vary in size inversely with the size of r, as shown in formula (2.3.7.). When no estimate of **r** can be made, one has no choice but simply to apply the Case 3 procedure to the one sample of paired differences **Z**, keeping in mind that the d_z' unit is σ_z. With an estimate of **r** available, a preferable procedure is to use as the ES index

$$(2.3.8) \qquad d_4' = \frac{m_X - m_Y}{\sigma},$$

Note that this is identically the same index as the **d** of formulas (2.2.1) and (2.2.2), the difference between means standardized by the within-population σ. As was the case for d_3', all the interpretive material (e.g., **U, r, r²**) of Section 2.2 holds. However, for correct power values, the value located in the power tables is *not* d_4', but rather

$$(2.3.9) \qquad d = \frac{d_4'}{\sqrt{1-r}}$$

As in Case 3, this procedure leads to an overestimate of power which is trivial for all but small samples, since the tables assume $2(n-1)$ degrees of freedom where only $n-1$ are actually available.

The advantages of matching can now be made readily apparent. Consider an investigation which is to concern itself with the question of a sex difference in some aptitude variable. Assume that elementary school boys and girls each have population $\sigma = 16$, and one wishes to detect a difference in raw population means of 8 points, using samples of $n = 40$ subjects. Assume the test is to be performed at the two-tailed .05 level ($a_2 = .05$). The relevant power table is 2.3.5.

Case 0. Since the plan is to work with independent samples of 40 boys and 40 girls, we use $n = 40$ and

$$d = \frac{|m_A - m_B|}{\sigma} = \frac{8}{16} = .5$$

to find power = .60.

Case 4. Instead of independent samples of boys and girls, the investigator plans to draw 40 brother–sister pairs to detect the 8 points difference. There is the same ES, namely,

$$d_4' = \frac{|m_x - m_y|}{\sigma} = \frac{8}{16} = .5.$$

However, he estimates the **r** between brothers and sisters on this aptitude variable as .6 and in Table 2.3.5 for **n** = 40 and

$$d = \frac{d_4'}{\sqrt{1 - r}} = \frac{.5}{\sqrt{1 - .60}} = \frac{.5}{.6325} = .79,$$

he finds power $\cong$ .93. Thus, given the same 8 point or .5 standardized difference between means to detect, the use of the matched pairs design with an estimated matching **r** of .60 has resulted in power of .93 instead of only .60.

Note that if **r** were .40 instead of .60, he would look for the value

$$d = \frac{.5}{\sqrt{1 - .40}} = \frac{.5}{.7746} = .65,$$

and find power $\cong$ .81 (by linear interpolation), a lesser increase because the matching **r** is smaller.

Illustrative Examples

2.6 An educational researcher has developed two different programed tests for teaching elementary algebra. From a high school grade, he selects 50 pairs of pupils so that the two members of each pair have IQs within 3 points of each other. He randomly assigns the members of each pair to the A and B programs, and following instruction, tests all subjects on a common algebra achievement test. He wishes to detect a difference [formula (2.3.8)]

$$d_4' = \frac{m_A - m_B}{\sigma} = .4,$$

a small to medium value, using the a_2 = .05 significance criterion. It would not be correct to look for the value in the power table d_4' = .40, because this value does not take into account the advantageous effect of matching. The appropriate ES for this situation is [formula (2.3.9)]:

$$d = \frac{d_4'}{\sqrt{1 - r}} = \frac{.4}{\sqrt{1 - r}}.$$

r is the population correlation between IQ-matched pairs in algebra achievement. It is also the population r between IQ and algebra achievement.[4] From past educational research, or from the sample data (if this power analysis is being performed *post hoc*), he can estimate the population r as .55. Thus,

$$d = \frac{.4}{\sqrt{1 - .55}} = \frac{.4}{.6708} = .60.$$

If he were lacking a basis for estimating r, the investigator would have reached the same result if he had postulated that the ES he was seeking to detect in terms of paired differences in the achievement test, $A - B = Z$ units, was [from formula (2.3.5)] $d_Z' = .42$, so that, in Case 3 fashion, he would use the power tables for $d = .42\sqrt{2} \cong .60$ [formula (2.3.4)].

Thus, in either instance, summarizing his specifications:

$$a_2 = .05, \qquad d = .60, \qquad n = 50.$$

From Table 2.3.5, column $d = .60$, row $n = 50$, he finds power $= .84$.

Note that had the same problem been undertaken with *independent* random samples of 50 cases with the same ES, namely $d = .40$, power would be only .50 (Table 2.3.5). The effect of matching with an r of .55 makes the effective d equal to .60 with a resultant large increase in power (from .50 to .84).

2.7 Many behavioral science researchers use the "own-control" principle, i.e., each subject is observed under two conditions, X and Y, and the experimental issue is the existence of a difference between m_X and m_Y. Thus, X, Y constitute the paired observations and the significance test is a straightforward instance of Case 4. Sometimes Y and X represent "before" and "after" some intervening experimental manipulation whose effect on a dependent variable is to be scrutinized. (In their failure to control for other concomitants of time, such studies may be misleading.)

Consider a study to appraise the efficacy of prescribing a program of diet and exercises to a group of overweight soldiers. The researcher gets from each subject his "before" weight X, prescribes the program, and checks the "after" weight Y 60 days later. The study employs a sample of 80 subjects. The researcher wishes to know the power of a test at $a_1 = .01$ to detect a mean loss ($Z = X - Y$) of 4 lb where the estimate of the population $\sigma = 12$ lb. Thus [from formula (2.3.8)], $d_4' = 4/12 = .33$. He may estimate

---

[4] Strictly speaking, this is true only if matching on IQ had been perfect. The postulated matching (within 3 points) approaches closely enough to make the equation of the two r's substantially accurate.

that under these circumstances the population **r** of before with after weight would be in the vicinity of .80. Thus, his effective **d** [from formula (2.3.9)] is

$$\mathbf{d} = \frac{.33}{\sqrt{1 - .80}} = \frac{.33}{.4472} = .74.$$

Alternatively, he might have avoided the need to estimate **r** and reasoned that, considering the distribution of weight loss Z, he wanted to detect a mean loss of about .5 of the standard deviation of weight *losses*, i.e. [formula (2.3.5)]

$$\mathbf{d_z}' = \frac{\mathbf{m_z}}{\sigma_\mathbf{z}} = .5.$$

To find the effective **d**, $.5\sqrt{2} = .71$, or, in this instance, about the same value (.74) found from the approach via formula (2.3.9).

Summarizing the specifications:

$$\mathbf{a}_1 = .01, \qquad \mathbf{d} = .74, \qquad \mathbf{n} = 60.$$

In Table 2.3.1 (for $\mathbf{a}_1 = .01$), in the row $\mathbf{n} = 60$, columns $\mathbf{d} = .70$ and .80, we find respectively power of .93 and .98 between which linear interpolation gives power of approximately .95. Thus, the researcher is almost certain of detecting a mean loss of 4 lb at the $\mathbf{a}_1 = .01$ level, with $\mathbf{n} = 60$.

Note how a relatively small $\mathbf{d_4}'$ of .33 becomes a **d** for table entry of .74 which yields a high power value because of the effectiveness of "own-control" matching. Such large matching **r**'s are not infrequent in own-control designs in behavioral science.

2.4   SAMPLE SIZE TABLES

The tables in this section use values for the significance criterion, the ES to be detected, and the *desired power* to determine the sample size. They would therefore be of primary utility in the planning of experiments to provide a basis for the decision as to how many sampling units (**n**) are to be used. Although decisions about sample size in behavioral science are frequently made by appeal to tradition or precedent, ready availability of data, or intuition (Cohen, 1965, p. 97ff), unless Type II error rate considerations contribute to the decision, they can hardly be rational.

2.4.1   CASE 0: $\sigma_A = \sigma_B$, $\mathbf{n}_A = \mathbf{n}_B$. As was done in Section 2.3 for the power tables, the use of the sample size tables is first described for the conditions for which they were optimally designed, Case 0, where they yield the sample size, **n**, for each of two independent samples drawn from normal populations having equal variances. Their use in other cases is described later. Tables are used for **a**, **d**, and the desired power;

1. Significance Criterion, **a**. The same values of **a** are provided as for the power tables. For each of the following **a** levels, a table is provided: $a_1 = .01$ ($a_2 = .02$), $a_1 = .05$ ($a_2 = .10$), $a_1 = .10$ ($a_2 = .20$), $a_2 = .01$ ($a_1 = .005$), and $a_2 = .05$ ($a_1 = .025$).

2. Effect Size, **d**. This value is defined and interpreted as above [formulas (2.2.1, 2.2.2)] and used as in the power tables. The same provision is made: .10 (.10) .80 (.20) 1.40.

To find **n** for a value of **d** not provided, an adequate approximation is given by substituting in the following:

$$(2.4.1) \qquad\qquad n = \frac{n_{.10}}{100d^2} + 1$$

where $n_{.10}$ is the necessary sample size for the given **a** and desired power at $d = .10$, and **d** is the nontabulated ES. Round the result to the nearest integer.[5]

3. Desired Power. The sample size tables list desired values of .25, .50, .60, 2/3, .70 (.05), .95, .99.

Some comment about the selection of the above values is in order. The .25 value is given only to help provide a frame of reference in sample size determination; it seems very unlikely that a behavioral scientist would normally *desire* only one chance in four of rejecting a null hypothesis. The values are about equally spaced between .50 and .99. An exception to this equality of power interval is the provision of power of 2/3. This was made so as to give the sample size at which the odds are two to one that a given **d** would be detected.

Entries for desired power values of .99, .95, and .90 are offered. This makes possible the setting of Type II error risk equal to the conventional Type I, or **a**, risks of .01, .05, and .10. There are conceivable research circumstances where, given an alternate-hypothetical value of **d**, the investigator may wish to equalize his Type I (**a**) and Type II (**b** = 1 − power) risks. The tables will accommodate this demand and provide the **n** values to accomplish this aim at conventional **a** levels.

---

[5] The +1 in the formula is optimal for tests at $a_2 = .05$ ($a_1 = .025$). Slightly greater accuracy is obtained if constants other than 1 are added at other **a** levels, as follows:
   +1.5 at $a_2 = .01$ ($a_1 = .005$) and $a_1 = .01$ ($a_2 = .02$),
   + .7 at $a_1 = .05$ ($a_2 = .10$), and
   + .4 at $a_1 = .10$ ($a_1 = .20$).
These constants are empirical and were determined by averaging discrepancies over the range power $\geq .70$, $.20 \leq d \leq 1.00$.

Table 2.4.1

n to detect d by t test

$a_1 = .01 \ (a_2 = .02)$

Power	.10	.20	.30	.40	.50	.60	.70	.80	1.00	1.20	1.40
.25	547	138	62	36	24	17	13	10	7	5	4
.50	1083	272	122	69	45	31	24	18	12	9	7
.60	1332	334	149	85	55	38	29	22	15	11	8
2/3	1552	382	170	97	62	44	33	25	17	12	9
.70	1627	408	182	103	66	47	35	27	18	13	10
.75	1803	452	202	114	74	52	38	30	20	14	11
.80	2009	503	224	127	82	57	42	33	22	15	12
.85	2263	567	253	143	92	64	48	37	24	17	13
.90	2605	652	290	164	105	74	55	42	27	20	15
.95	3155	790	352	198	128	89	66	51	33	23	18
.99	4330	1084	482	272	175	122	90	69	45	31	23

$a_1 = .05 \ (a_2 = .10)$

Power	.10	.20	.30	.40	.50	.60	.70	.80	1.00	1.20	1.40
.25	189	48	21	12	8	6	5	4	3	2	2
.50	542	136	61	35	22	16	12	9	6	5	4
.60	721	181	81	46	30	21	15	12	8	6	5
2/3	862	216	96	55	35	25	18	14	9	7	5
.70	942	236	105	60	38	27	20	15	10	7	6
.75	1076	270	120	68	44	31	23	18	11	8	6
.80	1237	310	138	78	50	35	26	20	13	9	7
.85	1438	360	160	91	58	41	30	23	15	11	8
.90	1713	429	191	108	69	48	36	27	18	13	10
.95	2165	542	241	136	87	61	45	35	22	16	12
.99	3155	789	351	198	127	88	65	50	32	23	17

$a_1 = .10 \ (a_2 = .20)$

Power	.10	.20	.30	.40	.50	.60	.70	.80	1.00	1.20	1.40
.25	74	19	9	5	3	3	2	2	2	2	2
.50	329	82	37	21	14	10	7	5	4	3	2
.60	471	118	53	30	19	14	10	8	5	4	3
2/3	586	147	65	37	24	17	12	10	6	4	3
.70	653	163	73	41	27	19	14	11	7	5	4
.75	766	192	85	48	31	22	16	13	8	6	4
.80	902	226	100	57	36	26	19	14	10	7	5
.85	1075	269	120	67	43	30	22	17	11	8	6
.90	1314	329	146	82	53	37	27	21	14	10	7
.95	1713	428	191	107	69	48	35	27	18	12	9
.99	2604	651	290	163	104	73	53	41	26	18	14

Table 2.4.1 *(continued)*

Power	.10	.20	.30	.40	.50	.60	.70	.80	1.00	1.20	1.40
					$a_2 = .01$ ($a_1 = .005$) d						
.25	725	183	82	47	31	22	17	13	9	7	6
.50	1329	333	149	85	55	39	29	22	15	11	9
.60	1603	402	180	102	66	46	34	27	18	13	10
2/3	1810	454	203	115	74	52	39	30	20	14	11
.70	1924	482	215	122	79	55	41	32	21	15	12
.75	2108	528	236	134	86	60	45	35	23	17	13
.80	2338	586	259	148	95	67	49	38	25	18	14
.85	2611	654	292	165	106	74	55	43	28	20	15
.90	2978	746	332	188	120	84	62	48	31	22	17
.95	3564	892	398	224	144	101	74	57	37	26	20
.99	4808	1203	536	302	194	136	100	77	50	35	26

Power	.10	.20	.30	.40	.50	.60	.70	.80	1.00	1.20	1.40
					$a_2 = .05$ ($a_1 = .025$) d						
.25	332	84	38	22	14	10	8	6	5	4	3
.50	769	193	86	49	32	22	17	13	9	7	5
.60	981	246	110	62	40	28	21	16	11	8	6
2/3	1144	287	128	73	47	33	24	19	12	9	7
.70	1235	310	138	78	50	35	26	20	13	10	7
.75	1389	348	155	88	57	40	29	23	15	11	8
.80	1571	393	175	99	64	45	33	26	17	12	9
.85	1797	450	201	113	73	51	38	29	19	14	10
.90	2102	526	234	132	85	59	44	34	22	16	12
.95	2600	651	290	163	105	73	54	42	27	19	14
.99	3675	920	409	231	148	103	76	58	38	27	20

However, in the judgment of the author, for most behavioral science research (although admitting of many exceptions), power values as large as .90–.99 would demand sample sizes so large as to exceed an investigator's resources. Even when, with much effort or at much cost, these large **n**'s can be attained, they are probably inefficient, given the nature of statistical inference and the sociology of science.

Why not seek power approaching 1.00, or equivalently, **b** risks close to zero? Why not use the simple principle, "the smaller the Type II error, the better"? For reasons that parallel the rejection of this principle as an operational principle for setting **a** levels. Other things equal, if **a** is made vanishingly small, power becomes quite small. Similarly, if **b** is made very small (desired power very large), other things being equal, required sample sizes become very large. The behavioral scientist must set desired power values as well as desired **a** significance criteria on the basis of the consideration of the seriousness of the consequences of the two kinds of errors and the cost of obtaining data. He cannot literally place a dollar value on the "cost" of each kind of error, as can the industrial quality control engineer who uses exactly the same formal statistical inferential procedures. He can, however, approximate this approach by subjectively weighing the gravity of these two possibilities and the cost of generating data (but see Overall & Dalal, 1965).

The view offered here is that more often than not, the behavioral scientist will decide that Type I errors, which result in false positive claims, are more serious and therefore to be more stringently guarded against than Type II errors, which result in false negative claims. The notion that failure to find is less serious than finding something that is not there accords with the conventional scientific view.

It is proposed here as a convention that, when the investigator has no other basis for setting the desired power value, the value .80 be used. This means that **b** is set at .20. This arbitrary but reasonable value is offered for several reasons (Cohen, 1965, pp. 98–99). The chief among them takes into consideration the implicit convention for **a** of .05. The **b** of .20 is chosen with the idea that the general relative seriousness of these two kinds of errors is of the order of .20/.05, i.e., that Type I errors are of the order of four times as serious as Type II errors. This .80 desired power convention is offered with the hope that it will be ignored whenever an investigator can find a basis in his substantive concerns in his specific research investigation to choose a value *ad hoc*.

Returning to the Case 0 use of the **n** tables and summarizing, the investigator finds (*a*) the table for the significance criterion (**a**) he is using, and looks for (*b*) the standardized difference between the population means (**d**) along the horizontal stub and (*c*) the desired power along the vertical stub. These determine **n**, the necessary size of *each* sample to detect **d** at the **a** significance criterion with the desired power.

Illustrative Examples

2.8 Reconsider example 2.1 for the Case 0 use of the power tables in which an experimental psychologist is studying the effect of opportunity to explore a maze on subsequent maze-learning in rats. As described there, initially he wished to detect an ES of **d** = .50 at **a**$_2$ = .05. His plan to use **n** = 30 animals in each of his E and C groups resulted in a power estimate of .47. He will likely consider this value too low. Now let us assume that he wishes power to be .80 and wants to know the sample size necessary to accomplish this. His specifications thus are

$$\mathbf{a}_2 = .05, \quad \mathbf{d} = .50, \quad \text{power} = .80.$$

In Table 2.4.1 for $\mathbf{a}_2 = .05$, column $\mathbf{d} = .50$, row power $= .80$, $\mathbf{n}$ ($= \mathbf{n}_C = \mathbf{n}_E$) equals 64. He will need two samples of 64 animals each to have an .80 probability of detecting $\mathbf{d} = .50$ at $\mathbf{a}_2 = .05$. Thus, under these conditions, he will have to slightly more than double his planned $\mathbf{n}$ of 30 per group to go from power of .47 to power of .80.

If, on the other hand, he had reason to anticipate a higher $\mathbf{d}$, say of .80 (our conventional definition of a large ES), which he wished to detect with the same power at the same $\mathbf{a}$ level, then

$$\mathbf{a}_2 = .05, \quad \mathbf{d} = .80, \quad \text{power} = .80.$$

In the same Table 2.4.1 for $\mathbf{a}_2 = .05$, column $\mathbf{d} = .80$, row power $= .80$, he finds $\mathbf{n} = 26$ animals per group.

Alternatively, if he had reason to expect $\mathbf{d} = .20$ (our conventional definition of a small ES), for the same significance criterion and desired power, the specifications are:

$$\mathbf{a}_2 = .05, \quad \mathbf{d} = .20, \quad \text{power} = .80.$$

Again in Table 2.4.1 for $\mathbf{a}_2 = .05$, column $\mathbf{d} = .20$, the same row power $= .80$, $\mathbf{n}$ is 393 for *each* group.

This example illustrates dramatically the importance of putting oneself in the position to estimate ES in experimental planning. Depending on whether one posits $\mathbf{d} = .20$ or .80, for representative conditions (i.e., $\mathbf{a}_2 = .05$, power $= .80$), one needs two samples of 26 or 393 animals for the Case 0 design. It seems fairly apparent that experimental planning can hardly proceed in the absence of a prior rendering of judgment about the size of the effect one wishes to detect.

The researcher can, of course, reduce the $\mathbf{n}$ demanded by making his specifications less stringent with regard to either the significance level or the desired power (or both), if there are tolerable alternatives.

Thus, to take an extreme case with regard to the significance criterion, he can both increase his $\mathbf{a}$ risk to .10 and further define "the existence of the phenomenon" in directional terms, i.e., predict that $\mathbf{m}_E < \mathbf{m}_C$. Keeping the other specifications for the original problem, he has:

$$\mathbf{a}_1 = .10, \quad \mathbf{d} = .50, \quad \text{power} = .80.$$

In Table 2.4.1 for $\mathbf{a}_1 = .10$, for column $\mathbf{d} = .50$, row power $= .80$, he finds $\mathbf{n}$ ($= \mathbf{n}_C = \mathbf{n}_E$) $= 36$, compared with $\mathbf{n} = 64$ for $\mathbf{a}_2 = .05$ (same $\mathbf{d}$ and power).

Or, he can increase his **b** risk and settle for a 2:1 chance of detecting his assumed **d** = .50, i.e.,

$$\mathbf{a}_2 = .05, \quad \mathbf{d} = .50, \quad \text{power} = 2/3.$$

In Table 2.4.1 for $\mathbf{a}_2 = .05$, for column $\mathbf{d} = .40$, row power = 2/3, he finds **n** ($= \mathbf{n}_C = \mathbf{n}_E$) = 47, again compared with **n** = 64 for power = .80 (same **a** and **d**).

If he relaxes both **a** and desired power as above simultaneously, the specifications are now

$$\mathbf{a}_1 = .10, \quad \mathbf{d} = .50, \quad \text{power} = 2/3.$$

In Table 2.4.1 for $\mathbf{a}_1 = .10$, for column $\mathbf{d} = .50$ and row power = 2/3, he finds **n** ($= \mathbf{n}_C = \mathbf{n}_E$) = 24 compared with 64 for more stringent **a** and power (for the same **d**).

Experimental planning will frequently involve the study of the **n** demanded by various combinations of levels of **a**, desired power, and possibly **d**, with a final choice being determined by the specific circumstances of a given research (for illustration, see example 3.4 in the next chapter). If no acceptable combination yields an **n** within the resources of the investigator, the feasibility of more powerful designs (e.g., Case 4 for matched pairs) should be considered.

2.9 Consider again the circumstances of the investigation of an endocrinological factor in schizophrenia, presented above in example 2.2. The design calls for a test of the significance of the difference between independent means of hospitalized schizophrenics and normal controls, and the investigator has large resources of patients and laboratory facilities. He anticipates a relatively small ES, namely **d** = .20, and wants to decide the necessary **n** for the research. He is prepared to use as a significance criterion $\mathbf{a}_2 = .05$, but in this instance wishes that his **b** (Type II) risk be of the same magnitude. That is, he wishes to incur no greater risk that he will fail to detect a hypothetical **d** = .20 than the risk that he will mistakenly conclude that a difference exists when **d** = 0. His specifications thus are

$$\mathbf{a}_2 = .05, \quad \mathbf{d} = .20, \quad \text{power} = 1 - \mathbf{b} = 1 - .05 = .95.$$

In Table 2.4.1 for $\mathbf{a}_2 = .05$, column $\mathbf{d} = .20$, row power = .95, he finds **n** ($= \mathbf{n}_A = \mathbf{n}_B$) = 651.

2.4.2 CASE 1: $\mathbf{n}_A \neq \mathbf{n}_B$, $\sigma_A = \sigma_B$. Case 1 is not common when the sample size tables are used in experimental planning, since normally the planning will presume the selection of samples of equal size. Equal-sized samples are desirable, since it is demonstrable that with a given number of cases available for division into two samples for experimentation, equal division yields greater power than does unequal division.

There are, however, situations in which the size of one of the two samples is fixed in advance by circumstances. Perhaps the resources to apply to a given experimental treatment are limited to some fixed number, or perhaps no more than a given number can be withheld for use as control subjects. In such instances, the fixed sample size (n_F) will in general be different from the other sample, whose size is at the experimenter's discretion (n_U). The tables entires, as in Case 0, are **a**, **d**, and desired power, and **n** is sought. To find n_U, substitute the fixed **n** (n_F) and the **n** read from the table in

$$(2.4.2) \qquad\qquad n_U = \frac{n_F\, n}{2n_F - n},$$

where n_F = the fixed sample size,
  n = the value read from the table, and
  n_U = the necessary sample size for the other sample.

When $n_F \leq \frac{1}{2}n$, a zero or negative denominator results, and the problem is insoluble for the given specifications. One must either increase n_F (usually not possible) or change desired power, **a**, or **d** so as to decrease **n**.

Illustrative Examples

2.10 An educational psychologist plans research which will compare the effectiveness of a computer-based program for teaching reading to illiterates with a standard lecture method. He wishes to detect a **d** = .30 (i.e., between "slight" and "moderate") and is only interested in testing whether the computer-based method (C) yields higher criterion scores than the standard method (S), i.e., a directional (one-tailed) test. He sets his significance criterion at .05 (= a_1) and wishes power to be .75. That is, if the C method is superior to the S method by **d** = .30, he is prepared to run a risk of .25 (= **b**) of failing to get significant results relative to the .05 risk he runs of concluding C's superiority when the means are equal. Now, if there were no restrictions of time or equipment availability, this would be a Case 0 problem with the specifications

$$a_1 = .05, \qquad d = .30, \qquad \text{power} = .75.$$

In Table 2.4.1 for a_1 = .05, column **d** = .30, row power = .75, he would find **n** = ($n_C = n_S$) = 120, i.e., samples of 120 cases are needed in each group.

But now consider the real possibility that limitations in time and availability of equipment make it impossible for him to have more than 80 subjects in the computer group, while he is relatively unrestricted in regard to the sample size for the standard group. Given the fixed n_F of 80, how many cases does he need in the standard group (n_U) to meet the same specifications? In formula (2.4.2), with $n_F = 80$ and $n = 120$ (from Table 2.4.1 at $a_1 = .05$), he finds

$$n_U = \frac{(80)(120)}{2(80) - 120} = 240.$$

Thus, the specifications for **a, d**, and power would be met with a fixed sample size of 80 in the C group, if he has 240 subjects in the standard group.

2.4.3   CASE 2: $\sigma_A \neq \sigma_B$, $n_A = n_B$. The **n** tables are used in Case 2 in exactly the same way as in Case 0. The inequality of population σ values results only in a standardization of the difference in population means by the root mean square of the population variances [formula (2.3.2)] instead of the common population standard deviation. This has no effect on the use of the **n** tables. Only **d** is affected, and only in its interpretation via **U** measures; its interpretation in terms of **r** and r^2 remain unaffected. See the discussion of the use of the power tables for Case 2, Section 2.3.3.

Illustrative Example

2.11 A clinical psychologist plans a study of the orienting reflex in which he will compare means of process paranoid schizophrenics (S) and employee controls (C). On the basis of past findings, he expects that the S group will show greater variability than the C group, but it is a mean difference he wishes to detect at the $a_2 = .05$ level with power of .90.

In considering setting his ES, he may proceed in either of the following ways (among others):

1.   He may hypothesize that the ES of S vs. C population membership is such that it accounts for about 10% of the variance of the combined populations. He notes from Table 2.2.1 that when $r^2 = .109$, $d = .7$. Note that the fact that the *within*-population variances of S and C are assumed to differ does not affect the validity of the r^2 interpretation. His specifications then are

$$a_2 = .05, \qquad d = .7, \qquad \text{power} = .90.$$

In Table 2.4.1 for $a_2 = .05$, column $d = .7$, row power = .90, he finds **n** ($= n_S = n_C$) = 44 cases.

2.   He may set the value of $d = .70$ (or any other), not on the basis of its r^2 equivalent, but directly. That is, he may hypothesize that the standardized

difference between the population means is .70. Since he is assuming that $\sigma_S^2 \neq \sigma_C^2$, the standardizing unit cannot be the common within-population standard deviation, but is instead the square root of the mean of the two variances, i.e., $\sqrt{(\sigma_S^2 + \sigma_C^2)/2}$ [formula (2.3.2)].

2.4.4 CASE 3: ONE SAMPLE OF **n** OBSERVATIONS. In using the **n** tables for the one-sample **t** test, the only departure from Case 0 is that which was discussed in connection with the power tables for Case 3, i.e., the appropriate value of **d** for table entry. The reader is referred to Section 2.3.4. for the relevant discussion of the details. Briefly, if one is testing, with a single sample, the null hypothesis that the population mean has some specified value, $H_0: m = c$, and scales his ES in the usual way as a standardized difference, namely [formula (2.3.3)]

$$d_3' = \frac{m - c}{\sigma},$$

one uses the **n** tables for the value of $d = d_3'\sqrt{2}$. The value of **n** will be underestimated, but only to a trivial degree, unless it is quite small (e.g., less than 10 or 15), when prudence might dictate using $n + 1$, instead of **n** cases.

Illustrative Example

2.12 A political scientist plans to appraise the status of the attitude toward the United Nations of the urban population of a new African republic. He will use an orally administered Thurstone Attitude Scale which has the property that a neutral response is scaled 6 (on an 11-point scale). His null hypothesis, then, is $H_0: m = 6$. Since he wishes to be able to conclude that the average is either "pro" or "anti," he plans a nondirectional test and wishes to use a stringent significance criterion, namely $a_2 = .01$. He also seeks the assurance of relatively high power, .90. Furthermore, he wants to be in a position to conclude that the population in question is, on the average, only trivially different from neutral if, when the data are in, he does not find **t** to be significant. He defines such a trivial difference as one no greater than a departure of .10 of the population mean from 6 ($= c$), expressed in population standard deviation units. But this .10 value is d_3' [formula (2.3.3)], the Case 3 ES measure, not **d**. To find **d**, d_3' must be multiplied by $\sqrt{2}$ [formula (2.3.4)]. The result is $d = .10\sqrt{2} = .1414$. The specifications are

$$a_2 = .01, \quad d = .1414, \quad \text{power} = .90.$$

In Table 2.4.1 for $a_2 = .01$, his **d** value is not tabled. Following the procedure of Section 2.4.1, formula (2.4.1), he finds row power $= .90$ and column **d** $= .10$, in order to find $n_{.10} = 2978$. He then substitutes this value and **d** $= .1414$ in formula (2.4.1) to find

$$n = \frac{2978}{100(.1414)^2} + 1 = 1490.$$

Thus, he will need to draw a random sample of 1490 urban dwellers to assure with .90 probability the detection at the $a_2 = .01$ level of a .10 standard deviation departure of the population **m** from neutrality (a value of 6).

2.4.5   CASE 4: ONE SAMPLE OF **n** DIFFERENCES BETWEEN PAIRED OBSERVATIONS. Here, again, the consideration involved in using the **n** tables are exactly the same as for the power tables and involve the determination of **d**. The issues are discussed in detail in Section 2.3.5, to which the reader is referred.

Summarizing for convenience, if the investigator has no basis for estimating the population matching **r** between the **X**, **Y** pairs, he has no recourse but to work with their difference, **Z** ($=$ **X** $-$)**Y** in the fashion of Case 3. That is, he indexes the effect size as [formula (2.3.5)]

$$\mathbf{d_z'} = \frac{\mathbf{m_z}}{\sigma_z},$$

with the standard deviation of the difference scores as the unit in which the the mean difference is expressed, and enters the **n** tables with $\mathbf{d} = \mathbf{d_z'}\sqrt{2}$, using formula (2.4.1) for "interpolation" when necessary.

If the investigator has a basis for estimating the matching **r**, he can define [formula (2.3.8)]

$$\mathbf{d_4'} = \frac{\mathbf{m_X} - \mathbf{m_Y}}{\sigma},$$

which is exactly the same index as the **d** of independent samples (2.2.1) and (2.2.2), and use the **n** tables with [formula (2.3.9)] for

$$\mathbf{d} = \frac{\mathbf{d_4'}}{\sqrt{1 - \mathbf{r}}}.$$

The **n** read from the tables (or the tables plus formula (2.4.1)) is the necessary number of *pairs* to detect $\mathbf{d_z'}$ or $\mathbf{d_4'}$ (for which we enter with **d**) at the **a** significance criterion with the desired power. The Case 4 **n** (as was true for the Case 3 **n**) is, in principle, an underestimate, but unless **n** is quite small, the degree of underestimation is so small that it can be ignored.

Illustrative Examples

2.13 In a child development study of maternal attitude toward children with cerebral palsy, data are to be gathered in the following way. Each mother to be selected has a child with cerebral palsy (P) and at least one other child within 3 years of age who is free of the disease (C). The mothers are to complete a series of attitude scales for each of their two children separately. For each scale, a comparison is planned between $\mathbf{m_P}$ and $\mathbf{m_C}$. Each mother's attitude toward her P child is "controlled" by her attitude toward her C child. The plan is to use $\mathbf{a_2} = .05$ as the significance criterion and power of .80. A conventional definition of a medium effect size, $\mathbf{d_4}' = .50$, is posited for each scale. Note that $\mathbf{d_4}'$ is simply the $\mathbf{m_P} - \mathbf{m_C}$ difference, standardized by the common within-population standard deviation [or, if $\sigma_P \neq \sigma_C$, their root mean square, σ', formula (2.3.2)]. What sample size of mothers is necessary for these specifications?

For table entry, we require $\mathbf{d}$ from formula (2.3.9) and hence an estimate of $\mathbf{r}$, the population correlation between attitude scale scores toward P and those toward C of such mothers, i.e., the within mother between child pairs $\mathbf{r}$. The investigator, drawing on relevant evidence from the research literature and on the judgment that all sources of individual differences in attitude between mothers (e.g., differences in education, personality factors, response style) are contributing to this correlation, estimates $\mathbf{r}$ (probably conservatively) as .40. Thus $\mathbf{d} = .50/\sqrt{(1 - .40)} = .50/.7746 = .645$. The specifications are

$$\mathbf{a_2} = .05, \qquad \mathbf{d} = .645, \qquad \text{power} = .80.$$

As will generally be the case in Case 4 applications, the necessary $\mathbf{d}$ value is not tabulated and formula (2.4.1) is used. In Table 2.4.1 for $\mathbf{a_2} = .05$, one finds for row power = .80 in column $\mathbf{d} = .10$, the $\mathbf{n}_{.10}$ value of 1571, and substitutes it together with $\mathbf{d}$ in formula (2.4.1):

$$\mathbf{n} = \frac{1571}{100(.645)^2} + 1 = 38.8.$$

Thus, a sample of 39 mothers is required. Note that if the research design had involved comparisons of the means of independent samples of P mothers with comparable C mothers (or equivalently if $\mathbf{r}$ were zero), 64 mothers of each type would have been needed (for the specifications $\mathbf{a_2} = .05$, power = .80, $\mathbf{d} = .50$).

2.14 A neuropsychologist plans an investigation of the effect of leg amputation on various aspects of sensory threshold and discrimination above the amputation (A). He plans to control each A observation by measurement of the amputee subject on the same area on the contralateral side (C). He specifies a two-tailed test with Type I error risk of .02 ($=\mathbf{a_2}$) and Type II error risk of .10 ($=\mathbf{b}$, hence, power $= .90$). In specifying the ES, he may reason along either of the following lines:

1.   He considers the distribution of the differences between the paired measures, $A - C = \mathbf{Z}$. He anticipates that the mean $\mathbf{Z}$ value for the population is of the order of .35 of a standard deviation of such differences (midway between operationally defined small and medium ES), i.e., $\mathbf{d_z}' = \mathbf{m_z}/\sigma_z = .35$ [formula (2.3.5)]. For table entry, he requires [formula (2.3.4)] $\mathbf{d} = \mathbf{d_z}'\sqrt{2} = .35(1.414) = .495$. His specifications thus are

$$\mathbf{a_2} = .02, \qquad \mathbf{d} = .495, \qquad \text{power} = .90.$$

In Table 2.4.1 for $\mathbf{a_1} = .01$ ($\mathbf{a_2} = .02$) at row power $= .90$, if he is content to use $\mathbf{d} = .50$, he finds[6] $\mathbf{n} = 105$. This is the number of amputee subjects (i.e., pairs of observations) he needs.

2.   Alternately, he may prefer to work with the standard deviation of the separate measures, σ ($= \sigma_A = \sigma_C$) as unit,[7] and conceive his ES as [formula (2.3.8)] $\mathbf{d_4}' = \mathbf{m_A} - \mathbf{m_C}/\sigma = .35$ (say). He must also posit a value of the population correlation coefficient between measures on the two limbs, $\mathbf{r}$. In considering how to estimate this $\mathbf{r}$, he may have information from normal (N) subjects that estimates this value for them as $\mathbf{r_N} = .70$. It seems reasonable to him that the effect of amputation may well be to reduce this correlation to a value in the range .40–.60, for his sample. To find the values of $\mathbf{d}$, he substitutes in formula (2.3.9):

for $\mathbf{r} = .40$, $\mathbf{d} = .35/\sqrt{(1 - .40)} = .452$,
for $\mathbf{r} = .60$, $\mathbf{d} = .35/\sqrt{(1 - .60)} = .553$.

Summarizing these specifications:

$$\mathbf{a_2} = .02, \qquad \mathbf{d} = \frac{.452}{.553}, \qquad \text{power} = .90.$$

These $\mathbf{d}$ values will require the use of formula (2.4.1). In Table 2.4.1 for $\mathbf{a_1} = .01$ ($\mathbf{a_2} = .02$), for row power $= .90$, and column $\mathbf{d} = .10$, he finds $\mathbf{n_{.10}} = 2605$, and substituting
for $\mathbf{d} = .452$ (i.e., $\mathbf{r} = .40$), $\mathbf{n} = 129$,
for $\mathbf{d} = .553$ (i.e., $\mathbf{r} = .60$), $\mathbf{n} = 86$.

---

[6] Otherwise, he uses formula (2.4.1), for which he reads out of the table $\mathbf{n_{.10}} = 2605$ and, substituting it and $\mathbf{d} = .495$, finds $\mathbf{n} = 107$ (or 108, see footnote 5).
[7] If there is reason to believe that $\sigma_A \neq \sigma_C$ (for example, $\sigma_A > \sigma_C$ is not unlikely), we revert to a Case 2 definition, and use [formula (2.3.2)] $\sigma' = \sqrt{(\sigma_A^2 + \sigma_C^2)/2}$ in place of σ in the definition of $\mathbf{d_4}'$, with no effect on what follows.

Note how critical is the effect on **n** of the value of **r** posited. Since **n** varies inversely with $\mathbf{d}^2$, and $\mathbf{d}^2$ varies inversely with $1 - \mathbf{r}$, the increase in the required **n** from a smaller correlation $\mathbf{r}_S$ to a larger one $\mathbf{r}_L$ will require an increase by a factor of $(1 - \mathbf{r}_S)/(1 - \mathbf{r}_L)$, in the case above, $(1 - .40)/(1 - .60) = 1.50$, i.e., a 50% increase in **n**.

This may suggest that the route to **d** by means of $\mathbf{d}_4{}'$ (which is equivalent to the Case 0 definition of **d**), because of its critical dependence on **r**, is less desirable than the previous alternative, which only requires the setting of ES in terms of $\mathbf{d}_Z$, and avoids the necessity of positing a value for **r**. This would, however, be a mistaken conclusion, since the decision about ES in terms of $\mathbf{d}_Z{}'$ carries with it an *implicit* value of **r**, as can be seen from the relationship [formula (2.3.7)] $\sigma_Z = \sigma\sqrt{2(1 - \mathbf{r})}$ [where σ is either the common population standard deviation or σ' from formula (2.3.2)]. Thus, if one proceeds to **d** from $\mathbf{d}_Z{}'$ in order to avoid the estimation of **r**, which is necessary to proceed to **d** from $\mathbf{d}_4{}'$, one has *implicitly* posited (by simple algebra)

$$(2.3.10) \qquad \mathbf{r} = 1 - \tfrac{1}{2}\left(\frac{\mathbf{d}_4{}'}{\mathbf{d}_Z{}'}\right)^2.$$

Thus, if the investigator would want to set $\mathbf{d}_4{}'$ at (let us say, for concreteness) .4, but because he has no idea of **r**, instead elects to set $\mathbf{d}_Z{}'$ at .6, he has in effect unwittingly assumed **r** to be

$$1 = \tfrac{1}{2}\left(\frac{.4}{.6}\right)^2 = .78,$$

i.e., a definite value. The point being emphasized is that **r** is inevitably a part of the **d** value, and one can estimate it either explicitly or implicitly. There are circumstances where the paired differences, **Z**, represent a "natural" basis of study with which the investigator has some familiarity. In such cases he more readily expresses the ES as $\mathbf{d}_Z{}'$, and the fact that an **r** is implicit in his value of **d** is only of academic interest. But, as we have seen, the use of **Z** to evade the estimation of **r** does not succeed; a definite value for **r** is merely being posited implicitly, rather than explicitly. It appears obviously preferable that the researcher at least know, by means of formula (2.3.10), what **r** is being implicitly posited when he uses $\mathbf{d}_Z{}'$, or employ the usually more natural approach via $\mathbf{d}_4{}'$ and come to terms with the problem of explicitly estimating **r** for formula (2.3.9).

2.15 An experimenter in a psychology laboratory is organizing a study to compare the effects of two reinforcement schedules on trials to response acquisition, using white rats. The design he will employ will utilize pairs of animals both of which come from the same litter and are free of obvious defects; he will randomly assign one to the A group and the other to the B group. He will consider the phenomenon he is interested in to be the superiority of the B over the A schedule, that is, more trials for A than B, and moreover wants to keep his Type I risk quite small. He then chooses $a_1 = .01$. The ES he anticipates is moderate, as indexed by $d_4' = .50$. On the basis of past work, he estimates the between litter-mates learning ability correlation as $r = .65$. His effective **d**, therefore, is [formula (2.3.9)] $.50\sqrt{1/(1 - .65)} = .845$. Finally, he wishes to have a probability of .95 of detecting this (assumed) large effect. Thus, summarizing,

$$a_1 = .01, \quad d = .845, \quad \text{power} = .95.$$

Recourse must be taken to formula (2.4.1). In Table 2.4.1 for $a_1 = .01$, row power $= .95$, $n_{.10} = 3155$ and in formula (2.4.1)

$$n = \frac{3155}{100(.845)^2} + 1 = 45.$$

Thus, 45 litter pairs will be needed.

2.5   THE USE OF THE TABLES FOR SIGNIFICANCE TESTING

2.5.1   GENERAL INTRODUCTION. As noted above in Section 1.5, provision has been made in the power tables to facilitate significance testing. Here, our focus shifts from research planning to the appraisal of research results, and from the consideration of the alternate-hypothetical state of affairs in the population to the palpable characteristics of the sample and their bearing on the null hypothesis.

Accordingly, we redefine our ES index, **d**, so that its elements are sample results, rather than population parameters, and call it d_s. For all tests of the difference between means of independent samples,

(2.5.1) $$d_s = \frac{\overline{X}_A - \overline{X}_B}{s},$$

where $\overline{X}_A$ and $\overline{X}_B =$ the two sample means, and
$\quad\quad\quad\quad s =$ the usual pooled within sample estimate of the population standard deviation,

that is,

(2.5.2) $$s = \sqrt{\frac{\sum(X_A - \overline{X}_A)^2 + \sum(X_B - \overline{X}_B)^2}{n_A + n_B - 2}},$$

Note that we have defined **s** quite generally so that it will hold for all cases involving two independent samples, whether or not sample sizes are equal.

Formula (2.5.1) should be interpreted literally for a directional (one-tailed) test and as an absolute difference [i.e., without sign, as in formula (2.2.2)] for the nondirectional (two-tailed) test.

Thus, d_s is the standardized mean difference for the sample. It is simply related to the **t** statistic by

$$(2.5.3) \qquad\qquad d_s = t\sqrt{\frac{n_A + n_B}{n_A n_B}},$$

$$(2.5.4) \qquad\qquad t = d_s\sqrt{\frac{n_A n_B}{n_A + n_B}}.$$

The value of d_s necessary for significance is called d_c, i.e., the criterion value of d_s. The second column of each of the power tables 2.3, headed d_c, carries these values as a function of **n**. Using these values, the investigator need not compute **t**; the standardized difference between his sample means, d_s, is compared with the tabled d_c values for his sample size. If the obtained d_s value equals or exceeds d_c, his results are significant at the **a** value for that table; otherwise, they are not significant.

The advantages of using this approach are twofold:

1.   The value **s** is approximately the mean of the separate sample standard deviations. The latter are almost always computed, and often known approximately even prior to computation, so that the sample d_s can be approximated at a glance once the sample means are determined. If such an approximate value of d_s is materially different from the tabulated d_c value, the significance decision can be made without any computation. Thus, the d_c values can be used for a quick check on the significance of results.

2.   A second advantage lies in the convenience of having the d_c values for many values of **n**. Most **t** tables provide criterion values of **t** for relatively few values for degrees of freedom; each power table provides d_c values for 68 entries of **n** between 8 and 1000.

In general, these advantages are probably not great. They are judged, however, to be useful with sufficient frequency to warrant the inclusion of the d_c values in the power tables.

The d_s concept has virtues which should be noted quite apart from its use in significance testing. In general, the equivalents of **d** in terms of non-overlap (**U**), correlation (**r**), and proportion of variance accounted for (r^2), described for the population in Section 2.2, also hold for the sample, subject to the restrictions described there and in section 2.3. One simply uses Table

2.2.1 with d_c as **d**. The **U** measures will hold only to the extent to which the samples approach the conditions of normal distribution, equal variability, and equal sample size, on which these measures are predicated. The (point biserial) **r** and r^2 equivalents, on the other hand, have no such restrictions. Further, their systematic use as an accompaniment to significance testing will frequently prove illuminating and has been advocated as a routine procedure (Cohen, 1965, pp. 101–104). Finally, formula (2.5.4) makes quite explicit the fact that a significance decision (from **t**) is a function both of the sample effect size (how much) and **n**, the amount of evidence brought to bear on the null hypothesis. Behavioral scientists too often use evidence in regard to significance (e.g., **t** values) as arbiters with which to judge the size of the effect or degree of relationship (e.g., as estimates of **d** values and their equivalents). The formula starkly exposes this error.

2.5.2   SIGNIFICANCE TESTING IN CASE 0. In Case 0, the use of the d_c values in the power tables 2.3 is quite straightforward. The investigator computes (or estimates) his sample d_c value and enters the appropriate power table for his **a**, in the row for his **n** ($= n_A = n_B$), and checks to see whether his d_s equals or exceeds the tabled d_c value. Whether significant or not, he may then wish to express his d_c in terms of one or more of the **U** indices, **r**, or r^2, using Table 2.2.1, or for greater accuracy, formulas (2.2.3)–(2.2.6).

Illustrative Example

2.16   Consider the conditions stated initially for example 2.1. Whatever the details of his expected ES (given there as **d** = .50), the experiment has been run at $a_2 = .05$ with two independent experimental and control samples of 30 cases each. He computes his sample result as a standardized difference between means [d_s, formula (2.5.1)] and finds that it equals .46. His specifications are simply

$$a_2 = .05, \qquad n = 30, \qquad d_s = .46.$$

In Table 2.3.5 for $a_2 = .05$ and $n = 30$, $d_c = .52$. Since his d_s value is smaller than d_c, his observed difference is not significant at $a_2 = .05$. (He learns incidentally that with samples of 30 cases, it takes a difference between means of about half a standard deviation to reach significance at $a_2 = .05$.)

He may go on to refer to Table 2.2.1 [or, for greater accuracy, formula (2.2.6)] from which he learns that the point biserial **r** between E versus C group membership and number of trials to learning is about .22 which, in turn, means that about .05 ($=\mathbf{r}^2$) of the total among rat variance in trials is associated with group membership, *in his sample.*

If, for the purpose of reporting in the literature, he wants the **t** value, it is very readily found for Case 0, where formula (2.5.4) simplifies (since $\mathbf{n_E} = \mathbf{n_C} = \mathbf{n}$) to

(2.5.5) $$\mathbf{t} = \mathbf{d_s}\sqrt{\frac{\mathbf{n}}{2}}$$

which is here

$$\mathbf{t} = .46\sqrt{15} = 1.78.$$

This example can be used as an illustration of approximate "at-a-glance" significance decisions. Assume, instead, that he finds the following sample means and standard deviations ($\mathbf{n} = 30$, $\mathbf{a_2} = .05$ criterion):

$$\mathbf{X_E} = 10.8, \qquad \mathbf{X_C} = 12.1,$$

$$\mathbf{s_E} = 3.81, \qquad \mathbf{s_C} = 4.24.$$

One notes at a glance that **s** is approximately 4 and the difference between means, 1.3. The latter is only about a third of **s**, hence $\mathbf{d_s} \approx .33$, clearly less than the $\mathbf{d_c} = .52$ for the specified conditions.

2.5.3   SIGNIFICANCE TESTING IN CASE 1, $\mathbf{n_A} \neq \mathbf{n_B}$. The inequality of the sample sizes in a **t** test for independent means provides no new problems in the use of $\mathbf{d_c}$. Formula (2.5.2) for **s**, the standardizing unit for the sample mean difference, is written for the (more general) case which provides for differing values of $\mathbf{n_A}$ and $\mathbf{n_B}$. In entering the tables, the value of **n** to be used is the harmonic mean of $\mathbf{n_A}$ and $\mathbf{n_B}$, which we have already described above when Case 1 was first discussed in Section 2.3.2 [formula (2.3.1)]:

$$\mathbf{n'} = \frac{2\mathbf{n_A}\mathbf{n_B}}{\mathbf{n_A} + \mathbf{n_B}}.$$

The tabulated $\mathbf{d_c}$ value for Case 1 is an overestimate, but a very slight one unless **n'** is both absolutely small (say less than 20) and much smaller than $(\mathbf{n_A} + \mathbf{n_B})/2$ (see Section 2.3.2).

Illustrative Example

2.17   Reconsider the conditions of example 2.3. Assume that the experiment has been performed, and the psychologist is appraising the results of his directional hypothesis at $\mathbf{a_1} = .05$ that the new psychotherapeutic technique B ($\mathbf{n_B} = 60$) yields a higher mean criterion rating than the standard technique A ($n_A = 90$). Using the sample means (which differ in the predicted direction) and **s**, he finds $d_s = .32$ [formula (2.5.1)]. He also computes [formula (2.3.1)]

$$n' = \frac{2(90)(60)}{90 + 60} = 72.$$

His specifications thus are

$$a_1 = .05, \qquad n' = 72, \qquad d_s = .32.$$

In Table 2.3.2 for $a_1 = .05$ at $n' = 72$, $d_c = .28$. His d_s value of .32 exceeds the criterion value, so he concludes that the mean for the new method is significantly higher than that of the old (at $a_1 = .05$) on the rating criterion.

If he had instead computed **t**, he would have found it to equal 1.92. If he then wanted to have a d_s value (for example, to express his results in terms of a **U** value, or **r**, or r^2), he can find it from formula (2.5.3):

$$d_s = 1.92 \sqrt{\frac{90 + 60}{(90)(60)}} = .32.$$

Or, alternatively, if he first computes d_s and requires the **t** value, he can find it from formula (2.5.4).

2.5.4   SIGNIFICANCE TESTING IN CASE 2: $\sigma_A \neq \sigma_B$, $n_A = n_B$. Case 2 specifies that the standard deviations of the two *populations* are not equal. It is included here to stress two facts. One is that the *sample* standard deviations are virtually never equal but that this does not matter in the relationships discussed above in Section 2.5.1. The other is that even if the *population* standard deviations are judged to be unequal (for example, on the basis of a variance ratio test), the relationship between d_s and **t** nevertheless holds, since it is purely algebraic, and further, that the interpretation of d_s in terms of **r** and r^2 continues to hold (but not in terms of the **U** indices).

An issue not to be confused with that of the **t**–d_s–**r** relationships is the question of the validity of the **t** test under conditions of population variance heterogeneity. As discussed above in Section 2.3.3, provided that the sample sizes are approximately equal, the validity of the **t** test is hardly affected by any but relatively extreme population variance discrepancies. Thus, the d_c values will remain approximately valid under nonextreme Case 2 conditions.

Illustrative Example

2.18   Consider again the wage survey by the labor economist of example 2.4. When the survey of men and women workers' ($n = 100$) weekly wages is completed, he proceeds to compare their means at the prespecified $a_2 = .01$ level. His expected population difference $\sigma_A \neq \sigma_B$ is reflected in the sample, where one variance is about twice the other (a highly significant difference with **n**'s of 100). He nevertheless proceeds to determine the d_s value as (say) .40. His specifications are:

$$a_2 = .01, \qquad n = 100, \qquad d_s = .40.$$

In Table 2.3.4. (for $a_2 = .01$) with $n = 100$, he finds $d_c = .37$. He concludes, at $a_2 = .01$, that there is a sex difference in mean wages in the population sampled, since d_s exceeds d_c. Since the effect of $\sigma_A \neq \sigma_B$ on the validity of the test is trivial for large *and equal* samples (Scheffé, 1959, p. 340) his conclusion is valid.

Note, incidentally, that the d_s turned out to be smaller than the **d** value he had posited in planning the experiment (see example 2.4). His smaller d_s is nevertheless significant because of the large power he had had against the ES of **d** = .50, namely .82. A good reason to seek high power is, of course, the real possibility that the d_s, when found, will prove smaller than the **d** expected in the planning. This leaves a margin for error, either judgmental or sampling, in the setting of **d**.

2.5.5 SIGNIFICANCE TESTING IN CASE 3: ONE SAMPLE OF **n** OBSERVATIONS. For those circumstances in which the null hypothesis takes the form: A single sample of **n** observations comes from a normal population whose mean is **c**, one must take into account the construction of the Tables 2.3, including the d_c values. The reader is reminded that the latter proceeded on the assumption of *two*-sample tests, with, therefore, the sampling error variance of two means. Thus, it is necessary in one-sample tests to adjust the tabulated d_c value. This proceeds very simply: To find the proper criterion value for one-sample tests, d_c', one finds:

(2.5.6) $$d_c' = d_c \sqrt{\tfrac{1}{2}} \quad \text{or} \quad .707 d_c.$$

This value is an overestimate, but a very slight one unless **n** is less than 30 (see Section 2.3.4).

As for the observed d_s value for Case 3, we follow the principle expressed in Section 2.5.1 and merely define d_s as we defined d_3' with sample values substituted for the population values of formula (2.3.3):

(2.5.7) $$d_s' = \frac{\overline{X} - c}{s}.$$

The prime is used to indicate that a one-sample test is involved. The relationship between $\mathbf{d_s}'$ and **t** as given in formulas (2.5.3) and (2.5.4) must be revised for one-sample tests, as follows:

$$(2.5.8) \qquad\qquad \mathbf{d_s't} = \sqrt{\frac{1}{\mathbf{n}}},$$

$$(2.5.9) \qquad\qquad \mathbf{t} = \mathbf{d_s'}\sqrt{\mathbf{n}}.$$

The first of these formulae may be useful when a **t** has been computed and a standardized sample ES index is desired; the second is of use when the **t** value is needed (e.g., for reporting results in an article).

Formula (2.5.9) [as well as formulas (2.5.4) and (2.5.5)] makes patent the dependence of the significance decision on both effect size in the sample ($\mathbf{d_s'}$) and the amount of evidence provided by the sample (**n**).

Illustrative Example

2.19   In example 2.5, an experimenter was planning a test on the effect of rearing rats in total darkness on their weight gain from birth to 90 days. The test is of the departure, in either direction, from an established standard value of 70 (= **c**). The sample used was of 60 cases, and the test was planned and performed at $\mathbf{a_2}$ = .10. He finds the sample mean gain to be $\overline{\mathbf{X}}$ = 68.8 and the standard deviation to be **s** = 8.1. From formula (2.5.7), he finds $\mathbf{d_s'}$ = (–).15. His specifications are:

$$\mathbf{a_2} = .10, \qquad \mathbf{n} = 60, \qquad \mathbf{d_s'} = .15.$$

In Table 2.3.6 for $\mathbf{a_2}$ = .10, **n** = 60, he finds $\mathbf{d_c}$ = .30. Since this is a one-sample test, he goes on to find $\mathbf{d_c'}$ = .30$\sqrt{\frac{1}{2}}$ = .21. Comparing his observed $\mathbf{d_s'}$ with the criterion $\mathbf{d_c'}$, he concludes that the sample mean departure from 70 is not significant at $\mathbf{a_2}$ = .10.

2.5.6   SIGNIFICANCE TESTING IN CASE 4: ONE SAMPLE OF **n** DIFFERENCES BETWEEN PAIRED OBSERVATIONS. The significance test of the difference between means of paired observations is a special case of the one-sample test (Case 3) where **c** = 0 (see discussion in Section 2.3.5). That is, the computations proceed by taking the **X**, **Y** pairs, of which there are **n**, and finding the differences, **X** – **Y** = **Z**. The result is a single sample of **n Z** observations. From this point one proceeds as in Case 3, the null hypothesis being that the population mean of these **Z** values is 0. Once the sample data are being analyzed, the issue of the population (or sample) **r** between **X** and **Y**, discussed in the power and sample size sections on Case 4 (Sections 2.3.5. and 2.4.5), plays no role in the computations of significance.

For case 4, we define d_s' as in formula (2.5.6), calling the variable Z instead of X and treating c as 0, i.e.,

$$(2.5.10) \qquad\qquad d_s' = \frac{\overline{Z}}{s}.$$

where s is the sample standard deviation of the Z values.

Note that this is the exact sample analog of formula (2.3.5).

Also as in Case 3, we must make the adjustment of the tables d_c value, to allow for sampling error variance of only one mean, (here, a mean difference) instead of the two on which the tables are based. This requires multiplying d_s' by $\sqrt{\tfrac{1}{2}}$ [formula (2.5.6)] to find the Case 4 criterion, d_c'.

As in Case 3, the relationship between d_s' and t as given in formulas (2.5.8) and (2.5.9) hold for Case 4. Thus, one can simply translate a d_s' value into t, if the latter value is required, or a t value into d_s', if one wants to express the size of the mean difference in the sample in standardized terms, that is, in terms of the standard deviation of the differences.

Finally, and again as in Case 3, the d_c' value is slightly underestimated, but to a degree which can be safely ignored unless n is small.

Illustrative Example

2.20   In example 2.6, an educational researcher was planning an experimental comparison of two programed texts in algebra by assigning the members of 50 IQ-matched pairs at random to the two texts, and, following instruction, testing their achievement. Assume that the experiment has been performed and the data marshalled for the significance test, to be performed at $a_2 = .05$, as specified in the plans.

The test is of the significance of the departure of the mean difference, $\overline{Z} = (\overline{X} - \overline{Y})$, from zero, which is equivalent to a test of $\overline{X} - \overline{Y} = 0$. He finds $\overline{Z} = -2.78$, s (of the Z's) $= 8.22$, and entering these in formula (2.5.10), $d_s' = (-).34$. (Since the test is nondirectional, the negative sign does not enter, other than to indicate the $\overline{X}$ is less than $\overline{Y}$.) His specifications are:

$$a_2 = .05, \qquad n = 50, \qquad d_s' = .34.$$

In Table 2.3.5 for $a_2 = .05$, $n = 50$, he finds $d_c = .40$. Since this is a one-sample test, he needs to find $d_c' = .40\sqrt{\tfrac{1}{2}} = .28$. Comparing his observed d_s' value of .34 with the criterion d_c' value of .28, he concludes that his departure from no difference of 2.78 (in favour of the X program) is significant at $a_2 = .05$. If a value of t is required, it can be found from formula (2.5.9) as $t = .34\sqrt{50} = 2.40$.

3

The Significance of
a Product Moment r_s

3.1 Introduction and Use

Behavioral scientists generally, and particularly psychologists with substantive interests in individual differences in personality, attitude, and ability, frequently take recourse to correlational anlysis as an investigative tool in both pure and applied studies. By far the most frequently used statistical method of expression of the relationship between two variables is the Pearson product-moment correlation coefficient, **r**.

r is an index of linear relationship, the slope of the best-fitting straight line for a bivariate (**X**, **Y**) distribution where the **X** and **Y** variables have each been standardized to the same variability. Its limits are -1.00 to $+1.00$. The purpose of this handbook precludes the use of space for a detailed consideration of the interpretations and assumptions of **r**. For this, the reader is referred to a general textbook, such as McNemar (1962), Hays (1963), or Blalock (1960).

When used as purely descriptive measure of degree of linear relationship between two variables, no assumptions need be made with regard to the shape of the marginal population distribution of **X** and **Y**, nor of the distribution of **Y** for any given value of **X** (or vice versa), nor of equal variability of **Y** for different values of **X** (homoscedasticity). However, when significance tests come to be employed, assumptions of normality and homoscedasticity are formally invoked. Despite this, it should be noted that, as in the case of the **t** test with means, moderate assumption failure here, particularly with large **n**, will not seriously affect the validity of significance tests, nor of the power estimates associated with them.

In this chapter we consider inference from a single correlation coefficient, r_s, obtained from a sample of **n** pairs (**X**, **Y**) of observations. There is only one population parameter involved, namely **r**, the population correlation co-efficient. It is possible to test the null hypothesis that the population **r** equals *any* value **c** (discussed in Chapter 4). In most instances, however, the behavioral scientist is interested in whether there is *any* (linear) relationship between two variables, and this translates into the null hypothesis, H_0: **r** = 0. Thus, in common statistical parlance, a significant r_s is one which leads to a rejection of the null hypothesis that the population **r** is zero. It is around this null hypothesis that this chapter and its tables are oriented. (For the test on a difference between two **r**'s, see Chapter 4.)

The significance test of r_s may proceed by means of the **t** distribution, as follows:

$$(3.1.1) \qquad t = \frac{r_s\sqrt{n-2}}{\sqrt{1-r_s^2}}$$

where **n** is the number of (**X**, **Y**) pairs in the sample, and the appropriate **t** distribution is that for **n** − 2 degrees of freedom.[1] As in tests on means, the **t** criterion for rejection depends on the **a** (significance) level and the directionality of the test:

1. If *either* a positive or a negative value of r_s is considered (*a priori*) evidence against the null hypothesis, the test is nondirectional, i.e., two tailed.

2. If the sign of r_s is specified in advance, that is, if only positive (or only negative) correlation is deemed relevant for rejecting the null hypothesis, the test is directional, i.e., one tailed.

A word about regression coefficients. When one variable of the **X**, **Y** pair, conventionally **Y**, can be looked upon as dependent upon **X**, one may speak of the regression of **Y** on **X**. The slope of the best-fitting line for predicting **Y** from **X**, when each is in its *original* ("raw") unit of measurement, is called the regression coefficient, B_{YX}. B_{YX} is simply the *un*standardized slope of **Y** on **X** and can be written simply as a function of **r** and the two standard deviations, σ_X and σ_Y:

$$(3.1.2) \qquad B_{YX} = r\,\frac{\sigma_Y}{\sigma_X} \; ;$$

---

[1] In the power tables, minimum values of r_s necessary for significance, given **a** and **n**, are provided in the criterion **r** (r_c) column. This obviates the necessity in most instances of computing **t** from formula (3.1.1) and interpolating for **df** in **t** tables. See Section 3.5 which describes this procedure in detail.

thus

(3.1.3) $$r = B_{YX} \frac{\sigma_X}{\sigma_Y} .$$

B_{YX}, being the slope of the regression line, indicates how many units of change in Y are produced by a unit change in X, where the units are the "raw" values of the respective variables. In some areas of behavioral science (e.g., economics, sociology) where such dependencies can be assumed, and where the units in which X and Y are measured are inherently meaningful (e.g., dollars, population densities), regression coefficients may be preferred to correlation coefficients. Also, regression coefficients remain constant under changes in the variability of X, while correlation coefficients do not.

A test of the significance of B, i.e., that it departs from zero in the population, is automatically provided from the test of r. A glance at formula (3.1.2) shows that B is zero if and only if r is zero.[2] The researcher accustomed to regression formulations in the two-variable case where X, Y pairs are sampled need only translate his problem (including the effect size) into correlation terms and proceed.

3.2   THE EFFECT SIZE: r

The ES index offers no difficulty here. The requirements for an ES index include that it be a pure (dimensionless) number, one not dependent on the units of the measurement scale(s). The population correlation coefficient, r, serves this purpose.

Thus, a general formulation of the power estimation problem is: One is going to test the significance (H_0: $r = 0$) of a sample r_s value at the a significance criterion with n pairs of observations; if the population r is some specified value (thus, the ES), what is the power of the test (the probability of rejecting the null hypothesis)? Tables 3.3 would be used to find the power value.

Similarly, a general formulation of the sample size estimation problem is: One plans to test the significance (H_0: $r = 0$) of a sample r_s value at the a significance criterion and wishes to detect some specified population r (this being the ES); he then specifies the desired power (probability of rejecting the null hypothesis). How many pairs of observations, n, would be necessary? Table 3.4 would be used to find the value of n.

---

[2] The reader may object that B is zero when σ_Y is zero whatever the value of r. However, when σ_Y is zero, r is indeterminate, that is, it is not meaningful to talk of correlation when one of the variables does not vary.

3.2.1   **r** AS PV AND THE SIZE OF CORRELATIONAL EFFECTS. One conceptually useful way to approach an understanding of **r** is to consider r^2 (as
already noted in Chapter 2).[3] The square of the correlation coefficient is
the proportion of variance (PV) in either of the two variables which may be
predicted by (or accounted for, or attributed to) the variance of the other,
using a straight-line relationship. Concretely, given an **r** of .50 between IQ
and course grades, $r^2 = .25$, so that 25% of the variance in course grades
for the members of this population may be attributed to differences among
them in IQ. (Of course, the attribution of causality is a logical or scientific
issue, and not one of statistical inference, as such.) Note, incidentally,
that the descriptive use of r^2 (as that of **r**) is not dependent on assumptions
of normality or homoscedasticity.

Measures of proportion of variance are usually more immediately
comprehensible than other indices in that, being relative amounts, they
come closer to the behavioral scientist's verbal formulations of relative magnitude of association. They have the additional virtue of providing a common
basis for the expression of different measures of relationships, e.g., standardized difference between means (**d**), variation among means (correlation
ratio), as well as **r**.

The only difficulty arising from the use of PV measures lies in the fact that
in many, perhaps most, of the areas of behavioral science, they turn out to
be so small! For example, workers in personality-social psychology, both
pure and applied (i.e., clinical, educational, personnel), normally encounter
correlation coefficients above the .50–.60 range only when the correlations
are measurement reliability coefficients. In PV terms, this effective upper
limit implies something of the order of one-quarter or one-third of variance
accounted for. The fact is that the state of development of much of behavioral
science is such that not very much variance in the dependent variable is
predictable. This is essentially merely another way of stating the obvious:
that the behavioral sciences collectively are not as far advanced as the
physical sciences. In the latter, we can frequently account for upwards of
99% of dependent variable variance, for example, in classical mechanics.[4]
Thus, when we consider **r** = .50 a large ES (see below), the implication that
.25 of the variance accounted for is a large proportion must be understood
relatively, not absolutely.

[3] Another possibly useful way to understand **r** is as a proportion of common elements
between variables. The implicit model for this interpretation is not compelling for most behavioral science implications (behavioral genetics may be one exception). McNemar (1962,
p. 132) offers a brief discussion of this interpretation, which may be useful in some instances.
[4] This is one way to understand the reason for the fact that applied statistical analysis
flourishes in the biological and social sciences and has only limited specialized applications
in pure physical science.

The question, "relative to what?" is not answerable concretely. The frame of reference is the writer's subjective averaging of PVs from his reading of the research literature in behavioral science. Since no one reads a stratified random probability sample of the behavioral science literature (whose definition would be no mean task), this average may be biased in a "soft" direction, i.e., towards personality–social psychology, sociology, and cultural anthropology and away from experimental and physiological psychology.

The preceding serves as an introduction to operational definitions of "small," "medium," and "large" ES as expressed in terms of r, offered as a convention. The same diffidence is felt here as in Section 2.2 (and other such sections in later chapters). A reader who finds that what is here defined as "large" is too small (or too large) to meet what his area of behavioral science would consider appropriate standards is urged to make more suitable operational definitions. What are offered below are definitions for use when no others suggest themselves, or as conventions.

SMALL EFFECT SIZE: $r = .10$. An r of .10 in a population is indeed small. The implied PV is $r^2 = .01$, and there seems little question but that relationships of that order in $\mathbf{X}$, $\mathbf{Y}$ pairs in a population would not be perceptible on the basis of casual observation. But is it too small?

It probably is not. First of all, it is comparable to the definition of a small ES for a mean difference (Chapter 2), which was $d = .2$, implying point biserial $r = .10$ (for populations of equal size). More important than this, however, is the writer's conviction that many relationships pursued in "soft" behavioral science are of this order of magnitude. Thurstone once said that in psychology we measure men by their shadows. As the behavioral scientist moves from his theoretical constructs, among which there are hypothetically strong relationships, to their operational realizations in measurement and subject manipulation, very much "noise" (measurement unreliability, lack of fidelity to the construct) is likely to accompany the variables. This, in turn, will attenuate the correlation in the population between the constructs *as measured*. Thus, if two constructs in theory (hence perfectly measured) can be expected to correlate .25, and the actual measurement of each is correlated .63 with its respective pure construct, the observed correlation between the two *fallible* measures of the construct would be reduced to $.25 \, (.63) \, (.63) = .10$. Since the above values are not unrealistic, it follows that often (perhaps more often than we expect), we are indeed seeking to reject null hypotheses about r_s when r is some value near .10.

We can offer no exemplification with known instances of population r's of the order of .10, by the very nature of the problem. In fields where correlation coefficients are used, one rarely if ever encounters low r_s's on samples large enough to yield standard errors small enough to distinguish them from **r**'s of zero.

MEDIUM EFFECT SIZE: **r** = .30. When **r** = .30, $r^2 = PV = .09$, so that our definition of a medium effect in linear correlation implies that 9% of the variance of the dependent variable is attributable to the independent variable. It is shown later that this level of ES is comparable to that of medium ES in differences between two means.

Many of the correlation coefficients encountered in behavioral science are of this order of magnitude, and, indeed, this degree of relationship would be perceptible to the naked eye of a reasonably sensitive observer. If we appeal to fields which use psychological tests, we find, for example, that Guilford writes that "the validity coefficient (**r** with criterion) for a single test may be expected in the range from .00 to .60, with most of them in the lower half of that range [1965, p. 146]."

When one considers correlations among tests of diverse abilities, average **r**'s run rather higher than .30. However, for example, for adolescents, correlations among representative tests of creativity average to almost exactly .30, and creativity tests have an average **r** with IQ of just below .30 (Getzels & Jackson, 1962, p. 20). In another area, scores on the two major variables of personality self-description, neuroticism (or trait anxiety) and extraversion correlate about − .30 in college students and in psychiatric populations (Jensen, 1965). In still another area, about 40% of the correlation coefficients among the nine clinical scales of the Minnesota Multiphasic Personality Inventory which are reported in the literature are in the .25–.35 range. Broadly speaking, it seems justifiable to identify as a medium ES in correlation, a value at the midpoint of the range of correlations between discriminably different psychological variables.

LARGE EFFECT SIZE: **r** = .50. The definition of a large correlational ES as **r** = .50 leads to $r^2 = .25$ of the variance of either variable being associated linearly with variance in the other. Its comparability with the definition of large ES in mean differences (**d** = .8) will be demonstrated below. Here, we may simply note that it falls around the upper end of the range of (nonreliability) **r**'s one encounters in those fields of behavioral science which use them extensively, e.g., differential, personality–social, personnel, educational, clinical, and counseling psychology. Thus, Ghiselli writing in an applied psychology framework states "the practical upper limit of predictive effectiveness . . . [is] . . . a validity coefficient of the order of .50 [1964, p. 61]." Guilford's figure, as noted above, is similar. We appeal to the mental-personality-social measurement field for our criterion because of its very heavy use of linear correlation, both historically and contemporaneously. One can, of course, find higher values of **r** in behavioral science. Reliability coefficients of tests, particularly of the equivalence variety, will generally run much higher. Also, if effects in highly controlled "hard" psychology (e.g., psychophysics) are studied by means of r's, they would frequently be distinctly higher than .50. But they are not generally so studied. It seems reasonable that the frame of reference used for conventional definitions of correlational ES should arise from the fields which most heavily use correlations.

The example which comes most readily to mind of this .50 level of correlation is from educational psychology, which gave birth to many of the concepts and technology of correlation methods in behavioral science (e.g., Galton, Spearman). Correlations between IQs or total scores from other comprehensive aptitude batteries correlate with school grades at values which cluster around .50. In contrast, when one looks at near-maximum correlation coefficients of personality measures with comparable real-life criteria, the values one encounters fall at the order of a medium ES, i.e., $r = .30$.

Thus, when a investigator anticipates a degree of correlation between two different variables "about as high as they come," this would by our definition be a large effect, $r = .50$.

3.2.2   COMPARABILITY OF ES FOR r WITH d. It is patently desirable that effect sizes given a qualitative label, e.g., "medium," when studied by means of one design or parameter, be comparable to effects given the same label when studied by another. An attempt has been made for the operationally defined small, medium, and large ES to be comparable across the different ES parameters necessitated by the variety of tests discussed in this book.

Strict comparability, defined in exact mathematical terms, poses numerous difficulties. First, several alternative definitions are possible. Consider PV, which seems a likely candidate. When a variable is measured on an ordered equal-interval scale, so that the variance concept is meaningful, we can express ES in terms of proportion of variance, as was done above and in Chapter 2. But when the dependent variable is a nominal scale, we can no longer define variance or PV, but would need to invoke from information theory a more general (and much less familiar) concept, amount of information or uncertainty. If we decide to retreat from nominal scale comparability and try to use PV as a "strictly" comparable base for ES for interval scales, we encounter two further difficulties. One is that we would need to specify alternate models which would lead to varying PV's. For example, in Section 2.2 we defined the populations as distinct "points" and therefore, the relevant r as the point biserial r (r_p). So conceived, PV $= r_p^2$. But if our model is changed so that the populations are adjacent along a scale so that when combined they define a normal distribution (e.g., an adult male population defined by a median cut into "tall" and "short" men), the correlation with height of some dependent variable would be given by the biserial r (r_b) (Guilford, 1965, pp. 317–321), so that $PV = r_b^2$. But since r_b is greater than r_p, their squares and hence their PVs would differ. Thus, the "same" difference between means would, depending on the strength of the model assumption, lead to different proportions of variance.

A further problem would arise in that, having somehow defined strictly comparable ES in PV terms, when the latter were then translated into more familiar measures, awkward values which are not convenient multiples would result. Thus, if a medium PV were defined as .10, this would lead to $d = .667$ (under the conditions defined in Section 2.2) and $r = .316$.

We are prepared to be content with less formal bases for comparability than purely mathematical ones, utilizing the "state of the science" in relevant areas of behavioral science, as we have done above. But we wish to be guided in our operational definitions by quantitative considerations, here specifically correlational comparability.

In Section 2.2, the d criteria for small, medium, and large ES were stated and translated into *point* biserial r (r_p) and r_p^2 (Guilford, 1965, pp. 322–325). The use of r_p assumes that population membership (X) is two-valued and "point" in character. The t test for r, which concerns us in this chapter, presumes normal distributions on both X and Y. Comparability in PV would demand that the biserial r (r_b), for which a normal distribution is assumed to underlie the X dichotomy, should be the basis of comparison. With populations of equal size (i.e., forming the dichotomy at the median),

$$(3.2.1) \qquad\qquad r_b = 1.253 r_p.$$

Thus, if we translate the d criteria to r_p (Table 2.2.1) and then, by means of formula (3.2.1) to r_b, and compare the latter with the ES criteria set forth above for r, we find the following:

ES	d	$r_p \times 1.253 = r_b$		r
Small	.20	.100	.125	.10
Medium	.50	.243	.304	.30
Large	.80	.371	.465	.50

Comparing the r_b equivalent to the r criteria of the present chapter, we find what are judged to be reasonably close values for small and large ES and almost exact equality at the very important medium ES level. Thus, the terms "small," "medium," and "large" mean about the same thing in correlation terms as we go from consideration of mean differences to consideration of **r**'s.

3.3 POWER TABLES

The tables in this section yield power values when, in addition to the significance criterion and ES = **r**, the sample size is specified. Thus, these power tables will find their greatest use in determining the power of a test of the significance of a sample r_s, *after* the data are gathered and the test is made. They can also be used in experimental planning by varying **n**, or ES (= **r**), or **a** to determine the consequence which such alternatives have on power.

Specifically, the power tables yield power values for the **t** test of H_0: **r** = 0, i.e., for the test of the significance of a product moment r_s, determined on a sample of **n** pairs of observations **X**, **Y** at the **a** significance criterion. The tables give values for **a**, **r**, and **n**:

1. Significance Criterion, **a**. Tables are provided for the following values of **a**: $a_1 = .01$, $a_1 = .05$, $a_1 = .10$; $a_2 = .01$, $a_2 = .05$, $a_2 = .10$, the subscripts referring to one- and two-tailed tests. Since power at a_1 is to an adequate approximation equal to power at $a_2 = 2a_1$ for power greater than .10, one can determine power at $a_2 = .02$ (from the $a_1 = .01$ table), $a_2 = .20$ (from $a_1 = .10$), $a_1 = .005$ (from $a_2 = .01$), and $a_1 = .025$ (from $a_2 = .05$).

2. Effect Size, ES. The ES index here is simply **r**, the population product-moment correlation coefficient. In directional (one-tailed) tests (a_1), **r** is understood as either positive or negative, depending on the direction posited in the alternate hypotheses, e.g., H_1: **r** = − .30. In nondirectional (two-tailed) tests, **r** is understood as absolute, e.g., "given a level of population **r** = .30, whether positive or negative. . . ."

Provision is made for **r** = .10 (.10) .90. Conventional definitions of ES have been offered above, as follows:

   small: **r** = .10,
   medium: **r** = .30,
   large: **r** = .50.

3. Sample Size, **n**. This is the number of *pairs* of observations **X**, **Y** in the sample. Provision is made for **n** = 8 (1) 40 (2) 60 (4) 100 (20) 200 (50) 500 (100) 1000.

The values in the body of the table are the power of the test times 100, i.e., the percentage of tests carried out under the given conditions which will result in the rejection of the null hypothesis, H_0: **r** = 0. The values are rounded to the *nearest* unit and are accurate to within ± 1 as tabled (i.e., to within .01).

Table 3.3.1

Power of t test of r = 0 at a_1 = .01

						r				
n	r_c	.10	.20	.30	.40	.50	.60	.70	.80	.90
8	789	02	03	05	08	13	22	37	60	88
9	750	02	03	06	10	16	27	44	69	93
10	715	02	03	06	11	19	32	52	76	96
11	685	02	04	07	13	22	37	58	82	98
12	658	02	04	08	14	25	42	64	86	99
13	634	02	05	09	16	28	46	69	90	99
14	612	02	05	10	18	31	51	74	92	*
15	592	02	05	10	20	34	55	78	94	
16	574	02	06	11	22	38	59	81	96	
17	558	03	06	12	23	41	63	84	97	
18	543	03	06	13	25	43	66	86	98	
19	529	03	06	14	27	46	69	89	98	
20	516	03	07	15	29	49	72	91	99	
21	503	03	07	16	31	52	75	92	99	
22	492	03	07	17	32	54	77	94	99	
23	482	03	08	18	34	56	79	95	*	
24	472	03	08	18	36	59	81	95		
25	462	03	08	19	37	61	83	96		
26	453	03	09	20	39	63	85	97		
27	445	03	09	21	41	65	87	98		
28	437	03	09	22	43	67	88	98		
29	430	03	10	23	44	69	89	98		
30	423	03	10	24	46	71	91	99		
31	416	04	11	25	47	73	92	99		
32	409	04	11	26	49	75	93	99		
33	403	04	11	27	51	76	93	99		
34	397	04	12	28	52	78	94	99		
35	392	04	12	29	54	79	95	*		
36	386	04	12	30	55	80	95			
37	381	04	13	30	56	82	96			
38	376	04	13	31	58	83	96			
39	371	04	13	32	59	84	97			
40	367	04	14	33	61	85	97			
42	358	04	15	35	63	87	98			
44	350	05	15	37	66	89	98			
46	342	05	16	39	68	90	99			
48	335	05	17	41	70	92	99			

Table 3.3.1 (continued)

n	r_c	.10	.20	.30	.40	.50	.60	.70	.80	.90
50	328	05	18	42	72	93	99	*	*	*
52	322	05	18	44	74	94	99			
54	316	05	19	46	76	95	*			
56	310	06	20	48	78	96				
58	305	06	21	49	80	96				
60	300	06	21	51	81	97				
64	290	06	23	54	84	98				
68	282	06	25	57	87	98				
72	274	07	26	60	89	99				
76	266	07	28	63	90	99				
80	260	07	29	66	92	99				
84	253	08	31	68	93	*				
88	248	08	33	70	94					
92	242	08	34	73	95					
96	237	09	36	75	96					
100	232	09	37	76	97					
120	212	11	45	85	99					
140	196	12	52	90	*					
160	184	14	59	94						
180	173	16	65	96						
200	164	18	70	98						
250	147	23	81	99						
300	134	28	88	*						
350	124	32	93							
400	116	37	96							
450	110	42	98							
500	104	46	99							
600	095	55	*							
700	088	63								
800	082	69								
900	078	75								
1000	074	80								

* Power values below this point are greater than .995.

Table 3.3.2

Power of t test of r = 0 at a_1 = .05

					r				
n	r_c	.10	.20	.30	.40	.50	.60	.70	.80	.90

n	r_c	.10	.20	.30	.40	.50	.60	.70	.80	.90
8	621	08	12	18	26	37	52	68	85	97
9	582	08	13	20	29	42	57	74	90	99
10	549	08	14	22	32	46	62	79	93	99
11	521	09	15	23	35	50	67	83	95	*
12	497	09	15	25	38	54	71	87	97	
13	476	09	16	26	40	57	74	89	98	
14	458	10	17	28	43	60	78	91	98	
15	441	10	18	30	45	63	81	93	99	
16	426	10	19	31	48	66	83	95	99	
17	412	10	19	33	50	69	85	96	*	
18	400	11	20	34	52	71	87	97		
19	389	11	21	36	54	73	89	97		
20	378	11	22	37	56	75	90	98		
21	369	11	22	39	58	77	92	98		
22	360	11	23	40	60	79	93	99		
23	352	12	24	41	62	81	94	99		
24	344	12	24	42	64	83	95	99		
25	337	12	25	44	65	84	95	99		
26	330	12	26	45	67	85	97	*		
27	323	13	26	46	68	86	96			
28	317	13	27	47	70	88	97			
29	311	13	28	49	71	89	97			
30	306	13	28	50	72	90	98			
31	301	13	29	51	74	90	98			
32	296	14	30	52	75	91	98			
33	291	14	30	53	76	92	99			
34	287	14	31	54	77	93	99			
35	283	14	32	55	78	93	99			
36	279	14	32	56	79	94	99			
37	275	15	33	57	80	95	99			
38	271	15	33	58	81	95	99			
39	267	15	34	59	82	95	*			
40	264	15	35	60	83	96				
42	257	16	36	62	85	97				
44	251	16	37	64	86	97				
46	246	16	38	66	88	98				
48	240	17	39	67	89	98				

Table 3.3.2 *(continued)*

n	r_c	.10	.20	.30	.40	.50	.60	.70	.80	.90
50	235	17	41	69	90	98	*	*	*	*
52	231	17	42	71	91	99				
54	226	18	43	72	92	99				
56	222	18	44	73	93	99				
58	218	19	45	75	94	99				
60	214	19	46	76	94	99				
64	207	20	48	79	95	*				
68	201	20	50	81	96					
72	195	21	52	83	97					
76	190	22	54	85	98					
80	185	22	56	86	98					
84	181	23	58	88	99					
88	176	24	59	89	99					
92	173	24	61	90	99					
96	169	25	63	91	99					
100	165	26	64	92	99					
120	151	29	71	96	*					
140	140	32	77	98						
160	130	35	82	99						
180	123	38	86	99						
200	117	41	89	*						
250	104	47	94							
300	095	54	97							
350	088	59	98							
400	082	64	99							
450	078	68	*							
500	074	72								
600	067	79								
700	062	84								
800	058	88								
900	055	91								
1000	052	94								

* Power values below this point are greater than .995.

Table 3.3.3

Power of t test of r = 0 at a_1 = .10

						r				
n	r_c	.10	.20	.30	.40	.50	.60	.70	.80	.90
8	507	15	22	30	41	53	67	81	92	99
9	472	15	23	32	44	58	72	85	95	99
10	443	16	24	34	47	61	76	88	97	*
11	419	16	25	36	50	65	79	91	98	
12	398	17	26	38	53	68	83	93	99	
13	380	17	27	40	55	71	85	95	99	
14	365	17	28	42	58	74	87	96	99	
15	351	18	29	44	60	76	89	97	*	
16	338	18	30	45	62	79	90	98		
17	327	19	31	47	64	81	92	98		
18	317	19	32	49	66	82	93	98		
19	308	19	33	50	68	84	94	99		
20	299	20	34	52	70	86	95	99		
21	291	20	35	53	72	87	96	99		
22	284	20	36	54	73	88	97	99		
23	277	21	36	56	75	89	97	*		
24	271	21	37	57	76	90	98			
25	265	21	38	58	78	91	98			
26	260	22	39	59	79	92	98			
27	255	22	40	61	80	93	99			
28	250	22	40	62	81	94	99			
29	245	23	41	63	82	94	99			
30	241	23	42	64	83	95	99			
31	237	23	43	65	84	95	99			
32	233	23	43	66	85	96	99			
33	229	24	44	67	86	96	99			
34	225	24	45	68	87	97	*			
35	222	24	45	69	88	97				
36	219	24	46	70	88	97				
37	216	25	47	71	89	98				
38	213	25	48	72	90	98				
39	210	25	48	73	90	98				
40	207	25	49	74	91	98				
42	202	26	50	75	92	99				
44	197	26	51	77	93	99				
46	192	27	53	78	94	99				
48	188	27	54	79	94	99				

Table 3.3.3 *(continued)*

n	r_c	.10	.20	.30	.40	.50	.60	.70	.80	.90
50	184	28	55	81	95	99	*	*	*	*
52	181	28	56	82	96	*				
54	177	29	57	83	96					
56	174	29	58	84	97					
58	171	30	59	85	97					
60	168	30	60	86	97					
64	162	31	62	88	98					
68	157	32	64	89	98					
72	153	33	66	90	99					
76	149	34	68	92	99					
80	145	35	70	93	99					
84	141	36	71	94	*					
88	138	36	73	95						
92	135	37	74	95						
96	132	38	75	96						
100	129	39	76	96						
120	118	42	82	98						
140	109	46	86	99						
160	102	49	90	*						
180	096	52	92							
200	091	55	94							
250	081	62	97							
300	074	67	99							
350	069	72	99							
400	064	76	*							
450	061	80								
500	057	83								
600	052	88								
700	048	91								
800	045	94								
900	043	96								
1000	041	97								

*   Power values below this point are greater than .995.

Table 3.3.4

Power of t test of r = 0 at a_2 = .01

						r				
n	r_c	.10	.20	.30	.40	.50	.60	.70	.80	.90
8	834	01	02	03	05	08	14	26	47	80
9	798	01	02	03	06	10	18	32	56	88
10	765	01	02	04	07	12	22	40	65	93
11	735	01	02	04	08	15	27	46	73	96
12	708	01	02	05	09	17	31	52	79	97
13	684	01	03	05	10	20	35	58	84	99
14	661	01	03	06	12	22	40	64	87	99
15	641	01	03	06	13	25	44	68	90	*
16	623	01	03	07	14	28	48	73	93	
17	606	01	03	08	16	30	52	77	95	
18	590	01	04	08	17	33	56	80	96	
19	575	02	04	09	19	36	59	83	97	
20	561	02	04	09	20	38	62	85	98	
21	549	02	04	10	21	41	66	88	98	
22	537	02	04	11	23	43	68	90	99	
23	526	02	04	12	25	46	71	91	99	
24	515	02	05	12	26	49	74	93	99	
25	505	02	05	13	28	51	76	94	*	
26	496	02	05	14	30	53	78	95		
27	487	02	06	14	31	55	80	96		
28	479	02	06	15	33	57	82	96		
29	471	02	06	16	34	60	84	97		
30	463	02	06	17	36	62	85	98		
31	456	02	07	17	37	64	87	98		
32	449	02	07	18	39	66	88	98		
33	442	02	07	19	40	67	89	99		
34	436	02	07	20	42	69	90	99		
35	430	02	08	20	43	71	91	99		
36	424	02	08	21	45	72	92	99		
37	417	02	08	22	47	74	93	99		
38	413	02	08	23	48	76	94	*		
39	408	02	09	24	49	77	95			
40	403	02	09	25	50	78	95			
42	393	03	09	26	53	81	96			
44	384	03	10	28	56	83	97			
46	376	03	11	29	58	85	98			
48	368	03	11	31	61	87	98			

Table 3.3.4 *(continued)*

n	r_c	.10	.20	.30	.40	.50	.60	.70	.80	.90
50	361	03	12	33	63	89	99	*	*	*
52	354	03	12	34	66	90	99			
54	348	03	13	36	68	91	99			
56	341	03	14	38	70	93	99			
58	336	03	14	39	72	94	*			
60	330	03	15	41	74	94				
64	320	04	16	44	77	96				
68	310	04	17	47	80	97				
72	302	04	19	50	83	98				
76	294	04	20	53	85	98				
80	286	04	21	56	87	99				
84	280	05	23	59	89	99				
88	273	05	24	61	91	99				
92	267	05	25	64	92	*				
96	262	05	27	66	94					
100	256	06	29	69	95					
120	234	07	35	78	98					
140	217	08	42	85	99					
160	203	09	49	90	*					
180	192	11	55	94						
200	182	12	61	96						
250	163	16	73	99						
300	149	20	82	*						
350	138	24	89							
400	129	28	93							
450	121	32	96							
500	115	37	97							
600	105	45	99							
700	097	53	*							
800	091	60								
900	086	67								
1000	081	72								

* Power values below this point are greater than .995.

Table 3.3.5

Power of t test of $r = 0$ at $a_2 = .05$

n	r_c	.10	.20	.30	.40	.50	.60	.70	.80	.90
						r				
8	707	06	07	11	16	25	37	54	75	94
9	666	06	08	12	19	29	43	62	82	97
10	632	06	08	13	21	33	49	68	87	98
11	602	06	09	14	23	36	54	73	91	99
12	576	06	09	16	26	40	58	78	93	99
13	553	06	10	17	28	44	63	82	95	*
14	532	06	10	18	30	47	66	85	96	
15	514	06	11	19	32	50	70	88	98	
16	497	07	11	21	35	53	73	90	98	
17	482	07	12	22	37	56	76	92	99	
18	468	07	12	23	39	59	79	94	99	
19	456	07	13	24	41	62	81	95	99	
20	444	07	14	25	43	64	83	96	*	
21	433	07	14	27	45	66	85	96		
22	423	07	15	28	47	69	87	97		
23	413	07	15	29	49	71	89	98		
24	404	07	16	30	51	73	90	98		
25	396	08	16	31	53	75	91	99		
26	388	08	17	33	54	76	92	99		
27	381	08	17	34	56	78	93	99		
28	374	08	18	35	58	80	94	99		
29	367	08	18	36	59	81	95	99		
30	361	08	19	37	61	83	95	*		
31	355	08	19	38	62	84	96			
32	349	08	20	39	64	85	97			
33	344	09	20	40	65	86	97			
34	339	09	21	42	67	87	97			
35	334	09	21	43	68	88	98			
36	329	09	22	44	69	89	98			
37	325	09	22	45	70	90	98			
38	320	09	23	46	72	91	99			
39	316	09	23	47	73	91	99			
40	312	09	24	48	74	92	99			
42	304	10	25	50	76	93	99			
44	297	10	26	52	78	94	99			
46	291	10	27	54	80	95	*			
48	285	10	28	55	82	96				

Table 3.3.5 (continued)

n	r_c	.10	.20	.30	.40	.50	.60	.70	.80	.90
							r			
50	279	11	29	57	83	97	*	*	*	*
52	273	11	30	59	85	97				
54	268	11	31	61	86	98				
56	263	11	32	62	87	98				
58	259	12	33	64	89	98				
60	254	12	34	65	90	99				
64	246	12	36	68	91	99				
68	239	13	38	71	93	99				
72	232	13	39	73	94	*				
76	226	14	41	76	95					
80	220	14	43	78	96					
84	215	15	45	80	97					
88	210	15	47	82	98					
92	205	16	48	83	98					
96	201	16	50	85	98					
100	197	17	52	86	99					
120	179	19	59	92	*					
140	166	22	66	95						
160	155	24	72	97						
180	146	27	77	98						
200	139	29	81	99						
250	124	35	89	*						
300	113	41	94							
350	105	46	97							
400	098	52	98							
450	092	56	99							
500	088	61	99							
600	080	69	*							
700	074	76								
800	069	81								
900	065	85								
1000	062	89								

* Power values below this point are greater than .995.

Table 3.3.6

Power of t test of r = 0 at a_2 = .10

					r				
n	r_c	.10	.20	.30	.40	.50	.60	.70	.80	.90
8	621	11	14	19	27	38	52	68	85	97
9	582	11	15	21	30	42	57	74	90	99
10	549	11	15	22	33	46	62	79	93	99
11	521	12	16	24	35	50	67	83	95	*
12	497	12	17	25	38	54	71	87	97	
13	476	12	17	27	40	57	74	89	98	
14	458	12	18	28	43	60	78	91	98	
15	441	12	19	30	45	63	81	93	99	
16	426	12	19	31	48	66	83	95	99	
17	412	13	20	33	50	69	85	96	*	
18	400	13	21	34	52	71	87	97		
19	389	13	22	36	54	73	89	97		
20	378	13	22	37	56	75	90	98		
21	369	13	23	39	58	77	92	98		
22	360	13	24	40	60	79	93	99		
23	352	14	24	41	62	81	94	99		
24	344	14	25	42	64	83	95	99		
25	337	14	26	44	65	84	95	99		
26	330	14	26	45	67	85	96	*		
27	323	14	27	46	68	86	96			
28	317	14	27	47	70	88	97			
29	311	15	28	49	71	89	97			
30	306	15	29	50	72	90	98			
31	301	15	29	51	74	90	98			
32	296	15	30	52	75	91	98			
33	291	15	31	53	76	92	99			
34	287	15	31	54	77	93	99			
35	283	16	32	55	78	93	99			
36	279	16	32	56	79	94	99			
37	275	16	33	57	80	95	99			
38	271	16	34	58	81	95	99			
39	267	16	34	59	82	95	*			
40	264	16	35	60	83	96				
42	257	17	36	62	85	97				
44	251	17	37	64	86	97				
46	246	17	38	66	88	98				
48	240	18	39	67	89	98				

Table 3.3.6 *(continued)*

n	r_c	.10	.20	.30	.40	.50	.60	.70	.80	.90
50	235	18	41	69	90	98	*	*	*	*
52	231	18	42	71	91	99				
54	226	19	43	72	92	99				
56	222	19	44	73	93	99				
58	218	19	45	75	94	99				
60	214	20	46	76	94	99				
64	207	20	48	79	95	*				
68	201	21	50	81	96					
72	195	22	52	83	97					
76	190	22	54	85	98					
80	185	23	56	86	98					
84	181	24	58	88	99					
88	176	24	59	89	99					
92	173	25	61	90	99					
96	169	26	63	91	99					
100	165	27	64	92	99					
120	151	29	71	96	*					
140	140	32	77	98						
160	130	35	82	99						
180	123	38	86	99						
200	117	41	89	*						
250	104	47	94							
300	095	54	97							
350	088	59	98							
400	082	64	99							
450	078	68	*							
500	074	72								
600	067	79								
700	062	84								
800	058	88								
900	055	91								
1000	052	94								

* Power values below this point are greater than .995.

Illustrative Examples

3.1 A personality psychologist has performed an experiment in which he obtained paired measures on a sample of 50 subjects. One of these variables is a questionnaire score on extraversion, the other a neurophysiological measure which his theory posits should relate to the former. His hypothesis is formulated as nondirectional and he selects $a_2 = .05$ as his significance criterion. Although his theory dictates a strong relationship, unreliability and lack of high construct validity of his measures (e.g., social desirability variance in his questionnaire measure) lead him to expect only a medium ES, hence he posits $r = .30$ ($PV = r^2 = .09$). What is the power of the test of the significance of r_s he performs? His specifications are

$$a_2 = .05, \qquad r = .30, \qquad n = 50.$$

In Table 3.3.5 (for $a_2 = .05$), column $r = .30$, row $n = 50$, power $= .57$. Thus, a significance test with 50 subjects at an $a_2 = .05$ criterion has not much more than a 50–50 chance of rejecting the null hypothesis when the population $r = .30$.

It may be argued that a theory which leads to so nonobvious a prediction as the correlation of measured electrical events in the nervous system with responses to complex social and intrapersonal questionnaire items combined in a certain specific way, should at least predict the *direction* of the association. Indeed it does—it predicts a positive correlation. If the investigator would have been prepared to renounce all interest in discovering an unanticipated *negative* correlation (if such, despite his theory, should be the case), he would have formulated his null and alternate hypothesis directionally (H_0: $r \leq 0$, $H_1 : r = +.30$) and, leaving his other conditions unchanged, may have instead used a one-tailed significance criterion, thus:

$$a_1 = .05, \qquad r = .30, \qquad n = 50.$$

In Table 3.3.2 for $a_1 = .05$ (instead of Table 3.3.5 for $a_2 = .05$), column $r = .30$, row $n = 50$, power $= .69$. The use of a directional instead of a nondirectional test under these conditions (of a, r, and n) would result in his chance of rejecting the null hypothesis being improved from .57 to .69. Note that the formulation of this illustration is *not* intended to suggest any manipulation of the directionality of the test *after* the data are gathered. This is properly formulated in advance and maintained. However, these tables may be used in experimental planning for seeking an optimum strategy. This could include the decision as to whether to state the hypothesis directionally or nondirectionally and would lead to such comparisons as the above. If we take this to be the case in the above example, the psychologist would then need to decide whether, under the given conditions, the gain in power from .57 to .69 is worth forgoing the possibility of concluding that **r** is negative. This decision will be made, of course, on substantive and not statistical grounds.

3.2 An educational psychologist is consulted by the dean responsible for admission at a small college with regard to the desirability of supplementing their criterion for admission by using a personality questionnaire. The plan is to administer the test to entering freshmen and determine whether scores on this test (**X**) correlate with freshman year grade point average (**Y**). Following discussion it is determined that it can be assumed that for entering freshmen **X** is not correlated with the selection criterion, so that its correlation with **Y**, if any, represents incremental validity beyond present selection practices.[5] The decision is made that if **r** = .10, then it is worth adding to the selection procedure. Each annual freshmen class numbers about 500. The educational psychologist first seeks to determine power under these conditions if the decision to proceed is made at the $a_2 = .01$ and $a_2 = .05$ criteria. His specifications are

$$a_2 = .01, \quad r = .10, \quad n = 500,$$
$$a_2 = .05, \quad r = .10, \quad n = 500.$$

In Table 3.3.4 for $a_2 = .01$, with column **r** = .10 and row **n** = 500, power = .37. Then in Table 3.3.5 (for $a_2 = .05$) for the same column and row, power = .61.

The educational psychologist finds himself dissatisfied with these results, since, even with the $a_2 = .05$ risk, he has only a three in five chance of detecting **r** = .10. He checks the consequence of $a_2 = .10$ (Table 3.3.6) for these conditions and finds power = .72, the same as for $a_1 = .05$ (Table 3.3.2). Thus, even if he were to use an $a_2 = .10$ criterion (which he and the dean judge to be too large a risk in this situation), or an $a_1 = .05$ criterion (which would mean eliminating the possibility of a valid conclusion that **r** is of sign opposite from the one anticipated), he would have power of not quite three in four. Since even liberalizing conditions which are unacceptable in the situation yield power values not as high as desired, he considers other possibilities.

The psychologist considers the possibility of an experimental plan which involves combining the data for two successive years, so that **n** will equal about 1000. The conditions now are

$$a_2 = .01, \quad r = .10, \quad n = 1000,$$
$$a_2 = .05, \quad r = .10, \quad n = 1000.$$

---

[5] Alternatively, what follows can be considered to be concerned with the *partial* correlation of **X** and **Y**, holding constant the current selection criterion. Power or sample size estimates for null hypothesis tests of partial (or part) correlations are given approximately by the tables in this chapter, provided the number of variables excluded is not large.

He uses Table 3.3.4 (for $a_2 = .01$), with column $r = .10$ and row $n = 1000$, and finds power $= .72$. Then, he considers Table 3.3.5 (for $a_2 = .05$) and finds power $= .89$. He suggests to the dean that if two successive years' admissions can be used (resulting in an additional year's delay) and that if the alpha risk of $a_2 = .05$ is acceptably small, that a population $r = .10$ can be detected with probability of almost nine in ten. The dean might well find this procedure acceptable.

It may be noted that if **X** has a higher correlation with **Y** in the population, say $r = .20$, the various conditions posited above yield power values as follows:

		$n = 500$	$n = 1000$
(Table 3.3.4)	$a_2 = .01$	.97	$>.995$
(Table 3.3.5)	$a_2 = .05$	.99	$>.995$
(Table 3.3.6)	$a_2 = .10 \, (a_1 = .05)$	$>.995$	$>.995$

It is obvious that if **r** is as large as .20, it hardly matters what alpha criterion is chosen, and, moreover, it would certainly not pay to delay an additional year to bring **n** from 500 to 1000. This illustrates how crucial the ES decision may be in experimental planning.

3.3 An industrial psychologist is asked to perform an investigation of the relationship between weekly wages (which vary as a function of training and experience) and work output for a given job. The client's purpose is to decide on wage and qualification policy in a new venture. The economics of the situation are such that if an additional dollar a week in wage (**X**) is accompanied by as much as an additional 4 units (**Y**) of work output, it would be advantageous to hire the best qualified workers who will require the maximum salary. The ES is thus formulated in terms of a regression coefficient $B_{YX} = 4$. The industrial psychologist can obtain appropriate data on $n = 120$ workers and plans to perform a one-tailed test at the .01 level. The one-tailed test is justified on the grounds that the situation does not require distinguishing between a zero and a negative relationship in the null hypothesis—either will lead to the same decision (see Section 1.2 and Cohen, 1965, pp. 106–111, and ref.).

Since the ES is a regression coefficient, for use of Tables 3.3 and 3.4.1, it must be converted into **r**. For this, values or estimates of the relevant population standard deviations of **X** and **Y** are needed. Assume these values are available, and are $\sigma_X = 8$ and $\sigma_Y = 80$. Thus, from formula (3.1.3),

$$r = B_{YX} \frac{\sigma_X}{\sigma_Y} = (4) \frac{8}{80} = .40.$$

Thus, the specifications are

$$a_1 = .01, \qquad r = .40, \qquad n = 120.$$

In Table 3.3.1 (for $a_1 = .01$), with column $r = .40$ and row $n = 120$, power $= .99$. Thus, if the relationship in the population is such that a dollar increase in weekly pay is associated with an increase of 4 work units (which, given σ_Y and σ_X, implies $r = .40$), then, with $n = 120$, the probability that he will reject the null hypothesis at the $a_1 = .01$ criterion is .99. Note that these conditions happen to yield equality of alpha and beta risks at .01, a result which can, of course, be directly sought. For this, the sample size Tables (3.4) are somewhat more convenient.

3.4   Sample Size Tables

The tables in this section list values for the significance criterion, the $r \, (= \text{ES})$ to be detected, and the *desired power*. The number of paired observations (X, Y) required in the sample, n, is then completely determined. These tables are designed primarily for use in the planning of experiments, during which the decision on sample size is made. As already noted (Section 2.4), a rational decision on sample size requires, after the significance criterion and ES are formulated, attention to the question: How much power (or how little Type II error risk) is desired?

The use of these tables is subject to the same assumptions of normality and homoscedasticity as those applying to the power tables in the previous section (see Section 3.1). Tables give values for a, r, and desired power:

1. Significance Criterion, a. The same values of a are provided as for the power tables. Five tables are provided, one for each of the following nonparenthetic a levels: $a_1 = .01$ ($a_2 = .02$), $a_1 = .05$ ($a_2 = .10$), $a_1 = .10$ ($a_2 = .20$), $a_2 = .01$ ($a_1 = .005$), and $a_2 = .05$ ($a_1 = .025$).

2. Effect Size, ES. The population r serves as ES. For problems in which the effect size is expressed as a regression coefficient, it is converted to r by means of formula (3.1.3). The same provision for r is made as in the power tables: .10 (.10) .90. For r values other than the nine provided, the following formula, rounding to the nearest integer, provides an excellent approximation[6]:

(3.4.1) $$n = n_{.10} \left(\frac{.100}{z} \right)^2 + 2,$$

---

[6] A check on formula (3.4.1) was made by applying it to the 96 values for $a_1 = .005$, .025, .050, and .010, $r = .20$ (.10) .90 at power levels .50, .80, and .99. The mean discrepancy from the *rounded* values of Tables 3.4 was $+.01$, with a standard deviation of .46. No discrepancy exceeded 1.1. Since rounding error alone would result in a standard deviation of discrepancies of .32, the approximation is more than adequate.

where $n_{.10}$ is the necessary sample size for the given a and desired power at $r = .10$ (obtained from the table), and z is the Fisher z transformation for the nontabled r value. The constant $.100$ is the value of the z transformation when $r = .10$. Discussion of the Fisher z transformation is found in many statistics textbooks (e.g., McNemar, 1962; Hays, 1963). The next chapter contains an r to z transformation table (4.2.2).

3. Desired Power. As in Chapter 2, provision is made for desired power values of .25, .50, .60, $\frac{2}{3}$, .70 (.05), .95, .99. For discussion of the basis for selecting these values, the provision for equalizing a and b risks, and the rationale of a proposed convention of desired power of .80, see Section 2.4.

Summarizing the use of the n tables which follow, the investigator finds (a) the table for the significance criterion (a) he is using, and locates (b) the population r along the horizontal stub and (c) the desired power along the vertical stub. n, the necessary sample size to detect r at the a significance criterion with the desired power, is then determined. If the r value in his specifications is not provided in the tables, he (a) finds the table for the significance criterion he is using, and (b) enters it in column $r = .10$ and row for desired power, and reads out $n_{.10}$. He then finds in Table 4.2.2 of the next chapter the Fisher z value for his r, and enters it and $n_{.10}$ in formula (3.4.1) to compute n.

Illustrative Examples

3.4 Reconsider the conditions of example 3.1, in which a personality psychologist is concerned with the relationship between a neurophysiological measure and a questionnaire score on extraversion. As originally described, he wishes to detect an ES of $r = .30$ at $a_2 = .05$. His plan to use $n = 50$ subjects resulted in a power estimate of .57. He will almost certainly consider this value too low. Assume that he wishes power to be at the conventional .80 value and wants to know the sample size necessary for this. The specifications are

$$a_2 = .05, \quad r = .30, \quad \text{power} = .80.$$

In Table 3.4.1 for $a_2 = .05$, column $r = .30$, row power = .80, he finds $n = 84$. Thus, with these specifications of a and r, he will require 84 subjects to achieve power of .80.

What if this psychologist had instead anticipated a strong relationship between the two variables, $r = .50$ (our operational definition of a large ES), using the same a and power:

$$a_2 = .05, \quad r = .50, \quad \text{power} = .80.$$

Table 3.4.1

n to detect r by t test

Power	.10	.20	.30	.40	.50	.60	.70	.80	.90
				$a_1 = .01$ $(a_2 = .02)$					
				r					
.25	273	68	31	18	12	9	7	5	4
.50	540	134	59	31	20	14	10	7	5
.60	663	164	72	39	24	16	11	8	6
2/3	757	187	81	44	28	18	13	9	6
.70	809	200	87	48	29	19	13	9	6
.75	897	221	96	53	32	21	14	10	7
.80	998	246	107	58	36	23	16	11	7
.85	1126	277	120	65	40	26	17	12	8
.90	1296	319	138	75	45	29	20	13	8
.95	1585	389	168	91	55	35	23	16	10
.99	2154	529	228	123	74	47	31	20	13
				$a_1 = .05$ $(a_2 = .10)$					
				r					
.25	99	24	12	8	6	4	4	3	3
.50	277	69	30	17	11	8	6	5	4
.60	368	92	40	22	14	10	7	5	4
2/3	430	107	47	26	16	11	8	6	4
.70	470	117	51	28	18	12	8	6	4
.75	537	133	58	32	20	13	9	7	5
.80	618	153	68	37	22	15	10	7	5
.85	727	180	78	43	26	17	12	8	6
.90	864	213	93	50	31	20	13	9	6
.95	1105	272	118	64	39	25	16	11	7
.99	1585	389	168	91	55	35	23	15	10
				$a_1 = .10$ $(a_2 = .20)$					
				r					
.25	39	11	6	4	3	3	3	3	3
.50	165	42	19	11	7	5	4	3	3
.60	236	59	27	15	10	7	5	4	3
2/3	293	73	33	18	12	8	6	4	4
.70	326	81	36	20	13	9	6	5	4
.75	383	95	42	23	14	10	7	5	4
.80	450	112	49	27	17	11	8	6	4
.85	536	133	58	32	19	13	9	6	4
.90	655	162	71	39	24	16	11	7	5
.95	864	213	93	50	31	20	13	9	6
.99	1296	319	138	75	45	29	19	13	8

Table 3.4.1 (continued)

$$a_2 = .01 \; (a_1 = .005)$$

Power	.10	.20	.30	.40	.50	.60	.70	.80	.90
.25	362	90	40	23	15	11	8	6	5
.50	662	164	71	39	24	16	12	8	6
.60	797	197	86	47	29	19	13	9	7
2/3	901	222	96	53	32	21	15	10	7
.70	957	236	102	56	34	23	15	11	7
.75	1052	259	112	61	37	25	17	11	8
.80	1163	286	124	67	41	27	18	12	8
.85	1299	320	138	75	45	30	20	13	9
.90	1480	364	157	85	51	34	22	15	9
.95	1790	440	190	102	62	40	26	17	11
.99	2390	587	253	136	82	52	34	23	13

$$a_2 = .05 \; (a_1 = .025)$$

Power	.10	.20	.30	.40	.50	.60	.70	.80	.90
.25	166	42	20	12	8	6	5	4	3
.50	384	95	42	24	15	10	7	6	4
.60	489	121	53	29	18	12	9	6	5
2/3	570	141	62	34	21	14	10	7	5
.70	616	152	66	37	23	15	10	7	5
.75	692	171	74	41	25	17	11	8	6
.80	783	193	84	46	28	18	12	9	6
.85	895	221	96	52	32	21	14	10	6
.90	1046	258	112	61	37	24	16	11	7
.95	1308	322	139	75	46	30	19	13	8
.99	1828	449	194	104	63	40	27	18	11

The same table (Table 3.4.1 for $a_2 = .05$) for column $r = .50$, row power $= .80$ yields $n = 28$.

At the other extreme of our operational definitions, suppose he hypothesized $r = .10$ (a small ES), keeping the other specifications constant:

$$a_2 = .05, \qquad r = .10, \qquad \text{power} = .80.$$

In table 3.4.1 for $a_2 = .05$, for $r = .10$ and power $= .80, n = 783$.

Again we see how crucial anticipated ES is to the decision about sample size. Over our range from large to medium to small ES, the n's required go from 28 to 84 to 783. Reversing the argument, it is apparent that a decision about sample size *implies* some value for r (given a and desired power). Many experiments are undertaken as if the experimenter were anticipating a *very* large ES, since presumably he would not bother to do the experiment if he thought he had a low probability of rejecting the null hypothesis.

Another point incidentally illustrated here is the nonlinearity of the **r** scale: At any given desired power level, equal increments in **r** do *not* produce equal or even proportional decrements in necessary **n** (as is implicit in formula (3.4.1), i.e., **n** varies approximately as the square of the ratio of the **z** values).

Experimental planning may involve preparing tables in which, for alternative power levels, the **n**'s necessary under varying alternative ES values and alternative **a** criteria are assembled from Table 3.4.1 and scrutinized in the light of the substantive issues of the research. A possible table for this example is shown in Table 3.4.2.

TABLE 3.4.2

AN EXAMPLE OF A SAMPLE SIZE PLANNING TABLE

	Power								
	.70			.80			.90		
	ES = **r**			ES = **r**			ES = **r**		
	.20	.30	.40	.20	.30	.40	.20	.30	.40
a$_1$ = .01	200	87	48	246	107	58	319	138	75
a$_1$ = .05	117	51	28	153	68	37	213	93	50
a$_1$ = .10	81	36	20	112	49	27	162	71	39
a$_2$ = .01	236	102	56	286	124	67	364	157	85
a$_2$ = .05	152	66	37	193	84	46	258	112	61

An experimenter with such a table before him is in a position to make a choice of an experimental plan which is consonant both with his knowledge and informed hunches of his substantive field and with statistical analytic issues. Thus, he might decide after reviewing the table that he is prepared to expend the money and effort involved in running 84 or 85 subjects, but would prefer the 84 subjects called for when he posits **r** = .30 at power = .80 for **a**$_2$ = .05 rather than the 85 called for when, with more stringent **a**$_2$ = .01 and greater power = .90, he must posit **r** = .40; he may not consider the risk of assuming **r** so high worth the **a** and power advantage. He may consider least desirable the plan which calls for **n** = 81, which allows for a distinctly smaller ES or **r** = .20, but at the cost of less power (.70) and a large, one-tailed Type I risk (**a**$_1$ = .10) or equivalently an even larger two-tailed Type I risk (**a**$_2$ = .20).

3.5 A social psychologist is planning an experiment in which college students selected with regard to a personality questionnaire measure (**Y**) will be subjected to various alternative communications in a study of attitude change. Before this is undertaken, however, he considers it important that it be demonstrable that his measure (**Y**) *not* be related to a questionnaire measure of social desirability (**X**). He finds himself in the apparent position of having to prove the null hypothesis that $r = 0$, which is formally impossible.

However, instead of demanding of himself the impossible proof that $r = 0$, he may revise this to an attempt to demonstrate that r is trivially small, which is probably all that is ever meant by "no" relationship in behavioral science. He may consider an r no greater absolutely than .10 as meeting this criterion in this context. It now becomes possible to mount an experiment from which the conclusion that r is trivially small may properly be drawn. He sets up as the ES he wishes to detect $r = .10$. To assure himself a good chance of detecting this value if it should obtain, he demands relatively high power, say .90. Finally, he is prepared to run a large risk that he will mistakenly reject $r = 0$ in favor of $r = .10$ by setting $a_2 = .20$, since scientific caution here demands that the bias be *against* the null hypothesis. He now seeks the **n** which will satisfy these specifications, which, summarized, are

$$a_2 = .20, \qquad r = .10, \qquad power = .90.$$

Table 3.4.1 for $a_1 = .10$ ($a_2 = .20$), for column $r = .10$, row power = .90, yields **n** = 655. (Since both **X** and **Y** are obtained by group procedures, this large sample may well be within his resources.[7])

Assume that the data are collected and he finds $r_s = .04$, which is not significant at $a_2 = .20$. He can conclude that the population r is effectively zero. This is because, if the population r is as large as .10, it is unlikely ($b = 1 - power = 1 - .90 = .10$) that he would have failed to find r_s significant.

In this way, experiments can be organized which can accomplish what is really sought when we attempt to "prove null hypotheses." What we have done instead is to mitigate the null hypothesis to mean "trivially small" and set up this small value as the ES (alternate hypothesis) in an experiment which has enough power to detect it. If we then fail to reject the literal null hypothesis, we can conclude that the effect is effectively zero.

---

[7] An alternative design for the overall study, which does not depend on this r being trivially small (but makes other assumptions), would be a factorial design (**Y** levels by communications) analysis of covariance in which the attitude change measure would be the dependent variable and the social desirability control measure (**X**) would be the covariate or "adjusting" variable.

3.6 A research clinical psychologist is preparing an investigation of rate of decay of the orienting reflex (OR) in various psychopathological patient groups. An issue arises as to whether the OR is appreciably related to amount of confusion as rated by trained observers (C). In the context of the study, he decides that if the proportion of variance in OR associated with C is as large as .10, he wants to perform a preliminary experiment at the $a_2 = .10$ level which will have power of .90 to detect it. Since $PV = r^2 = .10$, $ES = r = \sqrt{.10} = .32$, a value not provided in Table 3.4.1. He thus takes recourse to formula (3.4.1), which requires $n_{.10}$ (from Table 3.4.1 for $a_2 = .10$) and z, the Fisher z transformation of an r of .32. The latter is found in Table 4.2.2 of the next chapter to be $z = .332$. $n_{.10}$ is found in Table 3.4.1 for $a_2 = .10$ in column $r = .10$, row power = .90, as 864. Entering these values in formula (3.4.1),

$$n = 864 \left(\frac{.100}{.332} \right)^2 + 2 = 80.9.$$

Thus, if he is to have a .90 probability of detecting $r = .32$ ($PV = r^2 = .10$) at the $a_2 = .10$ level, he will need a sample n of 81 cases.

If, on reconsideration, he decides he would prefer to use the more stringent $a_2 = .05$ level and is prepared to operate with .85 power to detect the same $PV = .10$, all that changes is the $n_{.10}$ value. He uses Table 3.4.1 for $a_2 = .05$, row $r = .10$, power = .85, and finds $n_{.10} = 895$. Substituting in formula (3.4.1),

$$n = 895 \left(\frac{.100}{.332} \right)^2 + 2 = 83.1,$$

a slightly larger value.

3.5 THE USE OF THE TABLES FOR SIGNIFICANCE TESTING OF r

Although the major purpose of this handbook is the exposition and facilitation of power analysis, the power tables contain criterion values of the ES *in the sample* necessary to reach statistical significance. These values facilitate the testing of null hypotheses when the sample results are determined.

The power tables in this chapter (Tables 3.3.1–3.3.5) contain, in the r_c column, the sample r_s necessary to attain the significance level of the table for the sample size of the row in which it appears. The r_c is taken as absolute (of either sign) for nondirectional (two-tailed) tests, and as of the appropriate sign in directional (one-tailed) tests. These values are of the same kind as appear in some statistical texts, but provide many more values, both for a and for n.

Illustrative Examples

3.7   Consider the analysis of the data arising from the experiment relating extraversion to a neurophysiological measure given in example 3.1. Assume that the data have been collected as planned, and the sample r_s is found to equal $-.241$. The specifications for the significance test are

$$a_2 = .05, \quad n = 50, \quad r_s = -.241.$$

Table 3.3.5 (for $a_2 = .05$) is used for $n = 50$, and the r_c value is found to equal .279. Since .241 (the sign is ignored because the test is two-tailed) is smaller than r_c, the null hypothesis is not rejected.

3.8   Reconsider the condition of example 3.2, where the validity of a personality questionnaire to predict freshman grade point average is under study. Assume that prior to data collection, the decision is made to test the null hypothesis at $a_2 = .05$ and $n = 500$. When the data are collected, r_s is found to equal .136. Thus,

$$a_2 = .05, \quad n = 500, \quad r_s = .136.$$

In Table 3.3.5 (for $a_2 = .05$) at $n = 500$, the criterion value r_c is found to be .088. Since r_s exceeds this, the null hypothesis is rejected, and it is concluded that there is a (nonzero) relationship between the questionnaire measure and grade point average.

3.9   The industrial psychologist in example 3.3 designed an experiment using 120 paired observations to determine whether a regression coefficient of wages on work unit output was significant at $a_1 = .01$. In that example, it was demonstrated how the regression coefficient could be converted to an **r** and the tables of this chapter could be applied. In planning, his alternate hypothesis was $r = .40$. When the sample data were analyzed, the r_s was found to equal $+.264$. The following specifications, then, are the conditions for his test of the null hypothesis that population $r = 0$:

$$a_1 = .01, \quad n = 120, \quad r_s = +.264.$$

He uses Table 3.3.1 (for $a_1 = .01$) at row $n = 120$ and finds that $r_c = .212$. Since his sample r_s exceeds the $a_1 = .01$ criterion value .212, *and is of the proper sign* (since the test was directional), the null hypothesis is rejected. Note that rejecting $H_0 : r = 0$ means rejecting $H_0 : B = 0$, i.e., if the correlation is not zero, neither is the regression coefficient (as discussed in Section 3.1).

Note, too, that although the sample r_s of .264 is much smaller than the anticipated population **r** of .40 which figured in the experimental planning, it is nevertheless significantly different from zero. (This comes about because the power of the experiment to detect an $r = .40$ was very high, .99.) The rejection of the null hypothesis does *not* warrant the conclusion that the specified alternate hypothesis (anticipated ES) is true, only that the null hypothesis is false (subject of course to the Type I risk).

4

Differences between Correlation Coefficients

4.1 INTRODUCTION AND USE

This chapter is concerned with the testing under various specified conditions of hypotheses concerning differences between population correlation coefficients. The previous chapter was devoted to a frequently occurring special case of this issue, namely, the difference between a population r and zero. In the present chapter, other cases are considered: the difference between two population r's when a sample is available from each (Cases 0 and 1), and the difference between a population r and any specified hypothetical value (Case 2).

Interest in relationships in behavioral sciences transcends the simple question of whether a relationship exists (Chapter 3). Whether the degree of relationship between two variables is greater in one natural population or given experimental condition than it is in another, is an issue that arises with some frequency. A related issue involves the question of whether, in a population or condition, the degree of relationship differs from some specified value, not necessarily zero. Tests of these issues are available through Fisher's z transformation of r (e.g., McNemar, 1962, 139–140; Hays, 1963, 530–533; Blalock, 1960, 305–307), and the power analyses in this chapter relate to these tests.

The above informal statement requires closer specification. By "relationship," linear correlation indexed by the Pearson product-moment correlation coefficient, r, is intended. The usual normality and homoscedasticity assumptions are formally assumed for the r's involved (McNemar, 1962, Chapter 9), but even with considerable departure from these assumptions, the validity of tabled **a** and power values is not greatly affected, particularly for large samples.

The material in this chapter will be organized into "cases," according to the specific hypothesis and sample(s) employed:

Case 0. r_s values from equal size samples to test $r_1 = r_2$.

Case 1.   The same hypothesis, but $n_1 \neq n_2$.

Case 2.   One sample drawn from a population to test $r = c$.

A word about differences between independent regression coefficients. As such, the procedures and tables of this chapter do not provide a basis for power analysis of the test of $H_0 : B_1 - B_2 = 0$. Note, however, that if the standard deviations of **X** and **Y** can be assumed equal over the two populations (i.e., $\sigma_{X_1} = \sigma_{X_2}$, $\sigma_{Y_1} = \sigma_{Y_2}$), the test of the equality of **r**'s is equivalent to the test of equality of **B**'s.

4.2   THE EFFECT SIZE INDEX: **q**

The detectability of a difference in magnitude between population **r**'s is not a simple function of the difference. That is, if we were to define $j = r_1 - r_2$ and try to use **j** as our ES, we would soon discover that the detectability of **j**, under fixed conditions of **a** and **n**, would *not* be constant, but would depend on where along the **r** scale the difference **j** occurred. As a concrete example, when

1. $r_1 = .50$ and $r_2 = .25$, $j = .50 - .25 = .25$; and when

2. $r_1 = .90$ and $r_2 = .65$, $j = .90 - .65 = .25$ also.

But for these two *equal* differences of $j = .25$, given $a_2 = .05$ and $n = 35$ (for example), the power to detect the first difference $(.50 - .25)$ is only .22, while the power for the second $(.90 - .65)$ is .80. Thus, **r** does not supply a scale of equal units of detectability, and so the difference between **r**'s is not an appropriate ES index.

The Fisher **z** transformation of **r** provides a solution to the problem. When **r**'s are transformed by the relationship

(4.2.1) $$z = \tfrac{1}{2} \log_e \frac{1+r}{1-r},$$

equal differences between **z**'s are equally detectable. Thus, we define as our ES index

(4.2.2) $$q = z_1 - z_2 \quad \text{(directional)}$$
$$= | z_1 - z_2 | \quad \text{(nondirectional)}.$$

Thus, unlike $r_1 - r_2, z_1 - z_2 = q$ gives values whose detectability does *not* depend on whether the z's (and hence the r's) are both small or both large. The power and sample size tables of this chapter provide entry for $q = .10$ (.10) .80 (.20) 1.40.

To facilitate the conversion of $r_1 - r_2$ to $z_1 - z_2 = q$ values, Tables 4.2.1 and 4.2.2 have been provided. Table 4.2.1 yields q values as a function of $r_1 - r_2$; Table 4.2.2 is the usual r to z transformation table.

Table 4.2.1

r_1 values as a function of r_2 and $q = z_1 - z_2$

r_2	.10	.20	.30	.40	.50	.60	.70	.80	1.00	1.20	1.40
.00	10	20	29	38	46	54	60	66	762	834	885
.05	15	25	34	42	50	57	64	69	782	848	896
.10	20	29	38	46	54	60	66	72	801	862	905
.15	25	34	42	50	57	64	69	74	818	874	914
.20	29	38	46	54	61	67	72	76	834	886	922
.25	34	43	50	58	64	69	74	78	850	897	930
.30	39	47	54	61	67	72	77	80	864	907	937
.35	43	51	58	64	70	75	79	82	878	916	943
.40	48	55	62	68	73	77	81	84	890	925	949
.45	53	59	66	71	76	79	83	86	902	933	955
.50	57	63	69	74	78	82	85	87	914	941	960
.55	62	67	73	77	81	84	87	89	924	949	965
.60	66	71	76	80	83	86	88	90	935	956	970
.65	70	75	79	83	86	88	90	92	944	962	975
.70	75	79	82	85	88	90	92	93	953	968	979
.75	79	83	85	88	90	92	93	94	962	974	983
.80	83	86	89	90	92	94	95	96	970	980	987
.85	88	90	91	93	94	95	96	97	978	985	990
.90	92	93	94	95	96	97	97	98	986	990	994
.95	96	97	97	98	98	98	99	99	993	995	997

Table 4.2.1 is generally more convenient for use in power analysis and when r_1 and r_2 are of the same sign. Assume both positive and $r_1 > r_2$. Given r_2, the smaller, read across to r_1, the larger. When r_1 is found, it is used to determine q, the column heading, which is the difference between the z transformations of the r's, i.e., $q = z_1 - z_2$. For example, if you wished to detect a difference between population r's of .25 $(= r_2)$ and .50 $(= r_1)$, the table provides the difference q between their respective z values, as follows: Locate in the first

Table 4.2.2

Transformation of Product Moment r to z*

r	z	r	z	r	z	r	z
.00	.000	.25	.255	.50	.549	.75	0.973
.01	.010	.26	.266	.51	.563	.76	0.996
.02	.020	.27	.277	.52	.576	.77	1.020
.03	.030	.28	.288	.53	.590	.78	1.045
.04	.040	.29	.299	.54	.604	.79	1.071
.05	.050	.30	.310	.55	.618	.80	1.099
.06	.060	.31	.321	.56	.633	.81	1.127
.07	.070	.32	.332	.57	.648	.82	1.157
.08	.080	.33	.343	.58	.662	.83	1.188
.09	.090	.34	.354	.59	.678	.84	1.221
.10	.100	.35	.365	.60	.693	.85	1.256
.11	.110	.36	.377	.61	.709	.86	1.293
.12	.121	.37	.388	.62	.725	.87	1.333
.13	.131	.38	.400	.63	.741	.88	1.376
.14	.141	.39	.412	.64	.758	.89	1.422
.15	.151	.40	.424	.65	.775	.90	1.472
.16	.161	.41	.436	.66	.793	.91	1.528
.17	.172	.42	.448	.67	.811	.92	1.589
.18	.182	.43	.460	.68	.829	.93	1.658
.19	.192	.44	.472	.69	.848	.94	1.738
.20	.203	.45	.485	.70	.867	.95	1.832
.21	.213	.46	.497	.71	.887	.96	1.946
.22	.224	.47	.510	.72	.908	.97	2.092
.23	.234	.48	.523	.73	.929	.98	2.298
.24	.245	.49	.536	.74	.950	.99	2.647

*This table is abridged from Table 19.2 in Owen, D.B., *Handbook of Statistical Tables.* Reading, Mass.: Addison–Wesley, 1962. Reproduced with the permission of the publishers. (Courtesy of the U.S. Atomic Energy Commission.)

column the value $r_2 = .25$, then read across to $r_1 = .50$, and at the top of the column, find $q = .30$.

Since one cannot have both convenient multiples of .10 for q and simultaneously convenient multiples of .05 for both r_1 and r_2, the use of Table 4.2.1 may require interpolation in q. Thus, for $r_1 = .25$, $r_1 = .60$, entry in the row for $r_2 = .25$ yields $q = .40$ for $r_1 = .58$ and $q = .50$ for $r_1 = .64$. Linear interpolation gives the approximate value of $q = .433$.

Alternatively, for exact values of q, Table 4.2.2 may be used to locate $r_1 = .60$ and $r_2 = .25$ and their respective z values found: $z_1 = .693$, $z_2 = .255$. Then, $q = .693 - .255 = .438$. Note that in either case, interpolation would be needed when this nontabled q value is used in the power tables (but not for sample size determination[1]).

Table 4.2.2 would also be used when r_1 and r_2 are of different signs. For example, for $r_1 = +.60$ and $r_2 = -.25$, the respective z values are found from Table 4.2.2 as $z_1 = +.693$ and $z_2 = -.255$. Then $q = z_1 - z_2 = +.693 - (-.255) = .948$.

Finally, Table 4.2.2 will be necessary to find q_s when the power tables are used for significance testing, as described in Section 4.5.

In practice, the need to use nontabled values of q in power and sample size determination will not arise frequently. This is because one rarely has so highly specified an alternate hypothesis in terms of r_1 and r_2 values that one must find power or sample size for a value of q which is not tabled. A less exact specification of the $r_1 - r_2$ difference permits the use of the nearest tabled value of q in Table 4.2.1 and the later tables of this chapter. Indeed, the even less exact procedure of defining q as "small," "medium," or "large" with the operational definitions proposed below will suffice for many purposes.

4.2.1   "SMALL," "MEDIUM," AND "LARGE" DIFFERENCES IN CORRELA-TION.   To provide the behavioral scientist with a frame of reference in which to appraise differences in degree of correlation, we attach specific values of q to the adjectives "small," "medium," and "large" to serve as operational definitions which are offered as conventions. This conforms to the general plan which has been followed with each type of statistical test in this handbook. Again, the reader is urged to avoid the use of these conventions, if he can, in favor of exact values provided by theory. However, it is less likely here than, say, in testing differences between means, that contemporary theory will lead to exact alternative-hypothetical values of q.

EQUAL UNITS AND AMOUNTS OF RELATIONSHIP.   Differences in "amounts" of relationship expressed in Fisher z's, i.e., q values, are not generally

---

[1] As will be seen below, determining n from the sample size table (Table 4.4.1) requires no interpolation. For nontabled values of q, formula (4.4.1) is used.

familiar to behavioral scientists. Indeed, the intuitive concept "amount" of relationship requires specification for it to be useful. It is frequently pointed out in textbooks in applied statistics that r is "an *index* number, not a measurement on a linear scale of equal units" (Guilford, 1965, p. 103), and that in consequence equal changes in r do not represent equal changes in amount of relationship at different points along the range of possible values. (It has already been stated above that equal differences in population r's are not equally detectable.)

There are, however, simple functions of r which more closely accord with intuitive notions about amounts of relationship so that differences in these functions are equal in some acceptable sense.

One of these functions has already been encountered. Given an r for a population of X, Y pairs, r^2, the "coefficient of determination," is the proportion of variance (PV) in either variable which is linearly accounted for by the other. Thus, the quantity $r_1^2 - r_2^2$ represents amount of change in the proportion of variance accounted for; equal amounts of PV change can be meaningfully understood as equal amounts of change in amount of relationship, anywhere along the r scale. In this sense, the r_1, r_2 pairs .38, .10 and .88, .80 represent equal differences in amount of relationship, since in both pairs, $r_1^2 - r_2^2 = .134$—the larger r_1 of each pair accounts for 13.4% more variance than the smaller; similarly the pairs .60, .00 and .92, .70 ($r_1^2 - r_2^2 = .36$).

Another of those conversion functions is the complement of the coefficient of alienation, $1 - \sqrt{1 - r^2}$, expressed as percent and called **E**, the "index of forecasting efficiency" (Guilford, 1965, pp. 376–379). **E** indexes the amount of reduction in errors of prediction relative to the case where $r = 0$, when errors of prediction are measured by their standard deviation about the linearly predicted value. This standard deviation, called the "standard error of estimate," is reduced as r increases, and when $r = \pm 1$, becomes zero, so that **E** = 100%. When a pair of r's is converted to a pair of **E**'s, the index $\mathbf{E}_1 - \mathbf{E}_2$, in the sense of amount of reduction in error standard deviation, represents another meaningful rendition of the concept "differences in amount of relationship" which is independent of where on the r scale the difference occurs. In this sense, the r_1, r_2 pairs .38, .10 and .53, .40 represent (approximately) equal differences in amount of relationship, since in both pairs, $\mathbf{E}_1 - \mathbf{E}_2 = 7\%$—the larger r_1 of each pair results in an additional 7% reduction of standard error of estimate over the smaller r; similarly the pairs .50, .25 and .64, .50 (where $\mathbf{E}_1 - \mathbf{E}_2 = 10\%$).

The difference functions $r_1^2 - r_2^2$ and $\mathbf{E}_1 - \mathbf{E}_2$ are not equivalent, yet each offers a reasonable rendition of "equal differences in amount of relationship." Our ES index, $q = z_1 - z_2$ was chosen on the criterion of equal detectability, rather than equal amounts. Fortunately, over the most frequently encountered values of the correlation scale, equal q values yield not grossly unequal values of either $r_1^2 - r_2^2$ or $E_1 - E_2$. Thus equal detectability over much of the correlation scale represents approximately equal "differences in amount of relationship" as rendered either by difference in proportion of variance accounted for or by percent reduction in the standard error of estimate. In the description of our operational definitions of "small," "medium," and "large" q values, each will be interpreted in the latter terms and the range of approximate constancy will be described for each.

SMALL EFFECT SIZE: $q = .10$. A small difference between correlations is defined as $q = .10$. The following pairs of r's illustrate this amount of difference: .00, .10; .20, .29; .40, .48; .60, .66; .80, .83; .90, .92; .95, .96 (Table 4.2.1).

When the smaller r_2 falls between .25 and .80, a $q = .10$ implies $r_1^2 - r_2^2$ falling in the range .05–.08. (Outside these r_2 limits, $r_1^2 - r_2^2$ is below .05). Thus one can generally think of a small difference in correlation as one for which the population of larger r has an X, Y percentage shared variance 5–8% larger than that of the population with the smaller r.

In terms of difference between amounts of relationship expressed in forecasting efficiency terms for r_2 between .25 and .95, $q = .10$ implies $E_1 - E_2$ values of 3–5%. (For r_2 outside these limits, $E_1 - E_2$ is smaller than 3%.)

MEDIUM EFFECT SIZE: $q = .30$. With $q = .30$ taken to define a medium ES, we find (Table 4.2.1) the following pairs of r's illustrating this amount of difference: .00, .29; .20, .46; .40, .62; .60, .76; .80, .89; .90, .94; .95, .97.

When the smaller r_2 falls between .15 and .75, $q = .30$ implies a difference between r^2 falling between .15–.23. Taking a narrower range of r_2 between .25 and .70, $r_1^2 - r_2^2$ falls between .18–.23. Thus, over the middle of the correlation scale, a medium difference in correlation can be understood as one for which the population of larger r has a percentage of shared variance between X and Y which is about 20% larger than that of the smaller r. Outside these ranges of r_2, the shared variance difference is less; for low r_2, it reaches a minimum value (for $r_2 = .00$, $r_1 = .29$) of .084.

Interpreted in forecasting efficiency terms, for r_2 between .25 and .90, $q = .30$ implies $E_1 - E_2$ values of 10–15%, values outside these r_2 limits again yielding smaller discrepancies in $E_1 - E_2$.

LARGE EFFECT SIZE: $q = .50$. A large difference in r's is operationally defined as one which yields $q = .50$. Pairs of r's illustrating this degree of difference are: .00, .46; .20, .61; .40, .73; .60, .83; .80, .92; .90, .96; and .95, .98 (Table 4.2.1). Here it becomes particularly obvious how different is our approach via q from the simple difference $r_1 - r_2$.

Large differences, so defined, mean $r_1^2 - r_2^2$ values falling in the range .28 to .38 when r_2 (the smaller) falls between the limits .10–.70, or, taking a slightly narrower range for r_2 of .20 to .65, PV differences of .32 to .38. Thus, a large difference in r's in the middle of the scale is taken to mean one which involves about a third of the total variance.

In terms of difference in forecasting efficiency, when r_2 lies between .20 and .80, $E_1 - E_2$ is within the limits of 20–25%. If the latter seems small to the reader, it should be pointed out that a substantial reduction of the standard error of estimate from its maximum value when $r = 0$ requires very large values of r. Thus, for example, when one considers the definition in Chapter 3 of a large ES, $r = .50$, one finds that its E value is only 13.4%. For E to be as much as 50%, r must be .866. Thus, a difference between E's of 20–25% should be consonant with the intuitive conception of a large difference between amounts of correlation.

Comparison with Definitions for Significance Test of r. We can reinterpret the operational definitions of "small," "medium," and "large" ES of Chapter 3 on significance testing of a single r in the light of the q of the present chapter. Since $q = z_1 - z_2$, and $r_2 = 0$ transforms to $z_2 = 0$, given the definitions of Chapter 3 of $ES = r = .10, .30,$ and .50, these become respectively $q = .10, .31,$ and .55. They are thus approximately comparable with the q values .10, .30, and .50 of the present chapter. However, the set $r = .10, .30,$ .50 yields smaller values when expressed as r^2 and E differences from zero than those of the middle range described above. Thus the ES definitions for *differences* in relationship expressed as shared variance or reduction in error of prediction are larger than the ES definitions for significance testing of a single r.

4.3   POWER TABLES

When the significance criterion, ES, and sample size are specified, the tables in this section can be used to determine power values. Their major use will thus be after a research is performed or at least planned. They can, of course, also be used in research planning by varying n, ES, or a, or all three, to see the consequences to power of such alternatives.

4.3.1   CASE 0: $n_1 = n_2$. The power tables are designed to yield conveniently power values for the normal curve test of the difference between the Fisher transformations of the r,s ($q = z_1 - z_2$) of two independent samples of equal size (see McNemar, 1962, pp. 139–140 for assumptions). This is designated Case 0; other cases are described and illustrated in later sections. Tables give values for $a, q,$ and n:

1. Significance Criterion, a. Six tables are provided for the following values of a: $a_1 = .01, a_1 = .05, a_1 = .10, a_2 = .01, a_2 = .05, a_2 = .10$, where the subscripts refer to one- and two-tailed tests. Since power at a_1 is to an adequate approximation equal to power at $a_2 = 2a_1$ for power greater than

Table 4.3.1

Power of Normal Curve Test of $r_1 = r_2$
via Fisher z transormation at $a_1 = .01$

n	q_c	.10	.20	.30	.40	.50	.60	.70	.80	1.00	1.20	1.40
							q					
8	1.471	02	02	03	05	06	08	11	14	23	33	46
9	1.343	02	02	04	05	07	10	13	17	28	40	54
10	1.243	02	03	04	06	08	11	15	20	32	47	62
11	1.163	02	03	04	06	09	13	18	23	37	53	68
12	1.097	02	03	05	07	10	15	20	26	42	59	74
13	1.040	02	03	05	08	11	16	22	30	46	64	79
14	.992	02	03	05	08	12	18	25	33	51	69	83
15	.950	02	03	06	09	14	20	27	36	55	73	86
16	.912	02	03	06	10	15	21	29	39	59	77	89
17	.879	02	04	06	10	16	23	32	42	63	80	92
18	.849	02	04	07	11	17	25	34	45	66	83	93
19	.822	02	04	07	12	18	26	36	47	69	86	95
20	.798	02	04	07	12	19	28	39	50	72	88	96
21	.775	02	04	08	13	20	30	41	53	75	90	97
22	.755	02	04	08	14	22	32	43	56	78	92	98
23	.736	02	05	08	14	23	33	46	58	80	93	98
24	.718	02	05	09	15	24	35	48	60	82	94	99
25	.701	02	05	09	16	25	37	50	63	84	95	99
26	.686	02	05	10	16	26	39	52	65	86	96	99
27	.672	02	05	10	17	28	40	54	67	87	97	99
28	.658	02	05	10	18	29	42	56	69	89	97	*
29	.645	02	05	11	19	30	44	58	71	90	98	
30	.633	03	06	11	20	31	45	60	73	91	98	
31	.622	03	06	11	20	32	47	62	75	92	98	
32	.611	03	06	12	21	34	48	63	76	93	99	
33	.601	03	06	12	22	35	50	65	78	94	99	
34	.591	03	06	13	23	36	52	67	79	95	99	
35	.582	03	06	13	23	37	53	68	81	95	99	
36	.573	03	07	13	24	38	54	70	82	96	99	
37	.564	03	07	14	25	40	56	71	83	96	*	
38	.556	03	07	14	26	41	57	73	85	97		
39	.548	03	07	15	26	42	59	74	86	97		
40	.541	03	07	15	27	43	60	75	87	98		
42	.527	03	07	16	29	45	63	78	89	98		
44	.514	03	08	17	30	48	65	80	90	99		
46	.502	03	08	18	32	50	68	82	92	99		
48	.490	03	08	18	33	52	70	84	93	99		

Table 4.3.1 (continued)

n	q_c						q					
		.10	.20	.30	.40	.50	.60	.70	.80	1.00	1.20	1.40
50	.480	03	09	19	35	54	72	86	94	99	*	*
52	.470	03	09	20	36	56	74	87	95	*		
54	.461	03	09	21	38	58	76	89	96			
56	.452	04	10	22	39	60	78	90	96			
58	.444	04	10	23	41	62	79	91	97			
60	.434	04	10	23	42	63	81	92	97			
64	.421	04	11	25	45	67	84	94	98			
68	.408	04	12	27	48	70	86	95	99			
72	.396	04	12	29	51	73	88	96	99			
76	.385	04	13	30	54	76	90	97	99			
80	.375	04	14	32	56	78	92	98	*			
84	.365	05	15	34	59	80	93	98				
88	.357	05	15	36	61	82	94	99				
92	.349	05	16	37	63	84	95	99				
96	.341	05	17	39	66	86	96	99				
100	.334	05	18	41	68	88	97	99				
120	.304	06	21	49	77	93	99	*				
140	.281	07	25	56	84	97	*					
160	.263	07	29	63	89	98						
180	.247	08	33	69	92	99						
200	.234	09	37	74	95	*						
250	.206	12	47	86	99							
300	.191	13	54	91	99							
350	.177	16	62	95	*							
400	.165	18	69	97								
450	.156	20	75	98								
500	.148	23	80	99								
600	.135	27	87	*								
700	.125	32	92									
800	.117	37	95									
900	.110	42	97									
1000	.104	46	98									

* Power values below this point are greater than .995.

Table 4.3.2

Power of Normal Curve Test of $r_1 = r_2$
via Fisher z transformation at $a_1 = .05$

							q					
n	q_c	.10	.20	.30	.40	.50	.60	.70	.80	1.00	1.20	1.40
8	1.040	07	09	12	16	20	24	30	35	47	60	71
9	.950	07	10	13	17	22	27	33	40	54	67	78
10	.879	07	10	14	19	24	30	37	44	59	73	83
11	.822	07	11	15	20	26	33	40	48	64	77	88
12	.776	08	11	16	21	28	36	44	52	68	82	91
13	.736	08	12	16	23	30	38	47	56	72	85	93
14	.701	08	12	17	24	32	41	50	59	76	88	95
15	.672	08	12	18	25	34	43	53	62	79	90	96
16	.645	08	13	19	27	36	45	56	65	82	92	97
17	.622	08	13	20	28	37	48	58	68	84	94	98
18	.606	09	14	20	29	39	50	61	71	86	95	99
19	.582	09	14	21	30	41	52	63	73	88	96	99
20	.564	09	14	22	32	43	54	65	75	90	97	99
21	.548	09	15	23	33	44	56	67	77	91	97	99
22	.534	09	15	24	34	46	58	70	79	92	98	*
23	.520	09	16	24	35	47	60	71	81	94	98	
24	.508	09	16	25	36	49	62	73	83	94	99	
25	.496	09	16	26	38	51	64	75	84	95	99	
26	.485	10	17	27	39	52	65	77	86	96	99	
27	.475	10	17	27	40	53	67	78	87	97	99	
28	.465	10	17	28	41	55	68	80	88	97	*	
29	.456	10	18	29	42	56	70	81	89	98		
30	.448	10	18	29	43	58	71	82	90	98		
31	.440	10	18	30	44	59	73	84	91	98		
32	.432	10	19	31	45	60	74	85	92	98		
33	.425	10	19	31	46	61	75	86	93	99		
34	.418	11	20	32	47	63	76	87	93	99		
35	.411	11	20	33	48	64	77	88	94	99		
36	.405	11	20	33	49	65	79	88	95	99		
37	.399	11	21	34	50	66	80	89	95	99		
38	.393	11	21	35	51	67	81	90	96	99		
39	.388	11	21	35	52	68	82	91	96	*		
40	.382	11	22	36	53	69	83	91	96			
42	.372	11	22	37	55	71	84	93	97			
44	.363	12	23	39	57	73	86	94	98			
46	.355	12	24	40	58	75	87	95	98			
48	.347	12	24	41	60	77	89	95	98			

Table 4.3.2 (continued)

n	q_c	.10	.20	.30	.40	.50	.60	.70	.80	1.00	1.20	1.40
50	.339	12	25	42	62	78	90	96	99	*	*	*
52	.332	13	26	44	63	80	91	97	99			
54	.326	13	26	45	65	81	92	97	99			
56	.320	13	27	46	66	82	93	97	99			
58	.314	13	28	47	67	84	93	98	99			
60	.308	13	28	48	69	85	94	98	*			
64	.298	14	29	50	71	87	95	99				
68	.289	14	31	53	74	89	96	99				
72	.280	14	32	55	76	90	97	99				
76	.272	15	33	57	78	92	98	*				
80	.265	15	34	59	80	93	98					
84	.258	16	35	60	82	94	99					
88	.252	16	37	62	83	95	99					
92	.247	16	38	64	85	95	99					
96	.241	16	39	66	86	96	99					
100	.236	17	41	68	87	97	99					
120	.231	19	45	74	92	99	*					
140	.199	21	50	80	95	99						
160	.186	22	55	84	97	*						
180	.175	24	59	88	98							
200	.166	26	63	91	99							
250	.146	30	73	96	*							
300	.135	34	79	98								
350	.125	37	84	99								
400	.117	40	88	*								
450	.110	44	91									
500	.104	47	93									
600	.095	53	96									
700	.088	59	98									
800	.082	64	99									
900	.078	68	*									
1000	.074	72										

* Power values below this point are greater than .995

Table 4.3.3

Power of Normal Curve Test of $r_1 = r_2$
via Fisher z transformation at $a_1 = .10$

n	q_c	.10	.20	.30	.40	.50	.60	.70	.80	1.00	1.20	1.40
8	.811	13	17	21	26	31	37	43	49	62	73	82
9	.740	13	17	22	28	34	40	47	54	67	79	87
10	.685	14	18	24	30	36	44	51	59	72	83	91
11	.641	14	19	25	31	39	47	55	62	76	87	94
12	.604	14	20	26	33	41	50	58	66	80	90	95
13	.573	14	20	27	35	43	52	61	69	83	92	97
14	.547	15	21	28	37	46	55	64	72	86	94	98
15	.523	15	21	29	38	48	57	67	75	88	95	98
16	.503	15	22	30	40	50	60	69	78	90	96	99
17	.484	15	23	31	41	52	62	72	80	91	97	99
18	.468	16	23	32	43	53	64	74	82	93	98	99
19	.453	16	24	33	44	55	66	76	84	94	98	*
20	.440	16	24	34	45	57	68	78	85	95	99	
21	.427	16	25	35	47	59	70	79	87	96	99	
22	.416	17	25	36	48	60	71	81	88	96	99	
23	.405	17	26	37	49	62	73	82	89	97	99	
24	.396	17	26	38	51	63	75	84	90	97	*	
25	.387	17	27	39	52	65	76	85	92	98		
26	.378	17	27	40	53	66	77	86	92	98		
27	.370	17	28	40	54	67	79	87	93	99		
28	.363	18	28	41	55	69	80	88	94	99		
29	.355	18	29	42	56	70	81	89	95	99		
30	.349	18	29	43	57	71	82	90	95	99		
31	.343	18	30	44	59	72	83	91	96	99		
32	.337	18	30	44	60	73	84	92	96	99		
33	.331	19	31	45	61	74	85	92	97	*		
34	.326	19	31	46	62	75	86	93	97			
35	.320	19	31	47	62	76	87	94	97			
36	.316	19	32	47	63	77	88	94	98			
37	.311	19	32	48	64	78	88	95	98			
38	.307	19	33	49	65	79	89	95	98			
39	.302	20	33	50	66	80	90	95	98			
40	.298	20	34	50	67	81	90	96	98			
42	.290	20	35	52	69	82	91	96	99			
44	.283	20	35	53	70	84	92	97	99			
46	.277	21	36	54	72	85	93	98	99			
48	.270	21	37	56	73	86	94	98	99			

Table 4.3.3. (continued)

n	q_c						q					
		.10	.20	.30	.40	.50	.60	.70	.80	1.00	1.20	1.40
50	.264	21	38	57	74	87	95	98	*	*	*	*
52	.259	22	39	58	76	88	95	99				
54	.254	22	39	59	77	89	96	99				
56	.249	22	40	60	78	90	96	99				
58	.244	22	41	61	79	91	97	99				
60	.240	23	42	63	80	92	97	99				
64	.232	23	43	65	82	93	98	*				
68	.225	24	44	67	84	94	98					
72	.218	24	46	68	86	95	99					
76	.212	25	47	70	87	96	99					
80	.207	25	48	72	88	97	99					
84	.201	26	50	73	90	97	99					
88	.197	26	51	75	91	98	*					
92	.192	27	52	76	92	98						
96	.188	27	53	78	93	98						
100	.184	28	54	79	93	99						
120	.168	30	60	84	96	99						
140	.155	32	65	89	98	*						
160	.145	35	69	92	99							
180	.136	37	73	94	99							
200	.129	39	76	96	*							
250	.113	44	84	98								
300	.105	47	88	99								
350	.097	51	91	*								
400	.091	55	94									
450	.086	58	96									
500	.081	62	97									
600	.074	67	99									
700	.069	72	99									
800	.064	76	*									
900	.061	80										
1000	.057	83										

*   Power values below this point are greater than .995.

Table 4.3.4

Power of Normal Curve Test of $r_1 = r_2$
via Fisher z transformation at $a_2 = .01$

						q						
n	q_c	.10	.20	.30	.40	.50	.60	.70	.80	1.00	1.20	1.40
8	1.629	01	01	02	03	04	05	07	09	16	25	36
9	1.487	01	01	02	03	04	06	09	12	20	31	44
10	1.377	01	02	02	03	05	07	10	14	24	37	52
11	1.288	01	02	02	04	06	08	12	16	28	43	59
12	1.215	01	02	03	04	06	10	14	19	32	49	65
13	1.152	01	02	03	05	07	11	16	22	37	54	71
14	1.098	01	02	03	05	08	12	17	24	41	59	76
15	1.052	01	02	03	06	09	13	19	27	45	64	80
16	1.010	01	02	04	06	10	15	21	30	49	69	84
17	.973	01	02	04	06	11	16	23	32	53	73	87
18	.940	01	02	04	07	11	18	26	35	56	76	90
19	.911	01	02	04	07	12	19	28	38	60	79	92
20	.884	01	02	04	08	13	20	30	40	63	82	93
21	.859	01	02	05	08	14	22	32	43	66	85	95
22	.836	01	03	05	09	15	23	34	46	69	87	96
23	.815	01	03	05	09	16	25	36	48	72	89	97
24	.795	01	03	05	10	17	26	38	51	75	91	98
25	.777	01	03	06	11	18	28	40	53	77	92	98
26	.760	01	03	06	11	19	29	42	55	79	93	99
27	.744	01	03	06	12	20	31	44	58	81	94	99
28	.728	01	03	07	12	21	32	46	60	83	95	99
29	.714	02	03	07	13	27	34	48	62	85	96	99
30	.701	02	03	07	13	23	36	50	64	86	97	99
31	.688	02	03	07	14	24	37	52	66	88	97	*
32	.676	02	04	07	15	25	39	54	68	89	98	
33	.665	02	04	08	15	26	40	55	70	90	98	
34	.654	02	04	08	16	27	42	57	72	91	98	
35	.644	02	04	08	16	28	43	59	73	92	99	
36	.634	02	04	09	17	29	44	61	75	93	99	
37	.625	02	04	09	18	30	46	62	76	94	99	
38	.616	02	04	09	18	31	47	64	78	95	99	
39	.607	02	04	10	19	32	49	65	79	95	99	
40	.599	02	04	10	20	34	50	67	81	96	*	
42	.583	02	05	11	21	36	53	70	82	97		
44	.569	02	05	11	22	38	56	72	85	97		
46	.556	02	05	12	24	40	58	75	87	98		
48	.543	02	05	12	25	42	61	77	89	98		

Table 4.3.4 *(continued)*

n	q_c	.10	.20	.30	.40	.50	.60	.70	.80	1.00	1.20	1.40
							q					
50	.531	02	05	13	26	44	63	79	90	99	*	*
52	.520	02	06	14	28	46	65	81	92	99		
54	.510	02	06	14	29	48	68	83	93	99		
56	.501	02	06	15	30	50	69	85	94	99		
58	.491	02	06	16	32	52	72	86	95	*		
60	.482	02	07	16	33	54	73	88	95			
64	.467	02	07	18	36	57	77	90	97			
68	.452	02	08	19	38	61	80	92	98			
72	.438	02	08	21	41	64	83	94	98			
76	.426	03	09	22	44	67	85	95	99			
80	.415	03	09	24	46	70	87	96	99			
84	.405	03	10	25	49	73	89	97	99			
88	.395	03	10	27	51	75	91	98	*			
92	.386	03	11	28	54	78	92	98				
96	.378	03	11	30	56	80	94	99				
100	.370	03	12	31	58	82	95	99				
120	.337	04	15	39	69	89	98	*				
140	.311	04	18	46	77	94	99					
160	.291	05	21	53	83	97	*					
180	.274	05	24	60	88	98						
200	.260	06	28	66	92	99						
250	.228	07	38	79	97	*						
300	.211	09	44	86	99							
350	.196	11	52	92	*							
400	.183	12	60	95								
450	.172	14	66	97								
500	.163	16	72	98								
600	.149	20	81	*								
700	.138	24	88									
800	.129	28	92									
900	.122	32	95									
1000	.115	37	97									

* Power values below this point are greater than .995.

Table 4.3.5

Power of Normal Curve Test of $r_1 = r_2$
via Fisher z transformation at a_2 = .05

n	q_c	.10	.20	.30	.40	.50	.60	.70	.80	1.00	1.20	1.40
							q					
8	1.240	05	06	08	10	12	16	20	24	35	48	60
9	1.132	05	06	08	11	14	18	23	28	41	55	68
10	1.048	05	07	09	12	15	20	26	32	46	61	75
11	.980	05	07	09	13	17	22	29	36	52	67	80
12	.924	06	07	10	14	19	25	32	40	56	72	84
13	.877	06	07	10	15	20	27	35	43	61	77	88
14	.836	06	08	11	16	22	29	38	47	65	80	91
15	.800	06	08	11	17	23	31	40	50	69	84	93
16	.769	06	08	12	17	25	33	43	53	72	86	95
17	.741	06	08	12	18	26	35	46	56	75	89	96
18	.716	06	09	13	19	28	38	48	59	78	91	97
19	.693	06	09	14	20	29	40	51	62	81	92	98
20	.672	06	09	14	21	30	42	53	65	83	94	98
21	.653	06	09	15	22	32	44	56	67	85	95	99
22	.636	06	09	15	23	33	46	58	69	87	96	99
23	.620	06	10	16	24	35	48	60	72	88	97	99
24	.605	06	10	16	25	36	49	62	74	90	97	*
25	.591	06	10	17	26	38	51	64	76	91	98	
26	.578	06	10	18	27	39	53	66	77	92	98	
27	.566	06	11	18	28	41	55	68	79	93	99	
28	.554	06	11	19	29	42	56	70	81	94	99	
29	.544	07	11	19	30	44	58	71	82	95	99	
30	.534	07	11	20	31	45	60	73	84	96	99	
31	.524	07	12	20	32	46	61	75	85	96	99	
32	.515	07	12	21	33	48	63	76	86	97	*	
33	.506	07	12	21	34	49	64	77	87	97		
34	.498	07	12	22	35	51	66	79	88	98		
35	.490	07	13	22	36	52	67	80	89	98		
36	.483	07	13	23	37	53	68	81	90	98		
37	.475	07	13	24	38	54	70	82	91	98		
38	.469	07	13	24	39	55	71	83	92	99		
39	.462	07	14	25	40	56	72	84	92	99		
40	.456	07	14	25	41	58	73	85	93	99		
42	.444	07	14	26	42	60	75	87	94	99		
44	.433	07	15	27	44	62	78	89	95	99		
46	.423	08	15	29	46	64	79	90	96	*		
48	.413	08	16	30	48	66	81	91	97			

Table 4.3.5 *(continued)*

							q					
n	q_c	.10	.20	.30	.40	.50	.60	.70	.80	1.00	1.20	1.40
50	.404	08	16	31	49	68	83	92	97	*	*	*
52	.396	08	17	32	51	70	84	93	98			
54	.388	08	17	33	52	71	36	94	93			
56	.381	08	18	34	54	73	87	95	98			
58	.374	08	18	35	55	75	33	96	99			
60	.367	08	19	36	57	76	89	96	99			
64	.355	09	20	38	60	79	91	97	99			
68	.344	09	21	40	63	81	93	98	*			
72	.334	09	22	42	65	84	94	98				
76	.324	09	23	44	68	86	95	99				
80	.316	10	24	46	70	87	96	99				
84	.308	10	25	48	72	89	97	99				
88	.301	10	26	50	74	90	97	*				
92	.294	10	27	52	76	92	98					
96	.287	10	28	53	78	93	98					
100	.281	11	29	55	80	94	99					
120	.256	12	33	63	86	97	*					
140	.237	13	38	70	91	99						
160	.221	14	43	76	94	99						
180	.208	16	47	81	96	*						
200	.198	17	51	85	98							
250	.173	20	62	92	99							
300	.161	23	68	96	*							
350	.149	26	75	98								
400	.139	29	80	99								
450	.131	32	85	99								
500	.124	35	88	*								
600	.113	41	93									
700	.105	46	96									
800	.098	51	98									
900	.093	56	99									
1000	.088	61	99									

* Power values below this point are greater than .995.

Table 4.3.6

Power of Normal Curve Test of $r_1 = r_2$
via Fisher z transformation at $a_2 = .10$

n	q_c						q					
		.10	.20	.30	.40	.50	.60	.70	.80	1.00	1.20	1.40
8	1.040	10	12	14	17	20	25	30	35	48	60	71
9	.950	11	12	15	18	22	28	33	40	54	67	78
10	.879	11	12	15	19	24	30	37	44	59	73	83
11	.822	11	13	16	20	26	33	40	48	64	77	88
12	.776	11	13	17	22	28	36	44	52	68	82	91
13	.736	11	13	18	23	30	38	47	56	72	85	93
14	.701	11	14	18	24	32	41	50	59	76	88	95
15	.672	11	14	19	26	34	43	53	62	79	90	96
16	.645	11	14	20	27	36	45	56	65	82	92	97
17	.622	11	15	20	28	38	48	58	68	84	94	98
18	.606	11	15	21	29	39	50	61	71	86	95	99
19	.582	11	15	22	31	41	52	63	73	88	96	99
20	.564	11	16	23	32	43	54	65	75	90	97	99
21	.548	12	16	23	33	44	56	67	77	91	97	99
22	.534	12	16	24	34	46	58	70	79	92	98	*
23	.520	12	17	25	35	48	60	71	81	94	98	
24	.508	12	17	25	37	49	67	73	83	94	99	
25	.496	12	17	26	38	51	64	75	84	95	99	
26	.485	12	18	27	39	52	65	77	86	96	99	
27	.475	12	18	27	40	54	67	78	87	97	99	
28	.465	12	18	28	41	55	68	80	88	97	*	
29	.456	12	19	29	42	56	70	81	89	98		
30	.448	12	19	30	43	58	71	82	90	98		
31	.440	12	19	30	44	59	73	84	91	98		
32	.432	12	20	31	45	60	74	85	92	98		
33	.425	13	20	32	46	61	75	86	93	99		
34	.418	13	20	32	47	63	76	87	93	99		
35	.411	13	21	33	48	64	77	88	94	99		
36	.405	13	21	34	49	65	79	88	95	99		
37	.399	13	21	34	50	66	80	89	95	99		
38	.393	13	22	35	51	67	81	90	96	99		
39	.388	13	22	36	52	68	82	91	96	*		
40	.382	13	22	36	53	69	83	91	96			
42	.372	13	23	38	55	71	84	93	97			
44	.363	13	24	39	57	73	86	94	98			
46	.355	14	24	40	58	75	87	95	98			
48	.347	14	25	41	60	77	89	95	98			

Table 4.3.6 *(continued)*

		q										
n	q_c	.10	.20	.30	.40	.50	.60	.70	.80	1.00	1.20	1.40
50	.339	14	25	43	62	78	90	96	99	*	*	*
52	.332	14	26	44	63	80	91	97	99			
54	.326	14	26	45	65	81	92	97	99			
56	.320	14	27	46	66	82	93	97	99			
58	.314	15	28	47	67	84	93	98	99			
60	.308	15	29	48	69	85	94	98	*			
64	.298	15	30	51	71	87	95	99				
68	.289	15	31	53	74	89	96	99				
72	.280	16	32	55	76	90	97	99				
76	.272	16	33	57	78	92	98	*				
80	.265	16	35	59	80	93	98					
84	.258	17	36	60	82	94	99					
88	.252	17	37	62	83	95	99					
92	.247	17	38	64	85	95	99					
96	.241	17	39	66	86	96	99					
100	.236	18	41	68	87	97	99					
120	.231	20	45	74	92	99	*					
140	.199	21	50	80	95	99						
160	.186	23	55	84	97	*						
180	.175	25	59	88	98							
200	.166	26	63	91	99							
250	.146	31	73	96	*							
300	.135	34	79	98								
350	.125	37	84	99								
400	.117	40	88	*								
450	.110	44	91									
500	.104	47	93									
600	.095	53	96									
700	.088	59	98									
800	.082	64	99									
900	.078	68	*									
1000	.074	72										

* Power values below this point are greater than .995.

(say) .10, the tables can also be used for power at $a_2 = .02, a_2 = .20, a_1 = .005$, and $a_1 = .025$.

2. *Effect Size*, ES. This is the difference between Fisher z-transformed r's, q, whose properties are described in Section 4.2. Tables 4.2.1 and 4.2.2 facilitate the conversion of r_1, r_2 pairs into q values. Provision in the power tables is made for $q = .10$ (.10) .80 (.20) 1.40. Conventional definitions of ES have been offered, as follows:

small: $q = .10$,   medium: $q = .30$,   large: $q = .50$.

3. *Sample Size*, n. This is the size of each of the two samples whose r_s's are being compared. Provision is made for $n = 8$ (1) 40 (2) 60 (4) 100 (20) 200 (50) 500 (100) 1000.

The values in the body of the table are the power of the test $\times 100$, i.e., the percentage of tests carried out under the given conditions which will result in the rejection of the null hypothesis. They are rounded to the nearest unit and are accurate to within ± 1 as tabled.

Illustrative Examples

4.1 A marriage counselor has been studying the issue of personality similarity as a factor in the quality of marriage relationships. He has gathered data on several personality questionnaire variables from 60 husband–wife pairs in marriages rated as harmonious (Group 1). and from another 60 pairs with marital difficulties (Group 2). The study design involves the determination of the husband–wife correlation in each group for each personality variable, followed by a test of the significance of the difference between the two groups' r_s's (for each variable), i.e., $H_0 : r_1 = r_2$. His significance criterion is $a_2 = .05$. Given that the ES is $q = .30$ (the operational definition of a medium difference), what is the power of each test? His specifications are

$$a_2 = .05,   q = .30,   n_1 = n_2 = n = 60.$$

To find the test's power, in Table 4.3.5 for $a_2 = .05$, column $q = .30$, and row $n = 60$, power $= .36$. Thus, his probability of a significant ($a_2 = .05$) result is only slightly greater than one in three if the two populations differ in degree of relationship by $q = .30$ (e.g., population r values of .20, .46, or .40, .62 or .60, .76 from Table 4.2.1, or, if of opposite sign, e.g., $-.15, .15$ or $-.10$, $+.20$).

If one posits large ($q = .50$) instead of medium ES, one finds in the same table and row, but for column $q = .50$, power $= .76$. Only if one is seeking to detect an ES of $q = .60$–.70 does power increase to the low nineties, but this ES implies r pairs such as .20, .70 or .40, .80 or opposite sign pairs of the order of $-.30$, $+.30$ or $-.10$, $+.50$.

4.2 A theory of psychopathology yields the derivation that the correlation between two variables **X**, **Y**, should be higher for paranoid schizophrenics than for catatonic schizophrenics. A research psychiatrist gathers the relevant data for 180 cases in each diagnostic group, in order to perform a one-tailed significance test at $a_1 = .01$. On the several alternative hypotheses that the difference in **r** is small ($q = .10$), medium ($q = .30$), and large ($q = .50$), what is the power in each instance? Specifications are

$$a_1 = .01, \qquad q = \begin{matrix} .10 \\ .30 \\ .50 \end{matrix}, \qquad n_1 = n_2 = n = 180.$$

In Table 4.3.1 for $a_1 = .01$, row $n = 180$, and for columns $q = .10, .30,$ and .50, one finds respectively power values of .08, .69, and .99. The extreme spread of these power values strongly suggests the importance of deciding how large the anticipated ES is (at least at this level of **n**). Depending on the ES, the experiment has either a poor, fairly good, or virtually certain probability of a significant result. If the result is not significant, the only conclusion that can be drawn is that the difference in degree of relationship between the populations favoring the paranoid schizophrenics, if any, is not large. Were the degree of relationship large, with power of .99 to detect a large effect, it would likely have been found. A medium or small difference may well exist; the latter possibility, in particular, is quite consonant with the results. Of course, given nonsignificant results, the investigator cannot conclude that a difference exists, whatever his *a priori* power.

4.3.2   CASE 1: $n_1 \neq n_2$. The tables will yield power values when, under the conditions for a valid test of the significance of the difference between two population **r**'s, samples of different sizes are drawn. In such cases, compute

(4.3.1)
$$n' = \frac{2(n_1 - 3)(n_2 - 3)}{n_1 + n_2 - 6} + 3,$$

and use the **n'** value in the **n** column of the table. Unless one of the **n**'s is very small (<10), the power value found is an exact value.[2] Also, all of the interpretative material of Section 4.3.1 on differences between degrees of relationship holds for Case 1.

Illustrative Example

4.3 A psycholinguist has developed and used in a series of researches a certain procedure (P_2) for measuring speech disruption whose population reliability (i.e., correlation between parallel forms) is estimated as falling in the .75–.85 range. For theoretical and practical reasons, he designs an alter-

---

[2] That is, it is as exact as the Case 0 value, i.e., accurate within ± 1.

native procedure (P_1) whose reliability compared to P_2 he wishes to assess. For practical reasons he is interested in the possibility that $r_1 > r_2$, but difference in the other direction would also be quite meaningful to theory. Thus a nondirectional test is indicated, and he elects to use $a_2 = .05$. If r_2 is approximately .80, he is interested in the possibility that r_1 is about .10 away (particularly if it is about .90). Reference to Table 4.2.1 indicates that the r pairs .75, .88; .80, .90; and .85, .93, all of which represent an ES $= q = .40$ (i.e., between medium and large), represent the order of magnitude involved. Now, he has accumulated data on the original procedure for $n_2 = 260$, and uses the new procedure on an independent sample of $n_1 = 51$. What is the power of the test?

$$a_2 = .05, \quad q = .40, \quad n_1 = 51 \neq 260 = n_2.$$

With unequal n, he finds [from formula (4.3.1)]

$$n' = \frac{2\,(51 - 3)(260 - 3)}{51 + 260 - 6} + 3 = \frac{2\,(48)(257)}{305} + = 384.$$

In Table 4.3.5 for $a_2 = .05$, column $q = .40$, and row $n' = n = 84$, power = .72. Thus, his chances are (not quite) three in four of detecting a difference of $q = .40$, given these conditions.

Note the implication of n'. His samples of 51 and 260, a total of 311 cases, yields as much power as two equal samples of 84 cases, a total of 168 cases. As previously noted in two-sample comparisons, for a given total number cases, optimal power for any specified conditions occurs when the total number is divided equally. That is, an equal division of his 311 cases would yield two samples of 155 cases, for which the power would be .93 (interpolating in Table 4.3.5), instead of the value of .72 for the actual unequal division.

4.3.3 CASE 2: ONE SAMPLE OF n OBSERVATIONS TO TEST r = c. Thus far we have considered the power of the normal curve test via the difference between Fisher's transformations of r's of two independent samples, where the null hypothesis is $r_1 = r_2$. The same transformation and test can be used to test the departure of the r of a single population from some specified value c. The null hypothesis for the one-sample test is r = c. The test is employed when, given a sample of n cases, the investigator's purpose is to determine whether the data are consonant with the hypothesis that the population r is .50 or .90 or −.25 or any other value. It is thus the general case of which the test of Chapter 3 that r is zero is a special case.

Although the special case r = c = 0 arises frequently in behavioral science, the r = c ≠ 0 form is also often encountered. It will be found useful in psychometric technology where experience has led to certain expectations or standards for values of reliability and validity coefficients which would then serve as values for c. In behavioral genetics or other areas of behavioral science where strong theory exists, derivations from theory may also yield specific values of c whose statistical testing brings important information.

For the one-sample case (Case 2), we define our ES as for the other cases, i.e., as the difference between z-transformed r's, but whereas in formula (4.2.2), $r_2 \rightarrow z_2$ is an estimable population parameter, here it is a constant, so that for Case 2

$$(4.3.2) \quad q_2' = z_1 - z_c \quad \text{(directional)}$$

$$= |z_1 - z_c| \quad \text{(nondirectional)},$$

where $z_1 =$ the Fisher z transformation of the alternative-hypothetical r as before and

$z_c =$ the Fisher z transformation of the null-hypothetical c.

There is no conceptual change: q_2' is the difference between the (alternate) population value (r_1) and the value specified by the null hypothesis (c) expressed, as before, in units of the z transformation. The interpretation of q_2' proceeds exactly as described in Section 4.2 with regard to Table 4.2.1, r^2, and E, and the operational definitions of small, medium, and large ES.

The tables, however, are not applied to the value q_2' since they are constructed for Case 0, where there are *two* sample statistics (z_1 and z_2) which *each* contribute sampling error variance to the observed sample difference, for a total variance of $2/(n-3)$. Here only one sample contributes sampling error variance, yielding half the amount, $1/(n-3)$. This is simply allowed for by finding

$$(4.3.3) \qquad\qquad q = q_2' \sqrt{2}.$$

The q value is sought in the tables, while q_2' is the ES index which is interpreted. This procedure is exact.[3]

If q_2' is chosen as a convenient multiple of .10, q will in general not be a multiple of .10. Thus the operational definitions of ES for q_2' of .10, .30, and .50 become, for the one sample test, $q = .14, .42,$ and $.71$. Linear interpolation between power values will provide values which are sufficiently close (within .01 or .02) for most purposes.

Illustrative Example

4.4 A social psychologist has developed a considerable body of data on attitudes toward the mentally ill. One of his scales yields an alternate-form correlation coefficient which he can estimate as being very close to .60 in the population. He has prepared a revision of this scale to improve its reliability but must weigh an improvement of reliability against the loss of comparability of a revised scale. He decides that if he could raise the population

---

[3] Unlike the one-sample test of a mean (Section 2.3.4) which proceeds by a **t** test with its dependence on varying **n** and **df**, the present test uses the normal curve for all **n**, and no overestimation of power occurs when the tables are used for the one-sample test of **r**.

reliability (correlation) to the middle seventies, say .76 (see Table 4.2.1), it would warrant the replacement of the original scale. Thus, he will perform a one-sample test to determine whether he can conclude that the revision is superior. As formulated, he has no interest in the possibility that the revision has lower reliability; thus his test is one-tailed (directional), and he selects as his significance criterion $a_1 = .05$. He administers the revised scale to a sample of 50 subjects.

The null hypothesis he is testing is, therefore, $r \leq .60$ with an alternative hypothesis (or ES) of $r = .76$. Informally stated, his research questions are: Does the revised scale have reliability in the population better than .60? For the power analysis, he asks: If it is as high as .76, what is the probability that I will conclude that it is better than .60 with $n = 50$ at $a_1 = .05$?

Reference to Table 4.2.1 shows that the .60, .76 values of r yield $q_2' = .30$ (and incidentally, why the author chose the value .76). Note that $q_2' = .30$ represents a medium effect. For table entry, we need $q = .30 \sqrt{2} = .424$. Summarizing the specifications

$$a_1 = .05, \qquad q = .424, \qquad n = 50.$$

In Table 4.3.2 for $a_1 = .05$ and row $n = 50$, he finds power in columns $q = .40$ and .50 to be .62 and .78, respectively. Linear interpolation between these values yields power at $q = .424$ of $(.424 - .40)(.78 - .62) + .62 = .66$. Thus, if $r = .76$, his $a_1 = .05$ test for $n = 50$ has a two in three chance of getting a significant result, warranting the conclusion that $r > .60$. Note that no mention has been made of the sample r_s he may have found; this is irrelevant to the power analysis, which may (or better, should) be performed prior to the data collection.

4.4 SAMPLE SIZE TABLES

The tables in this section list values of the significance criterion, the ES to be detected, and the *desired power*. One then finds the necessary sample size. Their primary utility lies in the planning of experiments to provide a basis for the decision as to the number of sampling units (n) to use.

4.4.1 CASE 0: $n_1 = n_2$. The use of the sample size tables first described is that for which they were optimally designed, Case 0, where they yield the sample size, n, for each of two independent samples whose population r's are to be compared. The description of their use in two other cases follows this subsection. Tables are entered with a, q, and desired power.

1. Significance Criterion, a. The same values of a are provided as in the power tables, a table for each of the following: $a_1 = .01$ ($a_2 = .02$), $a_1 = .05$ ($a_2 = .10$), $a_1 = .10$ ($a_2 = .20$), $a_2 = .01$ ($a_1 = .005$), and $a_2 = .05$ ($a_1 = .025$).

2. Effect Size, q. This value is defined and interpreted as above [formula

Table 4.4.1

n to detect $q = z_1 - z_2$ by Fisher
z Transformation of r

$a_1 = .01 \ (a_2 = .02)$

q

Power	.10	.20	.30	.40	.50	.60	.70	.80	1.00	1.20	1.40
.25	549	139	64	37	25	18	14	12	8	7	6
.50	1085	274	123	71	46	33	25	20	14	11	9
.60	1334	336	151	86	56	40	30	24	16	12	10
2/3	1523	383	172	98	64	45	34	27	18	14	11
.70	1628	409	184	105	68	48	36	28	19	14	11
.75	1804	453	203	116	75	53	40	31	21	16	12
.80	2010	505	226	128	83	59	44	34	23	17	13
.85	2265	568	254	144	93	66	49	38	26	19	15
.90	2606	654	292	166	107	75	56	44	29	21	16
.95	3157	792	353	200	129	91	67	52	35	25	19
.99	4333	1085	484	274	176	123	91	71	46	33	25

$a_1 = .05 \ (a_2 = .10)$

q

Power	.10	.20	.30	.40	.50	.60	.70	.80	1.00	1.20	1.40
.25	191	50	24	15	11	8	7	6	5	4	4
.50	544	138	63	37	25	18	14	11	8	7	6
.60	724	183	83	48	32	23	18	14	10	8	7
2/3	865	218	99	57	37	27	21	16	12	9	7
.70	944	238	108	62	41	29	22	18	12	10	8
.75	1079	272	123	70	46	33	25	20	14	10	9
.80	1240	312	140	80	52	37	28	22	15	12	9
.85	1441	362	163	93	61	43	32	25	17	13	10
.90	1716	431	193	110	72	51	38	30	20	15	12
.95	2167	544	243	138	90	63	47	37	25	18	14
.99	3157	792	353	200	129	91	67	52	35	25	19

$a_1 = .10 \ (a_2 = .20)$

q

Power	.10	.20	.30	.40	.50	.60	.70	.80	1.00	1.20	1.40
.25	77	21	11	8	6	5	4	4	4	--	--
.50	331	85	39	24	16	12	10	8	6	5	5
.60	474	121	55	32	22	16	13	10	8	6	5
2/3	589	150	68	40	26	19	15	12	9	7	6
.70	655	166	75	44	29	21	16	13	10	8	6
.75	768	194	88	51	34	24	19	15	11	8	7
.80	905	228	103	59	39	28	21	17	12	9	8
.85	1078	272	122	70	46	33	25	20	14	10	8
.90	1317	331	149	85	56	39	30	24	16	12	10
.95	1716	431	193	110	72	51	38	30	20	15	12
.99	2606	654	292	166	107	75	56	44	29	21	16

Table 4.4.1 *(continued)*

					$a_2 = .01$ ($a_1 = .005$)						
						q					
Power	.10	.20	.30	.40	.50	.60	.70	.80	1.00	1.20	1.40
.25	726	184	83	48	32	23	18	14	10	8	7
.50	1330	335	150	86	56	40	30	24	16	12	10
.60	1604	403	181	103	67	47	36	28	19	14	11
2/3	1811	455	204	116	75	53	40	31	21	16	12
.70	1925	484	217	123	80	56	42	33	22	16	13
.75	2116	531	238	135	88	62	46	36	24	18	14
.80	2339	587	263	149	96	68	51	39	26	19	15
.85	2613	655	293	166	107	75	56	44	29	21	16
.90	2979	747	334	189	122	86	64	49	33	24	18
.95	3566	894	399	226	146	102	76	59	39	28	21
.99	4809	1205	537	303	195	137	101	78	51	36	28

					$a_2 = .05$ ($a_1 = .025$)						
						q					
Power	.10	.20	.30	.40	.50	.60	.70	.80	1.00	1.20	1.40
.25	333	86	40	24	16	12	10	8	6	5	5
.50	771	195	88	51	34	24	19	15	11	8	7
.60	983	248	112	64	42	30	23	18	13	10	8
2/3	1146	289	130	74	49	35	26	21	14	11	9
.70	1237	312	140	80	52	37	28	22	15	12	9
.75	1391	350	157	90	59	42	31	25	17	13	10
.80	1573	395	177	101	66	47	35	28	19	14	11
.85	1799	452	203	115	75	53	40	31	21	15	12
.90	2104	528	236	134	87	61	46	36	24	18	14
.95	2602	653	292	165	107	75	56	44	29	21	16
.99	3677	922	411	233	150	105	78	60	40	29	22

(4.2.2)] and used as in the power tables. The same provision is made: .10 (.10) .80 (.20) 1.40.

To find **n** for a value of **q** not tabled, a good approximation is given by substituting in

$$(4.4.1) \qquad n = \frac{n_{.10} - 3}{100q^2} + 3,$$

where $n_{.10}$ is the necessary sample size for the given **a** and desired power at $q = .10$, and **q** is the nontabled ES. Round to the nearest integer.

3. Desired Power. Provision is made for entering the sample size tables with desired power values of .25, .50, .60, 2/3, .70 (.05) .95, .99. See the discussion in Section 2.4.1 on the selection of these values and considerations affecting choice in a given investigation. The suggestion of desired power =

.80 to serve as a convention, in the absence of other bases for choice, is reiterated here.

Summarizing the Case 0 procedure, the investigator finds (a) the table for the significance criterion (a) he is using, and looks for (b) the difference in z-transformed r's (q) along the horizontal stub and (c) the desired power along the vertical stub. He then finds n, the necessary size of *each* sample to detect q at the a significance criterion with the desired power.

Illustrative Examples

4.5   Reconsider example 4.1, where a research study in personality similarity between spouses as a factor in the quality of marital relationships is described. In its initial formulation, a medium difference in correlation, i.e., ES $= q = .30$ was posited, and the significance criterion of $a_2 = .05$ was to be used. If power of .80 is desired, what is the sample size necessary? The specifications thus are

$$a_2 = .05, \qquad q = .30, \qquad \text{power} = .80.$$

In Table 4.4.1 for $a_2 = .05$, column $q = .30$, and row power $= .80$, $n = 177$. The investigator will thus need samples of good and poor marital pairs with 177 couples in each in order to detect a $q = .30$ difference in z-transformed correlations at the $a_2 = .05$ level. If he reconsiders his specifications and is content to posit $q = .50$ instead, the sample size required in each group is 66.

4.6   In example 4.2, a study testing for a higher correlation of a given pair of variables in paranoid than in catatonic schizophrenics was described. The significance criterion is $a_1 = .01$. Assume that the investigator is content with power of .75 and poses the question: How many cases are required, assuming successively that $q = .10, .30,$ and .50?

$$a_1 = .01, \qquad q = \begin{matrix} .10 \\ .30, \\ .50 \end{matrix} \qquad \text{power} = .75.$$

In the section of Table 4.4.1 for $a_1 = .01$ and row power $= .75$, the values in columns $q = .10, .30, .50$ are found to be 1804, 203, and 75, respectively. He may then decide that he is content to try to detect a medium effect and plan to collect samples of 203 cases of each schizophrenic type. Alternatively, he may reconsider his significance criterion. If he sets it at $a_1 = .05$, he finds from Table 4.4.1 (specifications otherwise the same) n's of 1079, 123, and 46 for the three q levels; if he sets it at $a_1 = .10$, he finds in the next section of the table 768, 88, and 34. His explorations in sample size requirements can be summarized in tabular form:

DESIRED POWER = .75

			q	
		.10	.30	.50
Significance	.01	1804	203	75
level a_1	.05	1079	123	46
	.10	768	88	34

Depending on his resources for data gathering and the theory being tested, he can make a choice among these possibilities, or investigate others (non-directional a, q of .20, .40).

4.4.2 CASE 1: $n_1 \neq n_2$. One does not ordinarily *plan* to use samples of unequal size (since equal sample sizes are optimal), but Case 1 can occur in planning when a value of r_s is already available from a given sample or one sample's size is necessarily fixed by circumstances, so that the researcher's freedom in setting sample size is restricted to only one of the two samples. With one sample size fixed at n_F, this value will generally differ from that of the other sample, whose size is at the researcher's disposal (n_U). As in Case 0, given a, q, and desired power, Table 4.4.1 gives values for n. To find n_U, substitute the fixed sample size (n_F) and the n read from the table in

(4.4.2)
$$n_U = \frac{n_F(n + 3) - 6n}{2n_F - n - 3}.$$

(See Section 2.4.2 when denominator is zero or negative.)

Illustrative Example

4.7 Return to consider again the situation described in example 4.3. The issue is whether a new procedure (P_2) has a significantly different ($a_2 = .05$) parallel form correlation from that of an older procedure (P_1). The ES to be detected is $q = .40$, and a sample is already available to estimate the correlation of P_1, with $n_F = 260$. Assuming that he desires power of .90, what sample size n_U does he require for the test?

If he were unconstrained in the choice of n for both samples, i.e., if Case 0 conditions prevailed, his specifications would simply be

$$a_2 = .05, \quad q = .40, \quad \text{power} = .90.$$

In the section of Table 4.4.1 for $a_2 = .05$, with column $q = .40$ and row power = .90, one finds that samples of 134 cases each would be required. But in this instance, he already has one sample whose size is fixed at $n_F = 260$.

Thus, the other sample need only contain (substituting $n_F = 260$ and $n = 134$ in formula (4.4.2))

$$n_U = \frac{260(134 + 3) - 6(134)}{2(260) - 134 - 3} = 91 \text{ cases.}$$

Thus, the availability of a sample of $n_F = 260$ cases makes it possible for him to satisfy his specifications (attain power of .90 to detect $q = .40$ at $a_2 = .05$) with a sample for the new procedure of 91 cases.

4.4.3   CASE 2: ONE SAMPLE OF n OBSERVATIONS TO TEST $r = c$. In using the n tables for the one-sample test, the only departure from Case 0 is that which was discussed in connection with the power tables for Case 2, the proper value of q to be sought in the table (see Section 4.3.3 for details). Briefly, if one is testing with a single sample the null hypothesis that the population r has some specified value, i.e., $H_0 : r = c$, and scales his ES in the usual way, as a difference between z-transformed values of r_1 and c, namely $q_2' = z_1 - z_c$, then n value is determined for $q = q_2' \sqrt{2}$. If the resultant q is not tabled (a likely occurrence), he takes recourse to the procedure described in connection with formula (4.4.1).

Illustrative Example

4.8   We return to example 4.4, where a social psychologist, engaged in an attitude-scale revision effort, plans a test at $a_1 = .05$ of $H_0 : r \leq .60$ against the alternate $H_1 : r_1 = .76$. Instead of assuming a sample size and determining the resulting power, as was done in problem 4.4, let us here assume that he seeks the sample size necessary for power to be .95. Note that this is an instance in which the investigator wishes the two kinds of errors to be equal, i.e., Type I = .05, Type II = $b = 1 - .95 = .05$.

As before, for r's of .60 and .76, the difference in z units (Table 4.2.1) is .30, which is q_2'. To use the table we require $q = .30 \sqrt{2} = .4243$, as in problem 4.4. Thus, the specifications are

$$a_1 = .05, \qquad q = .4243, \qquad \text{power} = .95.$$

Since $q = .4243$ is not tabled, we follow the procedure described in Section 4.4.1. In the part of Table 4.4.1 for $a_1 = .05$, row power = .95, and column $q = .10$, find $n_{.10} = 2167$. Then substitute $n_{.10} = 2167$ and $q = .4243$ in formula (4.4.1) for the required n:

$$n = \frac{2167 - 3}{100 \, (.4243)^2} + 3 = 123.$$

Thus if $r = .76$, a one-sample test of $H_0 : r = .60$ performed at the $a_1 = .05$ level will have .95 probability of a significant result if the sample n is 123.

4.5 THE USE OF THE TABLES FOR SIGNIFICANCE TESTING

4.5.1. GENERAL INTRODUCTION. Provision has been made in the power tables to facilitate significance testing. Power analysis is largely concerned with the planning of experiments and thus with the alternate-hypothetical ES. Once the experiment is performed, attention turns to the assessment of the null hypothesis in the light of the sample data.

We accordingly redefine our ES index, q, so that its elements are sample statistics, rather than population values, and call it q_s. For cases 0 and 1, where the r's of two independent samples are being compared, the sample r_s values are transformed into sample Fisher z_s values, and

$$(4.5.1) \qquad q_s = z_{s_1} - z_{s_2} \qquad \text{(directional)}$$

$$= \left| z_{s_1} - z_{s_2} \right| \qquad \text{(nondirectional)}.$$

Thus, q_s is simply the difference in sample z values. It is related to the unit normal curve deviate (or "critical ratio") x, by[4]

$$(4.5.2) \qquad q_s = x \sqrt{\frac{n_1 + n_2 - 6}{(n_1 - 3)(n_2 - 3)}} \, ,$$

$$(4.5.3) \qquad x = q_s \sqrt{\frac{(n_1 - 3)(n_2 - 3)}{n_1 + n_2 - 6}} \, .$$

The relationships are stated here for the more general situation where the sample n's need not be equal. They simplify for the Case 0, equal n condition (see below).

The value of q_s necessary for significance is called q_c, i.e., the criterion value of q_s. The second column of the power Tables 4.3, headed q_c, carries these values as a function of n. Using these values, the investigator need not compute the normal curve deviate x. He simply finds the z transformations of his sample r_s's in Table 4.2.2, then finds their difference, q_s, and compares it with the tabled q_c value for his sample size. If the obtained q_s value equals or exceeds q_c, his obtained difference is significant at the a value for that table; otherwise, it is not.

4.5.2 SIGNIFICANCE TESTING IN CASE 0, $n_1 = n_2 = n$. In Case 0, where $n_1 = n_2 = n$, the relationships between q_s and the normal deviate x are simplified:

$$(4.5.4) \qquad q_s = x \sqrt{\frac{2}{n - 3}} \, ,$$

$$(4.5.5) \qquad x = q_s \sqrt{\frac{n - 3}{2}} \, .$$

---

[4] The unit normal curve deviate is frequently represented by the symbol z. We use x here to avoid confusion.

[Formula (4.5.4) was used in the computation of the q_c values of the power tables, x being the normal curve deviate for the a criterion.]

The Case 0 use of the q_c values is quite straightforward: The investigator looks up the z_s values for the two r_s's in Table 4.2.2, finds their difference, q_s [formula (4.5.1)], and uses the appropriate power table depending on a, in the row for his $n(= n_1 = n_2)$, checking whether his q_s value equals or exceeds the tabulated q_c value.

Illustrative Example

4.9   Consider the conditions of example 4.1, where a marriage counselor is studying the difference in husband–wife correlation on a series of personality variables between 60 marriages rates as harmonious (Group 1) and 60 having marital difficulties (Group 2). The significance criterion is $a_2 = .05$. When the data are analyzed, it is found for a specific variable **A** that r_{s_1} is .42 and r_{s_2} is .16. He looks up the z transformation of these r_s's and finds $z_{s_1} = .448$ and $z_{s_2} = .161$. Thus, $q_s = .448 - .161 = .287$. His specifications, thus, are

$$a_2 = .05, \qquad n = 60, \qquad q_s = .287.$$

In Table 4.3.5 (for $a_2 = .05$) for row $n = 60$, he finds under q_c the value .367. Since his q_s is smaller than q_c, his observed difference is not significant at $a_2 = .05$. [From formula (4.5.5), $x = .287 \sqrt{(60 - 3)/2} = 1.53$.]

Assume now that for another variable B, he finds $r_{s_1} = .35, r_{s_2} = - .14$. Transformed by means of Table 4.2.2, these r values yield, respectively, $z_{s_1} = .365, z_{s_2} = - .141$. By formula (4.5.1) for nondirectional tests,

$$q_s = |.365 - (- .141)| = |.506| = .506.$$

The specifications remain the same as for variable **A**, except that now $q_s = .506$. Since this exceeds the $q_c = .367$, the difference in correlation for variable **B** is significant at $a_2 = .05$. [From formula (4.5.5), $x = .506 \sqrt{(60 - 3)/2} = 2.70$.]

Consider now the results for a third variable, **C**. Assume he finds $r_{s_1} = - .20, r_{s_2} = - .06$. Transformed, these r values yield, respectively, $z_{s_1} = - .203, z_{s_2} = - .060$. By formula (4.5.1) for nondirectional tests,

$$q_s = | - .203 - (- .060)| = | - .143| = .143,$$

which is less than $q_c = .367$ and hence not significant at $a_2 = .05$. [From formula (4.5.5), $x = .143 \sqrt{(60 - 3)/2} = .76$.]

4.10 Example 4.2 described a study in clinical psychology which depended on comparing at the $a_1 = .01$ level correlations of two variables between (a) paranoid and (b) catatonic schizophrenics, r_{s_1} being predicted the larger. When samples of $n = 180$ are analyzed, it is found that $r_{s_1} = .60$, $r_{s_2} = .36$. When transformed, these yield $z_{s_1} = .693$ and $z_{s_2} = .377$. Thus $q_s = .693 - .377 = .316$. The specifications are

$$a_1 = .01, \qquad n = 180, \qquad q_s = .316.$$

Table 4.3.1 (for $a_1 = .01$) for row $n = 180$ and column q_c, yields the value .247. Since q_s (.316) exceeds the criterion value (.247), it can be concluded at $a_1 = .01$ that the relationship is significantly larger for the paranoids. [If desired, **x** can be found from formula (4.5.5) to be $.316\sqrt{(180-3)/2}$ = 2.97.] Note that if the r_s's for paranoids and catatonics were reversed, i.e., if the sample results were contrary to the predicted direction, no **q** values need be determined—the difference, being contrary to the predicted direction in a directional test, is nonsignificant whatever its magnitude.

To make another point, we assume instead that r_{s_1}, r_{s_2} turn out to be $+.15$, $-.14$ so that z_{s_1}, z_{s_2} are .151, $-.141$, and $q_s = .151 - (-.141) = .292$. Now, since $q_s = .292$ is greater than $q_c = .247$, the difference between r_s's is significant, i.e., we conclude that r_1 is (algebraically) greater than r_2. Note that this is true despite the fact that neither is significantly different (at the same $a_1 = .01$ level) from zero. (In Chapter 3, Table 3.3.1, r_c for $n = 180$ is .173, which neither value exceeds.) Thus, two-sample values departing *in opposite directions* from zero may be significantly different from each other while neither is significantly different from zero. There is no contradiction if nonsignificance is properly interpreted as the data not warranting the rejection of the null hypothesis. Thus, the results of each sample do not warrant the conclusion that its population **r** is not zero, but, together, they do warrant the conclusion that the population **r**'s differ (subject, of course, to the Type I error).

4.5.3. SIGNIFICANCE TESTING IN CASE 1, $n_1 \neq n_2$. The fact of inequality of sample sizes in significance testing using the tabled q_c values requires only finding the harmonic mean of the $(n-3)$'s, n', as described in Section 4.3.2 [formula (4.3.1)]:

$$n' = \frac{2(n_1 - 3)(n_2 - 3)}{n_1 + n_2 - 6} + 3.$$

In using Tables 4.3, values of n' are substituted for n. Otherwise, exactly the same procedure is followed as in Case 0.

If the normal curve deviate value **x** is desired, it is found using formula (4.5.3), or, if n' has been found, it is computationally simpler to substitute n' for n in formula (4.5.5).

Illustrative Example

4.11   Example 4.3 describes an investigation in psycholinguistics designed to improve the reliability (parallel forms correlation) of a speech disruption measure. The statistical test takes the form of comparing the r_s's for the new (P_1) and old (P_2) procedure at the $a_2 = .05$ significance level. Assume he finds $r_{s_1} = .89$ for $n_1 = 51$ and $r_{s_2} = .79$ for $n_2 = 260$. The transformed values are found to be $z_{s_1} = 1.422$ and $z_{s_2} = 1.071$, so that

$$q = |1.422 - 1.071| = |.351| = .351.$$

To use the table, find n' from formula (4.3.1):

$$n' = \frac{2(51 - 3)(260 - 3)}{51 + 260 - 6} + 3 = 84$$

(as before in example 4.3).

The specifications for significance testing of the sample difference are:

$$a_1 = .05, \qquad n' = 84, \qquad q_s = .351.$$

Table 4.3.5 for $a_2 = .05$, row $n = 84$, and column q_c, yields .308. Since q_s exceeds q_c, the difference in sample correlations is significant. (If desired, x may be found from formula (4.5.5) as $.351\sqrt{(84 - 3)/2} = 2.23$.)

Note that in planning (example 4.3), an ES of $q = .40$ was posited. Despite the fact that the observed difference $q_s = .351$ fell short of this, it was nevertheless significant. As has been noted previously, this can only occur when, for the planning specifications, power exceeds .50. (In this example, it was .72.)

4.5.4   SIGNIFICANCE TESTING IN CASE 2: ONE SAMPLE, $H_0 : r = c$. When the null hypothesis takes the form: The r of a population of paired values from which a sample of n observations has been randomly drawn equals c, an adjustment must be made of the tabled q_c value. Since the tables were constructed for Case 0 conditions (two samples of equal size), they are designed to allow for sampling error variance of two z_s's, while in Case 2 there is only one. To find the proper criterion for one-sample tests of $r = c$, one finds

(4.5.6) $$q_c' = q_c\sqrt{\tfrac{1}{2}} = .707q_c,$$

where q_c is the tabulated value for n.

As for the observed q_s value for Case 2, we follow the principle expressed in (4.5.1), and simply define q_s' as we defined q_2' [formula (4.3.2)], merely substituting the sample value of z_s for the population parameter z_1:

(4.5.7) $q_s' = z_s - z_c$ (directional)

     $= |z_s - z_c|$ (nondirectional)

The prime is used to denote that a one-sample test is involved. The relationships between q_s' and the normal deviate x for this case are now

(4.5.8) $$q_s' = x \sqrt{\frac{1}{n-3}},$$

(4.5.9) $$x = q_s' \sqrt{n-3}.$$

Formula (4.5.9) can be used if the exact value of the normal deviate ("critical ratio") is desired, e.g., for reporting results for publication.

Illustrative Example

4.12 In example 4.4, which was concerned with an attempt to improve the reliability of an attitude scale, a test of H_0: $r \leq .60$ at $a_1 = .05$ (i.e., predicting $r > .60$) with a sample of $n = 50$ was described. When the data are collected, the social psychologist finds $r_s = .72$. Can he safely conclude that the new scale has a population reliability coefficient (alternate form correlation) greater than .60? He converts these two values of r_s to z_s, and finds their difference:

$$q_s' = .908 - .693 = .215.$$

This is the sample ES. His specifications, then, are

$$a_1 = .05, \quad n = 50, \quad q_s' = .215.$$

In Table 4.3.2 (for $a_1 = .05$) with row $n = 50$, he finds in column q_c, .339. This would be the criterion for a two-sample test. For this one-sample case, he goes on to find [formula (4.5.6)] $q_c' = .339\sqrt{\frac{1}{2}} = (.707)(.339) = .240$. This is the relevant criterion value, and since $q_s' = .215$ is less than $q_c' = .240$, he *cannot* conclude at $a_1 = .05$ that the population reliability of the new procedure exceeds .60.

If he wishes to determine the exact normal curve deviate value x which would result from the test, he finds [formula (4.5.9)] $x = .215\sqrt{50-3} = .147$.

5

The Test that a
Proportion is .50 and the Sign Test

5.1 INTRODUCTION AND USE

It arises with some frequency in behavioral science that a null hypothesis takes the form that the fraction of a population of potential observations having some defined characteristic is one-half, i.e., $\mathbf{H}_0$: $\mathbf{P} = .50$. Examples come to mind from areas as diverse as political science (opinion or political polling), experimental psychology (learning theory, psychophysics), and behavior genetics. Thus, for example, the question as to whether or not there is majority support in the electorate for a course of action by the national administration could be approached by polling a suitably drawn sample and testing the null hypothesis that the proportion of the population in favor is .50; rejection of this null hypothesis leads to the conclusion. As another example, the ability of an experimental subject to detect a near-threshold stimulus which is presented on a random half of a series of trials can be assessed by testing the null hypothesis that on a very long series he would be correct in his judgments of present–absent on $\mathbf{P} = .50$ of the trials. The finding that the sample $\mathbf{P}$ is greater than .50 and significant would lead to the conclusion that he is (at least on some trials) making the perceptual discrimination. Research in extrasensory perception involving the calling of the side of a coin or the color of the suit of a playing card would test null hypotheses of the same form.

The fact that in many human populations the sexes are about equally divided leads to the relevance of the $\mathbf{P} = .50$ test in studies of sex differences. Thus, if an investigator is interested in the relationship between sex and a definable characteristic (say, falling into a given psychiatric diagnostic group or a political party), he can draw a random sample of a group having the characteristic and test the null hypothesis that the proportion of males is .50. Departure from .50 is taken as evidence for a sex difference in incidence of the characteristic, and therefore a relationship between sex and the characteristic.

The widest application of the test of H_0: $P = .50$ arises in the form of the nonparametric "Sign Test" (Siegel, 1956, pp. 68–75). Consider the following circumstances. We have a population of **X**, **Y** paired observations, and we are concerned with the relative magnitude of the **X**'s and **Y**'s. If we can merely say for each pair in a sample whether **X** is greater than **Y** (so that **X** − **Y** is *positive*) or **X** is less than **Y** (so that **X** − **Y** is *negative*), we have a basis for deciding whether the X population is stochastically larger or smaller than the Y population. By "stochastically larger (smaller)" we simply mean that in more than half of the **X**, **Y** pairs in the population, **X** is larger (smaller) than **Y**. Under these circumstances, the null hypothesis that the X and Y populations are stochastically equal is simply H_0: $P = .50$, where **P** is the proportion of pairs in which **X** (or **Y**) is larger.

Note that no assumption need be made about the shape of either the **X** or the **Y** distributions, or of their joint (bivariate) distribution. Indeed, it is not even necessary that the values of the variables be expressed in metric (i.e., interval or ratio scale) form: only "larger than" or "smaller than" judgments are required. Thus, the test is distribution-free, and since no estimation of population parameters are called for, nonparametric as well.

If stronger assumptions are permitted, specifically, if it can be assumed that **X** − **Y** = **Z** values are normally distributed and with equal variance, then the t test for dependent means of Section 2.3.5 is appropriate, and, for equal specifications, more powerful. Further, with large samples, moderate failure of these assumptions is tolerable. The investigator may nevertheless choose to perform the less powerful sign test as a "shortcut" or "approximate" test (Cohen, 1965, p. 119).

This test can equally be used for a test of the difference between correlated or dependent proportions (McNemar, 1962, pp. 52–56). If we assess **X** and **Y** as having some attribute present (1) or absent (0), then our **X**, **Y** pairs are either (1, 0), (0, 1), (1, 1), or (0, 0). We then discard the instances of the latter two possibilities, where we cannot make a judgment of "greater than." Now, if the proportions having the attribute differ between **X** and **Y**, then **P**, the proportion of differing **X**, **Y** pairs in which **X** is greater than **Y**, will depart from .50. Thus, the null hypothesis is again **P** = .50, and the methods of this chapter can be applied.

Yet another application of the same test is in testing the index of order association (Senders, 1958, pp. 455–456).

The statistical term for the test model under consideration is the "symmetrical binomial cumulative distribution." It is frequently referred to by this name in the statistical literature [see MacKinnon (1959, 1961) for some useful tables]. "Symmetrical" is used for $P = 1 - P = .50$; tests of other values of P proceed by means of other binomial cumulative distributions (see McNemar, 1962, pp. 41–46). The methods of the next chapter may be used to test the more general hypothesis H_0: $P = k$, where k is any proportion.

5.2 THE EFFECT SIZE INDEX: g

We index departure from $P = .50$ simply by the distance in units of proportion from .50, i.e.,

(5.2.1) $g = P - .50$ or $.50 - P$ (directional),
and

$g = |P - .50|$ (nondirectional).

In this form, our null hypothesis is that $g = 0$. A test of H_0: $P = .50$ when P_1 is actually .60 represents an alternate hypothesis or ES of $g = .60 - .50 = .10$. Unlike some of the other ES indices in this book, g is fortunately expressed in a unit which is immediately comprehensible to the behavioral scientist.

5.2.1 "SMALL," "MEDIUM," AND "LARGE" VALUES OF g. We offer as conventions operational definitions of qualitatively defined levels of ES here with, if anything, greater diffidence than in the previous chapters (see particularly the general discussion in Section 1.4). Since g is so transparently clear a unit, it is expected that workers in any given substantive area of the behavioral sciences will very frequently be able to set relevant ES values without the proposed conventions, or set up conventions of their own which are suited to their area of inquiry.

They are offered here for whatever use they may afford researchers in areas where effect sizes are obscure, for use with the sign test where experience in an area may not provide a guide, and for the sake of symmetry of exposition. One further reason lies in a larger effort to make behavioral scientists using statistical inference more aware of the sizes of the effects they are studying. It must be reiterated, however, that a basis for positing g which comes from theory or experience should automatically take precedence over these conventions.

SMALL EFFECT SIZE: $g = .05$. With $g = .05$ as the definition, we are considering a division of the population of .55:.45 as a small departure from the null (.50:.50). This may be considered either too large or too small a criterion, depending on the reader's perspective.

For a *normally distributed* population of differences, the division between the highest .55 and the lowest .45 of them comes at about one-eighth (.126) of their standard deviation away from their mean (see discussion of U_3, Section 2.2 and Table 2.2.1). If such a division obtained in a sign test, with .55 positive and .45 negative, the mean of the positive differences would be .85, and of the negative differences $(-).75$, when expressed in units of the (total) standard deviation of the differences. This may well seem like very little, less than "small," particularly when one considers that at $P = .50$, these tail means are .80 and $-.80$.

On the other hand, consider political polling. In a presidential election, a candidate who garners 55% of the popular vote is said to have won by a landslide. (In only 9 of the 24 presidential elections since 1872 did the popular plurality candidate get more than 55% of the vote; in only 3, more than 60%.) In opinion polling on closely divided issues (where it is most relevant), a .55:.45 division is sizable. Another relevant fact: the well-known excess of women over men among the aged amounts to a female–male sex ratio of .547:.453 in the population aged 65 and over (for the year 1960). Also the difference in vocabulary knowledge between adult siblings of opposite sex is such that in about 55% of the pairs who differ, the female will be superior [estimated from Wechsler (1958, p. 147)].

Thus, the $g = .05$ criterion for a small departure may be too large or too small from some specific viewpoint; it seems, however, a reasonable criterion for general use.

MEDIUM EFFECT SIZE: $g = .15$. A .65:.35 split is offered as a conventional definition of a medium departure from .50:.50. This is a 13:7 ratio, i.e., approximately 2:1. (If exactly 2 to 1 is desired, it is provided in the tables at $g = \frac{1}{6}$.)

In a normal distribution of differences, the highest .65 are cut off at .385 of a standard deviation away from the mean. Interpreted as a sign test with .65 positive differences, the mean of these differences is .96, while that of the negative differences is $(-).77$ (in standard units). Thus, if adult mixed-sex sibling pairs were given a standard Arithmetic Reasoning test, in about two-thirds of the cases where the siblings differed, the brothers would get the larger score [estimated from Wechsler (1958, p. 147)].

In more familiar terms, and returning to divisions in the popular vote in presidential elections, there never has been a division as extreme as .65:.35 since popular vote totals became available (1872). (The largest proportion polled was .625 by Roosevelt in 1936. Ironically, this was the year of the Literary Digest Poll debacle, when Landon's election was predicted by a socioeconomically biased sample.)

An instance of a division of the order of $g = .15$ can be drawn from mortality statistics. If one were to collect very large and equal random samples of Negro and white births, those dying before the age of one year would contain about twice as many Negroes as whites (.664 : .336 for males, .667 : .333 for females).[1]

Another instance of a medium effect size is the sex difference in incidence of manic-depressive psychosis: Authorities generally agree that the diagnosis is made about twice as frequently in females than in males, hence $P \cong .67$ and $g \cong .67 - .50 = .17$ (see Campbell, 1953, p. 70).

For another example, consider again *normally distributed* populations of differences between adult brother–sister pairs with regard to two intelligence subtest variables, arthmetic reasoning and a speeded digit-symbol substitution task. In the arithmetic subtest, in approximately .64 of the pairs, the brothers would obtain the higher score, and in the digit-symbol subtest, in the same proportion of the pairs the sisters would show superior performance (estimated from Wechsler (1958, p. 147)]. Thus, $g \approx .14$ in both instances, a medium departure.

LARGE EFFECT SIZE $g = .25$. We operationally define as a large ES a .75 : .25, or 3:1 split. In line with our orientation in setting the ES conventions, this should be a departure from .50 : .50 which is fairly obvious to the observer's naked eye, yet not so large as to render statistical analysis wholly superfluous (see Section 1.4).

In a normally distributed population of differences, the largest .75 of them are cut off at .674 of a standard deviation below the mean. When interpreted as a sign test with .75 positive differences, the mean of the positive differences would be 1.10 and the mean of the negative differences $(-).60$ (in standard units). Thus, there would be a half standard deviation separation between the means of the positive and negative tail segments.[2]

It is difficult to come by well-known examples to illustrate a departure from the null of $g = .25$, i.e., .75 : .25 population splits where .50 : .50 represents "no effect." For example, as already noted, no recorded popular vote for the U.S. presidency has approached this size, and no brother–sister difference in the area of human abilities, such as were used to illustrate small and medium ES are known which are of this magnitude.

An obvious example can be drawn from Mendelian genetic ratios. For the simple case of single gene complete dominance inheritance, the matings

---

[1] Based on a 10% sample from death certificates in 1964. Cited in "The New Information Please Almanac for 1966." New York: Simon and Schuster, 1965.

[2] The reader should not confuse this with the medium ES of $d = .5$ separation between means of different *whole* normal populations, standardized by their common *within* population standard deviation, used in connection with the **t** test (see Section 2.2). Here tail segments of a *single* normal population are involved, and the standardizing unit is the total standard deviation, a much larger unit than the within-population standard deviation.

of heterozygous parents yield offspring .25 of whom would manifest the recessive character. Thus, the ratio among phenotypes showing to not showing the recessive trait would be .25:.75, thus a departure of .25 from a null hypothesis which posits equal incidence of the two phenotypes.

One can find populations that split .75:.25, but they are not compelling examples unless there is a reasonable basis for stating a .50:.50 null hypothesis. For example, the proportion of adult single males in the U.S. is close to .25 (1960 U.S. Census), but to consider this a $g = .25$ departure from .50:.50 seems forced in the absence of any particular reason to posit an equiprobable null hypothesis for single/not single. Or, in other words, what effect is there none of if the proportion of single men were .50?

The area of sex differences has provided some useful illustrations of small and medium ES. On can find examples of large sex differences, but they are larger than our $g = .25$ criterion. Thus, when one identifies the sex distribution in samples of school children who are stutterers or behavior problems or who are diagnosed as reading disability cases or color blind, the departure from a no sex effect .50 incidence for boys is typically at least .30 (i.e., .80:.20), color blindness (usually a sex-linked recessive character) rising to about $g = .40$ (i.e., .90:.10).

One example of a $g = .25$ sex difference can be offered: If one were to draw large and equal samples of male and female arrests from police blotters in U.S. cities of over 2500 population, and then to identify the arrests for auto theft, 75% of them would be males!

5.3 POWER TABLES

The tables in this section yield power values when, in addition to the significance criterion and ES ($= g$), the sample size is specified. They should therefore be used in finding the power of the test of H_0: $P = .50$ (or $g = 0$), after the data are gathered. They can also be used in planning experiments by varying n, ES, or a, or all three, to determine the consequence to power of such alternative specifications. The tables give values for "nearest" a, g, and n:

1. *Significance Criterion*, a. Since frequencies are discrete, the (exact) binomial test cannot be performed at a constant conventional value of a, such as .05 or .01. For example, when a population $P = .50$, and a random sample of $n = 10$ cases is drawn, the probability (a_2) of a 10:0 or 0:10 distribution in the sample is .002, of a 9:1 or 1:9 distribution is .021, and of an 8:2 or 2:8 distribution is .109. No tests *at* $a_2 = .01$, .05, or .10 are possible because intermediate values for frequences between 10 and 9 and between 9 and 8 are not possible. Thus, for each value of n in each power table,

the exact value of a_1 or a_2 for the test is given. This is generally[3] the *nearest* available value to the conventional .01, .05, and .10 criteria.

Tables are provided for the following "nearest" values of a: $a_1 \approx .01$, $a_1 \approx .05$, $a_1 \approx .10$; $a_2 \approx .01$, $a_2 \approx .05$, $a_2 \approx .10$, the subscripts referring to one- and two-tailed tests. Since power at a_1 closely approximates power at $a_2 = 2a_1$, for power greater than .10, one can also determine power at $a_2 \approx .02$ (from the $a_1 \approx .01$ table), $a_2 \approx .20$ (from $a_1 \approx .10$), $a_1 \approx .005$ (from $a_2 \approx .01$, and $a_1 \approx .025$ (from $a_2 \approx .05$). In each instance one simply doubles or halves the exact values for a_1 or a_2 given in the table. These will, however, not necessarily be the nearest possible values to those desired.

2. Effect Size, ES. The ES index here is **g**, the discrepancy in the population from the null-hypothetical **P** = .50. In directional (one-tailed) tests (a_1), **g** is understood as either positive or negative, depending on the direction posited in the alternate hypothesis, e.g., H_1: $g = -.15$ (i.e., $P_1 = .35$). In nondirectional (two-tailed) tests, **g** is understood as absolute, e.g., "given a departure from .50 or .15, whether positive or negative. . . ."

Provision is made for $g = .05$ (.05) .40, and also $\frac{1}{6}$. Conventional definitions have been offered above, as follows:

small: $g = .05$ (.55:.45)

medium: $g = .15$ (.65:.35),

large: $g = .25$ (.75:.25).

3. Sample Size, **n**. This is the number of observations in the sample. Depending on the nature of the application of the test, observations may be single, or as in the "Sign Test," paired. Provision is made for **n** = 8 (1) 40 (2) 60 (4) 100 (20) 200 (50) 500 (100) 1000.

The values in the body of the table are the power of the test times 100, i.e., the percent of tests carried out under the given conditions which will result in the rejection of the null hypothesis, H_0: **P** = .50 at the exact level of **a** given in the third column. The values are accurate to two places, as given. For a few values of **n** (250, 350, and 450), exact binomial values are not available in published tables and the normal approximation was used.

[3] An occasional exception is made in order to provide more values. For example, when **n** = 16, a break of 12:4 or 4:12 is significant at $a_2 = .077$. This is given in Table 5.3.5 for $a_2 \approx .05$. A break of 11:4 or 4:11 is significant at $a_2 = .210$ and is given in Table 5.3.6 for $a_2 \approx .10$, even though .077 is closer to .10 than .210 is. This exception avoids duplicating the information in that line of the table in Table 5.3.6 and instead provides an additional line of values.

Table 5.3.1

Power of Sign Test (P = .50) at $a_1 \approx .01$

n	v	a_1	.05	.10	.15	1/6	.20	.25	.30	.35	.40
8	8	004	01	02	03	04	06	10	17	27	43
9	9	002	00	01	02	03	04	08	13	23	39
10	9	011	02	05	09	10	15	24	38	54	74
11	10	006	01	03	06	08	11	20	32	49	70
12	11	003	01	02	04	05	09	16	27	44	66
13	11	011	03	06	11	14	20	32	50	69	87
14	12	006	02	04	08	11	16	28	45	65	84
15	13	004	01	03	06	08	13	24	40	60	82
16	13	011	03	07	13	17	25	40	60	79	93
17	14	006	02	05	10	13	20	35	55	76	92
18	15	004	01	03	08	10	16	31	50	72	90
19	15	010	03	07	15	19	28	47	67	86	96
20	16	006	02	05	12	15	24	41	63	83	96
21	16	013	04	10	20	25	36	57	77	92	99
22	17	008	03	07	16	21	31	52	73	90	98
23	18	005	02	05	13	17	27	47	69	88	98
24	18	011	04	10	21	26	39	61	81	94	99
25	19	007	03	07	17	22	34	56	78	93	99
26	19	014	05	12	26	32	46	69	87	97	*
27	20	010	03	10	22	28	41	64	84	96	
28	21	006	02	07	18	23	36	60	82	95	
29	21	012	04	12	26	33	48	71	89	98	
30	22	008	03	09	22	29	43	67	87	97	
31	23	005	02	07	19	25	39	63	85	97	
32	23	010	04	12	27	34	50	74	91	98	
33	24	007	03	09	23	30	45	70	89	98	
34	24	012	05	14	31	39	55	79	94	99	
35	25	008	04	11	27	34	51	76	93	99	
36	26	006	03	09	23	30	47	73	91	99	
37	26	010	04	13	31	39	57	81	95	99	
38	27	007	03	11	27	35	52	78	94	99	
39	27	012	05	16	36	44	62	85	96	*	
40	28	008	04	13	31	40	58	82	96		
42	29	010	05	15	35	44	63	86	97		
44	30	011	05	17	39	49	67	89	98		
46	31	013	06	19	43	53	71	91	99		
48	33	007	04	14	35	45	64	88	98		

Table 5.3.1 (continued)

n	v	a_1	.05	.10	.15	1/6	.20	.25	.30	.35	.40
50	34	008	04	16	39	49	68	90	99	*	*
52	35	009	05	18	43	53	72	92	99		
54	36	010	06	20	46	56	76	94	99		
56	37	011	06	22	49	60	79	95	*		
58	38	012	07	24	53	63	81	96			
60	40	007	04	18	45	56	76	95			
64	42	008	06	22	52	63	82	97			
68	44	010	07	25	58	69	86	98			
72	46	012	08	29	63	74	89	99			
76	49	008	06	25	59	70	88	99			
80	51	009	07	29	64	75	91	99			
84	53	011	08	32	69	79	93	99			
88	55	012	09	36	73	83	95	*			
92	58	008	07	31	70	80	94				
96	60	009	08	35	73	84	95				
100	62	010	10	38	77	86	97				
120	73	011	12	47	85	93	99				
140	84	011	13	54	91	96	*				
160	95	011	15	60	94	98					
180	106	010	17	65	96	99					
200	117	010	18	69	98	99					
250**	144	010	22	80	99	*					
300**	171	009	26	87	*						
350**	197	010	33	93							
400	224	009	36	95							
450**	250	010	42	98							
500	277	009	45	98							
600	329	010	55	*							
700	381	011	63								
800	433	011	70								
900	485	011	76								
1000	537	010	80								

* Power values below this point are greater than .995.

** Normal approximation.

Table 5.3.2

Power of Sign Test (P = .50) at $a_1 \approx .05$

n	v	a_1	.05	.10	.15	1/6	.20	.25	.30	.35	.40
8	7	035	06	11	17	20	26	37	50	66	81
9	8	020	04	07	12	14	20	30	44	60	77
10	8	055	10	17	26	30	38	53	68	82	93
11	9	033	06	12	20	23	31	46	62	78	91
12	9	073	13	23	35	39	49	65	79	91	97
13	10	046	09	17	28	32	42	58	75	88	97
14	11	029	06	12	20	26	36	52	70	85	96
15	11	059	12	22	35	40	52	69	84	94	99
16	12	038	09	17	29	34	45	63	80	92	98
17	12	072	15	26	42	48	60	77	89	97	*
18	13	048	11	21	35	41	53	72	87	96	99
19	14	032	08	16	30	35	47	67	84	95	99
20	14	058	13	25	42	48	61	79	91	98	*
21	15	039	10	20	36	42	55	74	89	97	
22	15	067	15	29	47	54	67	84	94	99	
23	16	047	12	24	41	48	62	80	93	98	
24	17	032	09	19	36	42	56	77	91	98	
25	17	054	13	27	47	54	68	85	95	99	
26	18	038	10	23	41	48	63	82	94	99	
27	18	061	15	31	52	59	73	89	97	*	
28	19	044	12	26	46	54	68	86	96	99	
29	19	068	17	34	56	64	77	92	98	*	
30	20	049	14	29	51	58	73	89	97		
31	21	035	11	25	46	53	69	87	97		
32	21	055	15	32	55	63	77	92	98		
33	22	040	12	28	50	58	73	90	98		
34	22	061	17	35	59	67	81	94	99		
35	23	045	13	31	54	62	77	92	99		
36	23	066	18	38	63	71	84	95	99		
37	24	049	15	33	58	66	81	94	99		
38	25	036	12	29	53	62	77	93	99		
39	25	054	16	36	62	70	84	96	99		
40	26	040	13	32	57	66	81	95	99		
42	27	044	15	34	61	69	84	96	99		
44	28	048	16	37	64	72	86	97	*		
46	29	052	17	40	67	75	88	98			
48	30	056	18	42	70	78	90	98			

Table 5.3.2 *(continued)*

n	v	a_1	.05	.10	.15	1/6	.20	.25	.30	.35	.40
50	31	059	20	45	73	80	92	99	*	*	*
52	32	063	21	47	75	82	93	99			
54	34	038	15	38	68	77	90	98			
56	35	041	16	41	71	79	91	99			
58	36	043	17	43	73	81	93	99			
60	37	046	18	45	75	83	94	99			
64	39	052	20	49	79	86	95	*			
68	41	057	23	53	83	89	97				
72	44	038	18	47	79	87	96				
76	46	042	20	51	83	89	97				
80	48	046	22	55	85	92	98				
84	50	051	24	58	88	93	98				
88	52	055	25	61	90	95	99				
92	54	059	27	64	91	96	99				
96	57	041	22	59	90	95	99				
100	59	044	24	62	91	96	99				
120	70	041	26	68	95	98	*				
140	80	054	34	78	98	99					
160	91	048	35	81	99	*					
180	102	043	35	84	99						
200	112	052	42	89	*						
250**	139	050	45	93							
300	165	047	52	97							
350**	191	050	59	98							
400	217	049	64	99							
450**	243	050	68	*							
500	269	049	72								
600	321	047	78								
700	372	052	85								
800	424	048	88								
900	475	051	92								
1000	527	047	93								

* Values below this point are greater than .995, unless other values are specified.

** Normal approximation.

Table 5.3.3

Power of Sign Test (P = .50) at $a_1 \approx .10$

n	v	a_1					g				
			.05	.10	.15	1/6	.20	.25	.30	.35	.40
8	6	145	22	32	43	47	55	68	80	89	96
9	7	090	15	23	34	38	46	60	74	86	95
10	7	172	27	38	51	56	65	78	88	95	99
11	8	113	19	30	43	47	57	71	84	93	98
12	8	194	30	44	58	63	72	84	93	98	*
13	9	133	23	35	50	55	65	79	90	97	99
14	10	090	17	28	42	48	58	74	87	95	99
15	10	151	26	40	56	62	72	85	94	98	*
16	11	105	20	33	49	55	66	81	92	98	
17	11	166	29	45	62	67	78	89	96	99	
18	12	119	23	37	55	61	72	86	95	99	
19	13	084	17	31	48	54	67	83	93	98	
20	13	132	25	42	60	66	77	90	97	99	
21	14	095	20	35	54	60	72	87	96	99	
22	14	143	28	45	65	71	81	93	98	*	
23	15	105	22	39	59	65	77	90	97	*	
24	16	076	17	33	53	59	73	88	96	99	
25	16	115	24	42	63	70	81	93	98	*	
26	17	084	19	36	57	64	77	91	98		
27	17	124	26	46	67	73	84	95	99		
28	18	092	21	40	62	69	81	93	99		
29	18	132	28	49	70	77	87	96	99		
30	19	100	23	43	65	72	84	95	99		
31	20	075	19	38	60	68	81	94	99		
32	20	108	25	46	69	76	87	96	99		
33	21	081	21	41	64	71	84	95	99		
34	21	115	27	49	72	79	89	97	*		
35	22	088	22	44	68	75	86	96	99		
36	22	121	29	52	75	81	91	98	*		
37	23	094	24	46	71	78	89	97			
38	23	128	30	54	77	84	92	98			
39	24	100	26	49	74	80	91	98			
40	25	077	21	44	69	77	88	97			
42	26	082	23	47	72	80	90	98			
44	27	087	24	49	75	82	92	99			
46	28	092	26	52	77	84	93	99			
48	29	097	27	54	79	86	94	99			

Table 5.3.3 (continued)

n	v	a_1	.05	.10	.15	1/6	.20	.25	.30	.35	.40
50	30	101	29	56	81	87	95	99	*	*	*
52	31	106	30	58	83	89	96	*			
54	32	110	31	60	85	90	97				
56	33	114	33	62	86	91	97				
58	34	119	34	64	88	92	98				
60	36	078	26	56	83	89	96				
64	38	084	28	59	86	91	97				
68	40	091	31	63	88	93	98				
72	42	097	33	66	90	95	99				
76	44	103	35	69	92	96	99				
80	46	109	37	72	93	97	99				
84	48	115	39	74	95	97	*				
88	51	083	33	69	93	97	99				
92	53	087	35	72	94	97	*				
96	55	092	36	74	95	98					
100	57	097	38	76	96	98					
120	68	085	39	80	98	99					
140	78	102	47	87	99	*					
160	89	089	47	89	99						
180	99	102	53	93	*						
200	110	089	53	93							
250**	136	100	60	97							
300	162	092	66	98							
350**	187	100	74	99							
400	213	106	77	*							
450**	239	100	80								
500	265	097	83								
600	316	103	88								
700	367	106	92								
800	419	095	94								
900	470	097	96								
1000	521	097	97								

* Values below this point are greater than .995, unless other values are specified.

** Normal approximation.

Table 5.3.4

Power of Sign Test (P = .50) at $a_2 \approx .01$

						g					
n	v	a_2	.05	.10	.15	1/6	.20	.25	.30	.35	.40
8	8	008	01	02	03	04	06	10	17	27	43
9	9	004	01	01	02	03	04	08	12	23	39
10	10	002	00	01	01	02	03	06	11	20	35
11	10	012	02	03	06	08	11	20	32	49	70
12	11	006	01	02	04	05	09	16	27	44	66
13	12	003	01	01	03	04	06	13	23	40	62
14	12	013	02	04	08	11	16	28	45	65	84
15	13	007	01	03	06	08	13	24	40	60	82
16	14	004	01	02	05	06	10	20	35	56	79
17	14	013	02	05	10	13	20	35	55	76	92
18	15	008	01	03	08	10	16	31	50	72	90
19	16	004	01	02	06	08	13	26	46	68	88
20	16	012	02	05	12	15	24	41	63	83	96
21	17	007	01	04	09	12	20	37	59	80	95
22	18	004	01	03	07	10	16	32	54	77	94
23	18	011	02	05	13	17	27	47	69	88	98
24	19	007	01	04	10	14	23	42	66	86	97
25	19	015	03	07	17	22	34	56	78	94	99
26	20	009	02	06	14	19	30	52	75	92	99
27	21	006	01	04	11	15	26	47	71	90	99
28	21	013	03	07	18	23	36	60	82	95	*
29	22	008	02	06	15	20	32	56	79	94	99
30	23	005	01	04	12	17	28	51	76	93	99
31	23	011	02	07	19	25	39	63	85	97	*
32	24	007	02	06	16	21	34	59	83	96	
33	24	014	03	09	23	30	45	70	89	98	
34	25	009	02	07	20	26	41	66	87	98	
35	26	006	02	06	17	22	36	63	85	97	
36	26	011	03	09	23	30	47	73	91	99	
37	27	008	02	07	20	27	42	69	90	98	
38	27	014	03	11	27	35	52	78	94	99	
39	28	009	02	11	24	31	48	75	93	99	
40	29	006	02	09	21	27	44	72	91	99	
42	30	008	02	09	24	32	50	77	94	99	
44	31	010	03	10	28	36	55	81	96	*	
46	32	011	03	12	31	40	60	85	97		
48	33	013	04	14	35	45	64	88	98		

Table 5.3.4 *(continued)*

n	v	a_2	.05	.10	.15	1/6	.20	.25	.30	.35	.40
									g		
50	35	007	02	10	28	37	57	84	97	*	*
52	36	008	03	11	31	41	61	87	98		
54	37	009	03	13	35	45	66	89	99		
56	38	010	04	14	38	49	69	91	99		
58	39	012	04	16	42	52	73	93	99		
60	40	013	05	18	45	56	76	95	*		
64	43	008	03	15	41	52	74	94	99		
68	45	010	04	18	47	59	80	96	*		
72	47	013	05	21	53	65	84	98			
76	50	008	04	18	50	62	82	97			
80	52	010	05	21	55	67	86	98			
84	54	012	05	25	60	72	90	99			
88	57	007	04	21	57	69	88	99			
92	59	009	05	24	62	74	91	99			
96	61	010	06	27	66	78	93	*			
100	63	012	07	31	70	81	95				
120	75	008	06	32	75	86	97				
140	86	009	07	40	84	92	99				
160	97	009	09	47	89	95	*				
180	108	009	10	53	93	97					
200	119	009	11	59	95	99					
250**	146	010	15	72	99	*					
300	173	009	19	81	*						
350**	200	010	23	87							
400	226	011	29	93							
450**	253	010	32	95							
500	279	011	38	97							
600	332	010	45	99							
700	385	009	52	*							
800	437	010	60								
900	489	010	67								
1000	541	010	73								

* Values below this point are greater than .995, unless other values are specified.

** Normal approximation.

Table 5.3.5

Power of Sign Test (P = .50) at $a_2 \approx .05$

n	v	a_2	.05	.10	.15	1/6	.20	.25	.30	.35	.40
8	7	070	08	11	17	20	26	37	50	66	81
9	8	039	05	07	12	14	20	30	44	60	77
10	9	021	03	05	09	10	15	24	38	54	74
11	9	065	08	12	20	24	31	46	62	78	91
12	10	039	05	09	15	18	25	39	56	74	89
13	11	022	03	06	11	14	20	33	50	69	87
14	11	057	07	13	22	26	36	52	70	85	96
15	12	035	05	09	17	21	30	46	65	82	94
16	12	077	10	17	29	34	45	63	80	92	98
17	13	049	07	13	24	28	39	57	76	90	98
18	14	031	05	10	19	23	33	52	72	88	97
19	14	064	09	17	30	35	47	67	84	95	99
20	15	041	06	13	25	30	42	62	80	93	99
21	16	027	04	10	20	25	36	57	77	92	99
22	16	052	08	16	30	36	49	70	87	96	*
23	17	035	06	12	25	31	44	65	84	95	99
24	17	064	10	19	36	42	56	77	91	98	*
25	18	043	07	15	31	37	51	73	89	97	
26	19	029	05	12	26	32	46	69	87	97	
27	19	052	08	19	36	43	58	79	93	99	
28	20	.036	06	15	31	38	53	75	91	98	
29	20	061	10	22	41	48	64	83	95	99	
30	21	043	07	18	36	43	59	80	94	99	
31	22	029	06	14	31	38	54	77	93	99	
32	22	050	09	21	40	48	64	85	96	99	
33	23	035	07	17	36	43	60	82	95	99	
34	23	058	10	23	45	53	69	88	97	*	
35	24	041	08	20	40	48	65	86	97		
36	24	065	11	26	49	58	74	91	98		
37	25	047	09	22	45	53	70	89	98		
38	26	034	07	19	40	48	66	87	97		
39	26	053	10	25	49	57	74	91	98		
40	27	038	08	21	44	53	70	90	98		
42	28	044	09	24	48	57	74	92	99		
44	29	049	10	26	52	61	78	94	99		
46	30	054	11	29	56	65	81	95	99		
48	31	059	12	31	59	68	84	96	*		

Table 5.3.5 *(continued)*

n	v	a_2	.05	.10	.15	1/6	.20	.25	.30	.35	.40
50	32	065	13	34	62	71	86	97	*	*	*
52	34	036	09	26	54	64	81	96			
54	35	040	10	28	57	67	84	97			
56	36	044	11	30	60	70	86	97			
58	37	048	11	33	63	73	88	98			
60	38	052	12	35	66	76	90	98			
64	40	060	14	39	71	80	92	99			
68	43	038	11	34	67	77	91	99			
72	45	044	12	38	72	81	93	99			
76	47	050	14	42	76	84	95	*			
80	49	057	16	46	80	87	96				
84	52	038	12	41	76	85	96				
88	54	042	14	44	80	88	97				
92	56	047	15	48	83	90	98				
96	58	052	17	51	85	92	98				
100	60	057	18	54	87	93	99				
120	71	055	21	61	92	97	*				
140	82	052	22	67	95	98					
160	93	048	24	72	97	99					
180	104	044	25	76	98	99					
200	114	056	31	83	99	*					
250**	141	050	35	89	*						
300	167	057	43	94							
350**	194	050	46	96							
400	220	051	52	98							
450**	246	050	58	99							
500	272	054	62	*							
600	325	045	67								
700	377	054	74								
800	428	052	81								
900	480	049	85								
1000	531	054	89								

* Values below this point are greater than .995, unless other values are specified.

** Normal approximation.

Table 5.3.6

Power of Sign Test (P = .50) at $a_2 \approx .10$

n	v	a_2					g				
			.05	.10	.15	1/6	.20	.25	.30	.35	.40
8	6	289	31	37	45	49	56	68	80	90	96
9	7	180	20	26	35	39	47	60	74	86	95
10	8	109	13	18	27	30	38	53	68	82	93
11	8	227	25	32	44	48	57	61	84	93	98
12	9	146	17	24	35	40	49	65	79	91	97
13	10	092	11	18	28	32	42	58	75	88	97
14	10	180	21	30	43	48	59	74	87	95	99
15	11	118	15	23	35	41	52	69	84	94	99
16	11	210	25	35	50	55	66	81	92	98	*
17	12	143	18	27	42	48	60	77	89	97	*
18	13	096	13	21	36	41	53	72	87	96	99
19	13	167	21	32	48	54	67	83	93	98	*
20	14	115	15	26	42	48	61	79	91	98	
21	15	078	11	20	36	42	55	74	89	97	
22	15	134	18	30	48	54	67	84	94	99	
23	16	093	13	24	41	48	62	80	93	98	
24	16	152	20	34	53	60	73	88	96	99	
25	17	108	15	28	47	54	68	85	95	99	
26	18	076	11	23	41	48	63	82	94	99	
27	18	122	17	31	52	59	73	89	97	*	
28	19	087	13	26	46	54	68	86	96	99	
29	19	136	19	35	56	64	77	92	98	*	
30	20	099	15	29	51	58	73	89	97		
31	21	071	11	25	46	53	69	87	97		
32	21	110	17	33	55	63	77	92	98		
33	22	080	13	28	50	58	73	90	98		
34	22	121	18	36	59	67	81	94	99		
35	23	090	15	31	54	62	77	92	99		
36	23	132	20	39	63	71	84	95	99		
37	24	099	16	34	58	66	81	94	99		
38	25	073	13	29	53	62	77	93	99		
39	25	108	18	37	62	70	84	96	99		
40	26	081	14	32	57	66	81	95	99		
42	27	088	15	35	61	69	84	96	99		
44	28	096	17	37	64	72	86	97	*		
46	29	104	18	40	67	75	88	98			
48	30	111	20	42	70	78	90	98			

Table 5.3.6 *(continued)*

n	v	a_2	.05	.10	.15	1/6	.20	.25	.30	.35	.40
50	31	119	21	45	73	80	92	99	*	*	*
52	32	126	22	47	75	82	93	99			
54	34	076	16	38	68	77	90	98			
56	35	081	17	41	71	79	91	99			
58	36	087	18	43	73	81	93	99			
60	37	092	19	45	75	83	94	99			
64	39	103	21	49	79	86	95	*			
68	41	114	23	53	83	89	97				
72	44	076	18	47	79	87	96				
76	46	085	20	51	83	89	97				
80	48	093	22	55	85	92	98				
84	50	101	24	58	88	93	98				
88	52	109	26	61	90	95	99				
92	54	117	28	64	91	96	99				
96	57	082	23	59	90	95	99				
100	59	089	24	62	91	96	99				
120	70	082	26	68	95	98	*				
140	80	108	34	78	98	99					
160	91	097	35	81	99	*					
180	102	086	36	84	99						
200	112	104	42	89	*						
250**	139	100	45	93							
300	165	094	52	97							
350**	191	100	59	98							
400	217	099	64	99							
450**	243	100	68	*							
500	269	098	72								
600	321	094	78								
700	372	104	85								
800	424	097	88								
900	475	102	92								
1000	527	094	93								

* Values below this point are greater than .995, unless other values are specified.

** Normal approximation.

Illustrative Examples

5.1 A class in political science at a large state university undertakes a research project, as follows: There are about to be student government elections, and the class attempts to forecast the result by polling a random sample of 100 students who indicate they will vote. Two candidate slates are in contention, and, among other questions, respondents are asked their slate preference. A test is to be performed at the $a_2 \approx .05$ level of the null hypothesis that either slate will poll .50 of the votes. Assuming that, in fact, the present split in the student body is .55:.45, i.e., that $g = .55 - .50 = .05$, what is the power of the test? The specifications are;:

$$a_2 \approx .05, \quad g = .05, \quad n = 100.$$

In Table 5.3.5 (for $a_2 \approx .05$), one finds that the closest exact value to $a_2 = .05$ for $n = 100$ is $a_2 = .057$. At that level, for column $g = .05$, power equals .18. Thus, if the population split is .55:.45, there is only an 18% chance of detecting this slight edge at the $a_2 = .057$ level with $n = 100$.

Other things equal, what is the probability that a .60:.40 population split is detectable?

$$a_2 = .057, \quad g = .10, \quad n = 100.$$

In row $n = 100$ of Table 5.3.5 in column $g = .10$, one finds power of .54. Thus, there is only about an even chance of detecting a .60:.40 disparity in preference for the two slates with $n = 100$ at $a_2 = .057$. Under these conditions, apparently, a sample of 100 cases is insufficient for useful forecasting, unless **P** departs a great deal from .50. Note that one must posit $g = .15$, a population .65:.35 split 'hence a "landslide") for the power of the test to be usefully large (i.e., .87).

5.2 An experimental psychologist undertakes an investigation in which he randomly assigns the two members of 24 litter pairs of rats to an E (impoverished environment) and C (control) condition. At maturity, each of the pairs is brought together and a panel of three observers renders judgments as to which of the two is the more aggressive, a majority vote being determining. These circumstances call for a sign test. The null hypothesis is that $P_E \leq .50$, to be tested at $a_1 \approx .05$, against the directional alternative that $P_E > .50$, that is, that more of the E members would be judged aggressive, this being the expectation derived from his theory. The latter leads him to expect a strong effect, which he operationally defines as "large," i.e., $g = .25$. Thus, his exact alternate hypothesis is that the population $P_E = .50 + .25 = .75$. Given the latter, what is the power of the test? The specifications are:

$$a_1 \approx .05, \quad g = .25, \quad n = 24.$$

Note that although there are 48 animals involved, the observational unit is the pair, which can yield a positive (E > C) or a negative (E < C) difference in dominance, hence $n = 24$.

In Table 5.3.2 for $a_1 \approx .05$, one notes first that for row $n = 24$, the nearest to the .05 exact value of $a_1 = .032$. (The next most stringent criterion for a_1 at $n = 24$ is .076—see Table 5.3.3.) Reading over to column $g = .25$, one finds his power to be .77. Thus, if the effect is that large, he has a fairly good chance (about 3 in 4) of rejecting the null.

However, if the observational judgment about aggressiveness is difficult to make, as evidenced, for example, by many split decisions among the judges, he might reason that the large effect expected from theory may be attenuated by measurement (judgment) error, and that perhaps he should not expect more than a 2:1 rather than a 3:1 predominance of E members being judged the more aggressive, hence $g = P_E - .50 = \frac{2}{3} - \frac{1}{2} = \frac{1}{6}$. For this alternate hypothesis, that is for $g = \frac{1}{6}$ along row $n = 24$ (where $a_1 = .032$), the power = only .42. He might consider liberalizing his a_1 criterion, since the discreteness has forced him to use $a_1 = .032$ when he was prepared to work at $a_1 = .05$. He revises his specifications to

$$a_1 \approx .10, \qquad g = \tfrac{1}{6}, \qquad n = 24.$$

In Table 5.3.3 for $a_1 \approx .10$, he finds (as noted before) that at $n = 24$ he can work at the exact value $a_1 = .076$, which is not very far from his originally intended $a_1 = .05$ level. Reading over to $g = \frac{1}{6}$, he finds power = .59, which he may still find inadequate for his purpose.

5.3 An educational psychologist has designed an experiment to decide which of two alternative frame sequences more effectively teaches a small unit of plane geometry in a programed textbook. A group of 300 subjects was formed into 150 pairs, the members of each matched for available mathematical aptitude score, sex, and class. They were assigned textbooks differing only in whether the A or B version of the unit was included in their program. When the text was completed, the students were given a criterion problem and the "passers" were determined. The test performed involved finding whether the (correlated) proportions of passers in the A and B groups differ (McNemar, 1962, pp. 52–56), or, equivalently, whether, out of the pairs whose outcomes (pass or fail) *differ* (n_d), the proportion who had the A versions differ from .50. Note that this number cannot be known in advance, but varies inversely with the degree of between pair correlation, e.e., the stronger the relationship between pair members, necessarily the fewer pairs will have differing outcomes. He wishes to be able to reject the null hypothesis if, in the population, there is a .60:.40 split among those pairs who have differing outcomes, thus $g = .10$. As stated, the test is non-directional, and he has set $a_2 \approx .05$. He finds, after the experiment is completed, that in 60 of the 150 pairs, the pass–fail outcomes of the two members of the pair differ, i.e., $n_d = 60$. What is the power of the test? The specifications are:

$$a_2 \approx .05, \qquad g = .10, \qquad n = 60.$$

In Table 5.3.5 (for $a_2 \approx .05$) for $n = 60$, he first finds that the exact a_2 value for the test at that n is .052. In column $g = .10$, he finds power $= .35$. He might well consider this power value inadequate for his purpose. He reconsiders the plan.

It occurs to him that he can liberalize his significance driterion, since a Type I error in this situation is relatively tolerable. Thus:

$$a_2 \approx .10, \qquad g = .10, \qquad n = 60.$$

Now, in Table 5.3.6 (for $a_2 \approx .10$) for $n = 60$, he first finds that the exact a_2 value is .092, and for $g = .10$, finds power $= .45$. This still leaves him with a less than equiprobable chance of rejecting the null for these specifications.

He then decides to consider even further liberalization of his significance criterion: He can test at $a_2 \approx .20$ by using the $a_1 \approx .10$ criterion on a two-sided basis:

$$a_2 \approx .20, \qquad g = .10, \qquad n = 60.$$

In Table 5.3.3 for $a_1 \approx .10$, but used in a way that makes $a_2 \approx .20$, he first finds that for $n = 60$, the exact a_1 value is .078, so for his intended use, $a_2 = 2(.078) = .156$. For $g = .10$, he finds power $= .56$.

Although by progressively liberalizing his a_2 criterion from .052 to .156, he has increased power from .35 to .56, he may well decide that the latter value is still inadequate. If he cannot reasonably expect $g > .10$, his only recourse within this design is to increase n.

5.4   SAMPLE SIZE TABLES

The tables in this section give values for the significance criterion, the g ($=$ ES) to be detected, and the desired power. The sample size, n (i.e., the number which is the base of the sample proportion to be tested), is then determined. These tables are designed primarily for use in making the decision about sample size during the planning of experiments. As Section 2.4 points out, a rational decision on sample size requires, once a significance criterion and ES are formulated, attention to the question: how much power (how little Type II error risk) is desired?

Table 5.4.1

n to detect g in the Sign Test (P = .50)

Power	\multicolumn{9}{c}{$a_1 = .01$ ($a_2 = .02$) g}
	.05	.10	.15	1/6	.20	.25	.30	.35	.40
.25	274	69	32	27	19	14	11	7	7
.50	541	135	60	49	32	22	17	14	11
.60	665	166	73	59	42	27	19	14	11
2/3	759	189	83	67	47	30	19	17	11
.70	811	202	89	72	49	32	22	17	11
.75	899	223	98	79	54	34	25	17	14
.80	1001	248	109	88	60	37	27	19	14
.85	1127	279	122	98	67	42	30	19	17
.90	1297	321	140	112	77	50	32	22	17
.95	1571	388	169	135	92	56	37	27	19
.99	2154	530	230	184	124	75	50	35	25

Power	\multicolumn{9}{c}{$a_1 = .05$ ($a_2 = .10$) g}
	.05	.10	.15	1/6	.20	.25	.30	.35	.40
.25	95	28	13	13	8	8	5	5	5
.50	271	68	30	28	18	13	8	8	5
.60	360	90	42	35	23	16	11	8	8
2/3	430	107	47	37	28	18	13	11	8
.70	469	116	51	44	30	18	13	11	8
.75	536	133	58	49	35	23	13	11	8
.80	616	152	67	53	37	23	16	13	8
.85	716	177	77	62	44	28	18	13	11
.90	853	210	91	73	50	33	23	16	11
.95	1077	265	115	92	62	40	28	18	13
.99	1568	385	166	133	89	54	35	26	18

Power	\multicolumn{9}{c}{$a_1 = .10$ ($a_2 = .20$) g}
	.05	.10	.15	1/6	.20	.25	.30	.35	.40
.25	39	14	9	7	7	4	4	4	4
.50	164	46	21	19	14	9	7	4	4
.60	235	59	28	21	17	9	9	7	4
2/3	292	73	35	28	19	14	9	7	7
.70	325	81	37	30	21	14	9	7	7
.75	381	94	44	35	26	17	12	9	7
.80	449	111	48	39	28	19	14	9	7
.85	535	132	57	48	35	21	14	9	7
.90	654	161	70	56	39	26	19	12	9
.95	852	209	90	72	49	30	21	14	9
.99	1293	317	136	109	73	44	28	21	14

Table 5.4.1 *(continued)*

				$a_2 = .01$ $(a_1 = .005)$					
					g				
Power	.05	.10	.15	1/6	.20	.25	.30	.35	.40
.25	363	92	44	34	26	18	12	8	8
.50	663	166	74	60	42	26	18	12	12
.60	800	199	88	71	49	34	24	12	12
2/3	903	225	99	80	55	34	26	15	15
.70	960	239	105	85	58	39	26	15	15
.75	1054	262	115	93	64	39	26	15	15
.80	1165	289	127	102	70	44	32	15	15
.85	1301	322	141	114	78	49	34	24	18
.90	1483	367	160	129	88	54	37	26	18
.95	1775	438	191	153	104	64	44	32	21
.99	2392	589	255	205	139	84	55	39	26

				$a_2 = .05$ $(a_1 = .025)$					
					g				
Power	.05	.10	.15	1/6	.20	.25	.30	.35	.40
.25	166	44	20	17	12	9	6	6	6
.50	384	96	44	37	25	17	12	9	6
.60	489	122	54	44	32	20	15	9	9
2/3	570	142	62	50	37	25	17	12	9
.70	616	153	67	54	37	25	17	12	9
.75	692	172	75	61	44	28	17	15	9
.80	783	194	85	68	49	30	20	15	12
.85	895	221	97	78	53	32	25	17	12
.90	1047	259	113	90	61	40	28	17	15
.95	1294	319	138	111	75	49	32	23	17
.99	1827	449	194	155	105	63	42	30	20

As was pointed out above in Section 5.3, the use of the exact binomial test precludes the use of exact conventional significance criteria because of the discreteness of sample frequencies. In order to avoid the cumbersomeness of supplying the exact **a** values for each value of **n** read from the table, the values of **n** read from the table are to be interpreted as follows:

1. **n** *Less than 50.* The exact **a** value which was used is *no greater than* the stated value; it is the (discrete) value of **a** below the stated value. Thus, the actual **a** values for, say, the table for $a_2 = .05$ are more or less below .05. Accordingly, the power values, being for actual **a** generally less than nominal **a**, will be (slightly) lower than would be the case if the exact values could be used.

2. **n** *of 50 or More.* The normal approximation to the binomial was used, and the **n** values are the *nearest* integral number (as is true throughout the book), not the next largest.

Tables give values for **a**, **g**, and desired power.

1. Significance Criterion, **a.** The same values are provided as for the power tables, but as just noted, are for exact values not exceeding the nominal value when the value of **n** read from the table is less than 50. Five tables are provided, one for each of the following nonparenthetic **a** levels: $a_1 = .01$ ($a_2 = .02$), $a_1 = .05$ ($a_2 = .10$), $a_1 = .10$ ($a_2 = .20$), $a_2 = .01$ ($a_1 = .005$), and $a_2 = .05$ ($a_1 = .025$).

2. Effect Size, ES. The difference between the alternative-hypothetical value of **P** and .50 = **g**, the ES index. The same provision for **g** is made as in the power tables: .05 (.05) .40 and $\frac{1}{6}$. For **g** values other than the nine provided, the following formula, rounding to the nearest integer, provides a good approximation:

$$(5.4.1) \qquad\qquad n = \frac{n_{.05}}{400g^2} - K,$$

where $n_{.05}$ is the necessary sample size for the given **a** and desired power at **g** = .05 (obtained from the table), and **K** is a constant which varies with the desired power, as follows[4]:

Power:	.50	.60	$\frac{2}{3}$	.70	.80	.85	.90	.95	.99
K:	0	0.5	1.0	1.5	2.5	3.0	3.5	6.0	9.0

3. Desired Power. As in the previous chapters, provision is made for desired power values of .25, .50, .60, $\frac{2}{3}$, .70 (.05), .95, .99. For discussion of the basis for selecting these values, the provision for equalizing **a** and **b** risks, and the rationale of a proposed convention of desired power of .80, see Section 2.4.

Summarizing the use of the following **n** tables, the investigator finds (*a*) the table for the significance criterion (**a**) he is using, locates (*b*) the population (alternate-hypothetical) value of **g** and (*c*) the desired power along the vertical stub. He then finds **n**, the necessary sample size to detect **g** at (when **n** < 50, no more than) the **a** significance criterion with the desired power. If the **g** value in his specifications is not provided, he locates the value for

---

[4] The approximation is the normal approximation, thus the **n** found will be the estimated value *at* the **a** value necessary for the desired power. It will thus be comparable in its interpretation to the tabled values of **n** ≥ 50, i.e., the *nearest* number, not the next largest, as is the case with tabled values of **n** < 50.

$n_{.05}$ in the relevant **a** table in column **g** = .05 and the row for desired power. This is used, together with the value of **K** for the desired power, in formula (5.4.1) to compute **n**.

Illustrative Examples

5.4 Consider again the situation described in example 5.1, where a political science class undertakes a project involving polling a sample of the college student body with regard to student government elections. As described there originally, they wish to detect a .55:.45 division between two slates (hence, **g** = .05) at a_2 = .05. Their original intention to use **n** = 100 respondents who would express a preference led to power of .18. We may safely assume that this value is found inadequate. Assume now that they wish to have power at the proposed conventional value of .80 and seek the necessary sample size to achieve this. The specifications are:

$$a_2 = .05, \qquad g = .05, \qquad \text{power} = .80.$$

In Table 5.4.1 in the section for a_2 = .05, column **g** = .05, row power = .80, one finds **n** = 783. This is a very large sample, indeed, far larger than the originally intended **n** = 100. It thus takes many cases to detect a small ES (**g** = .05) with conventional desired power of .80.

If they posit instead that the division in the student population may be as large as .60:.40 (hence, **g** = .60 − .50 = .10), a value which falls between the operational definitions of small and medium ES for this test, what is the sample size required? The new specifications:

$$a_2 = .05, \qquad g = .10, \qquad \text{power} = .80.$$

In the same line (power = .80) of the same table (Table 4.5.1. in the section for a_2 = .05), for column **g** = .10, one finds **n** = 194.

5.5 The experimental psychologist of example 5.2 was studying the effects of an impoverished early environment on the aggressiveness of rats. Using litter pairs (one E and one C), the plan is, following the experimental manipulation, to have judgments rendered as to which pair member is the more aggressive. He intends a directional sign test at about a_1 = .05, predicting that the E member will be more frequently judged the more aggressive. Assume that although he anticipates a large *true* effect, because of expected judge unreliability, he posits as an alternate hypothesis $g = P_E - .50 = \frac{2}{3} - \frac{1}{2} = \frac{1}{6}$. He desires power to be .80. What is the required **n**? The specifications are

$$a_1 = .05, \qquad g = \tfrac{1}{6}, \qquad \text{power} = .80.$$

In the section of Table 5.4.1 for $a_1 = .05$ in column $g = \frac{1}{6}$ for row desired power $= .80$, he finds $n = 53$ litter pairs. Since $n > 50$, a normal curve test is envisaged.

Assume that this is a much larger experiment than he had planned to mount. He wonders how much reduction in n would occur if he reduced his desired power to .70, keeping the other specifications unchanged, i.e.,

$$a_1 = .05, \qquad g = \tfrac{1}{6}, \qquad \text{power} = .70.$$

In the $a_1 = .05$ section of Table 5.4.1, in column $g = \frac{1}{6}$, he now reads from row power $= .70$ that the necessary n is 44. Since $n < 50$, the specification is for an exact binomial sign test at $a_1 \leq .05$ and power $\geq .70$. To find the exact value of a_1 and power, he uses the *power* table for $a_1 \approx .05$, Table 5.3.2 for $n = 44$. He finds there in column a_1 that the exact value is .048 at which criterion column $g = \frac{1}{6}$ gives exact power .72.

This n is still rather large for his resources. While in the power Table 5.3.2, he glances upward along the a_1 column and notices that if he slightly liberalizes his a_1 criterion to .054 and applies it with $n = 39$, $g = \frac{1}{6}$, power $= .70$. Thus, he can save 5 $(= 44 - 39)$ litter pairs by working at $a_1 = .054$ instead of .048 and with power of .70 instead of .72, differences he might well consider trivial.

He glances a little further up the a_1 column and notes that if he further liberalizes his a_1 criterion to .066 this value can be used in a test where $n = 36$, at $g = \frac{1}{6}$, power $= .71$. He thus has essentially the same power at a saving of three more pairs, if he is prepared to use the $a_1 = .066$ significance criterion.

He decides that he is quite prepared for a_1 to exceed .05, but is uncomfortable about the $(1 - .71 =)$ .29 Type II (**b**) risk. In studying the test at $n = 36$, he notes that the risk ratio, .29:.066, is such that he runs about a 4 times larger risk of failing to obtain significance if $g = \frac{1}{6}$ than of getting a spuriously significant result if $g \leq 0$ (i.e., if the directional null hypothesis is true). Although, as was suggested in Section 2.4, such a ratio is consonant with the conventional scientific caution, an investigator's knowledge about the place of his specific research effort in his research context requires (certainly permits) that he set values for **a** and **b** and thus their ratio. Our experimental psychologist determines that he wishes to reduce the risk ratio, and is quite prepared to liberalize his a_1 criterion in order to increase his power to about .80. He thus changes his specifications to

$$a_1 = .10, \qquad g = \tfrac{1}{6}, \qquad \text{power} = .80.$$

Using again the sample size Table 5.4.1, but in the section for $a_1 = .10$, for column $g = \frac{1}{6}$, row power $= .80$, he finds $n = 39$. Since $n \leq 50$, the table assumes an exact binomial test, so $a_1 \leq .10$ and power $\geq .80$. To determine exact values, he turns to power Table 5.3.3 (for $a_1 \approx .10$) and, for row $n = 39$, sees that the exact $a_1 = .100$ and the exact power at $g = \frac{1}{6}$ is .80. (It is, of course, a coincidence that his specifications are met exactly.) His risk ratio is now $b = 1 - .80 = .20$ to $a_1 = .100$, exactly 2 to 1. He may proceed on the basis of these specifications, or seek others in the vicinity of $n = 39$, e.g., at $n = 38$, where power is .84 and the two risks are almost equal, .16:.128, or if he does not wish to exceed $a_1 = .10$, at $n = 40$ where the risk ratio is .23:.077, or at $n = 37$ where it is .22 to .094.

5.6 The test of the null hypothesis that $P = .50$ (or $g = 0$) as applied to a test of correlated proportions was illustrated in problem 5.3. In that problem, an education psychologist was comparing two alternate programed frame sequences in a unit of plane geometry, by forming matched pairs of students, supplying them with one or the other sequence, and determining whether they passed a criterion problem. For the test, only the pairs whose pass–fail outcomes differ are relevant, since the null hypothesis formulation is that among such pairs, $P = .50$ of them come from sequence A (or B).

If, as described initially in problem 5.3, he expects a .60:.40 split among the pairs with differing outcomes ($g = .10$), plans to use the $a_2 = .05$ significance criterion, and wishes power to be .75, his specifications are

$$a_2 = .05, \quad g = .10, \quad \text{power} = .75.$$

In the $a_2 = .05$ section of Table 5.4.1 with column $g = .10$ and row power = .75, he finds $n = 172$. Since this represents the number of pairs of *differing* outcome, which he anticpates to be one-third of total number of pairs, this means that these specifications require that he have a total of $3(172) = 516$ pairs or 1032 subjects in all. Assuming classes of 30 students, this would require some 35 classes in plane geometry!

Assume the validity of the exclamation point, specifically that in the entire city there are only 26 classes in plane geometry, and that furthermore, he is not sure he can get the cooperation of every last one of the teachers involved. He reconsiders his specifications, and, as in problem 5.3, realizes that the nature of the decision is such that he can afford a larger Type I error criterion, so he changes his specifications to

$$a_2 = .10, \quad g = .10, \quad \text{power} = .75.$$

In the section of Table 5.4.1 for $a_2 = .10$ in column $g = .10$, row power = .75, he finds $n = 133$. This means a total of 399 pairs on the expected one-third of total differing in outcome, or 788 students, or 26-27 classes. He *knows* that there will be some defections from the 26 classes in the city's high schools, so he decided to liberalize his **a** criterion to $a_2 = .20$. He reasons that in this situation, failure to detect the alternate-hypothetical .60:.40 discrepancy is almost as serious as a mistaken conclusion of the superiority of one sequence over the other. Since he is committed to a $1 - .75 = .25$ ($= \mathbf{b}$) risk of the former, he decides to raise the latter to .20 ($= \mathbf{a_2}$). What sample size is now demanded? The specifications are

$$\mathbf{a_2} = .20, \quad \mathbf{g} = .10, \quad \text{power} = .75.$$

In Table 5.4.1 the subtable for $\mathbf{a_2} = .20$ is used and for column $\mathbf{g} = .10$ and row power = .75, $\mathbf{n} = 94$, the number of differing pairs required. This, in turn, requires in all 3(94) = 282 pairs—or 564 students—a total of 19 classes which is close to the total number he can expect to get.

In the above example, we have manipulated only the significance criterion. In other problems where there is a fixed maximum $\mathbf{n}$ permitted by the resources (which, of course is true, in principle, for all research problems), other specifications instead of (or in addition to) the significance criterion may be more appropriately modified. Thus, some of the specifications which result in about the same required $\mathbf{n}$ from Table 5.4.1 are tabulated.

$\mathbf{a_2}$	$\mathbf{g}$	Power	$\mathbf{n}$
.01	$\frac{1}{6}$	.75	92
.02	.15	.75	98
.02	$\frac{1}{6}$	.85	98
.05	.10	.50	96
.05	.15	.85	97
.10	.10	.60	90
.10	.15	.90	91
.10	$\frac{1}{6}$	.95	92
.20	.15	.95	90

The investigator must weigh the alternative specifications for *his* problem from such a sample size table, and decide his best strategy. It was implicitly assumed in this problem that the investigator could not reasonably anticipate $\mathbf{g}$ greater than .10, nor was he prepared to tolerate less than 3:1 odds that, given a .60:.40 split, he would be able to make a definitive decision favoring the A or B sequences. This then left him to consider the significance criterion, which, given the nature of the problem, we saw he could liberalize.

5.7 A psychiatrist plans an experiment involving a single neurotic subject to determine whether, *for this subject*, psychoanalytic sessions following ingestion of a very small dosage of LSD are more productive than those following placebo. His purpose is to decide, after the experimental series, either to continue the psychoanalysis with LSD or without it (strictly, with placebo). The design is to determine randomly which of the sessions in each successive pair is to be an LSD session, the other to be placebo. Transcripts of the tape-recorded sessions are to be submitted to a panel of judges who must render a blind consensus judgment as to which session of each pair is the more productive.

He reasons that unless in the population[5] there is a superiority of the order of 4:1 favoring LSD sessions, he would just as soon not decide in its favor; hence he expects a population split of .80:.20, or $g = .80 - .50 = .30$. As formulated, the test is nondirectional and he decides that the significance criterion be $a_1 = .05$. Finally, if g is in fact .30, he wants to be fairly sure that he will reject the null and fixes the desired power at .90. How many session pairs does he require for these specifications, which are, in summary

$$a_1 = .05, \qquad g = .30, \qquad \text{power} = .90.$$

In Table 5.4.1 in the section for $a_1 = .05$ with column $g = .30$ and row power = .90, he finds $n = 23$. He will thus need 23 *pairs* of sessions to satisfy the specifications. Since the n is less than 50, he can determine the exact conditions of the binomial test by referring to the *power* table for the $a_1 = .05$ level, Table 5.3.2. In that table with $n = 23$, he sees that for the binomial test, the exact a_1 value is .047 at which, given $g = .30$, power = .93. He might look at other n values in the vicinity to see if they yield paired values of exact a_1 and exact power which he prefers to those at $n = 23$ (for example, at $n = 22$, $a_1 = .067$ with power = .94; at $n = 24$, $a_1 = .032$ with power = .91, etc.).[6]

It is insufficiently appreciated in many areas of the behavioral sciences that statistical investigations can be usefully undertaken with single subjects. The n of a study is the number of observations or instances, not necessarily the number of organisms or sets of organisms. Naturally, in investigations of single subjects, the populations to which generalizations can be made or inferences drawn are made up of instances or observations of *that* subject and cannot validly transcend him to populations of subjects. Still, such single subject experiments and their logically limited conclusions can be of either practical utility (as in the above example) or heuristic importance. For an

---

[5] The population here is, as is so often the case in behavioral sciences, an abstraction. It may be thought of as all the session pairs that might occur under the conditions specified.

[6] There is an alternative statistical-design strategy for problems of this kind which may well be superior to the preset fixed n described in this problem. "Sequential" tests proceed by assessing each experimental unit (usually a subject, but here, a session) as it becomes available and deciding whether to draw a conclusion or observe another experimental unit. Such tests require special procedures originally described by Wald (1947) and, less technically, by Fiske and Jones (1954).

example of an extreme philosophy of behavioral science oriented to singular propositions and some useful quantitative methods, the reader is referred to Stephenson (1953).

5.8 Assume that a certain mathematical model in signal detection predicts a proportion of success over a given series of trials to be .68, hence $g = .18$, while the null hypothesis is that $P = .50$. What is the n required, if the psychologist wishes power at .95 for a directional test at $a_1 = .05$, that is, equal a and b risks at .05? The specifications are

$$a_1 = .05, \quad g = .18, \quad \text{power} = .95.$$

Since $g = .18$ is not tabled, the psychologist must take recourse to formula (5.4.1), which requires $n_{.05}$, the n required under the conditions stated when $g = .05$.

In Table 5.4.1 in the section for $a_1 = .05$, at row power $= .95$, he finds in column $g = .05$ the value $1077 = n_{.05}$. Substituting that value, $g = .18$, and the value for K for power $= .95$ provided with formula (5.4.1), he finds

$$n = \frac{1077}{400(.18)^2} - 6.0 = 83.1 - 6.0 = 77.1.$$

Thus, the normal (or chi square) approximation test will yield a probability of .95 of rejecting H_0: $P = .50$ if the actual $P = .68$ when $n = 77$. (Note that since the test is directional, the standard normal curve deviate required for significance at the .05 level is ≥ 1.65. If the equivalent chi square form of the test is used, the criterion is the one tabled for one df ($u = 1$) at $a = .10$, namely 2.706.)

5.5 The Use of the Tables for Significance Testing

As was the case in previous chapters, the power tables provide a significance criterion column to facilitate the performance of the statistical test of the null hypothesis after the data are collected. This is particularly useful for the test of this chapter, since it obviates the necessity of using a separate set of tables for the binomial function.

For any given n, the significance criterion in the test of H_0: $P = .50$ is simply the number of observations in the larger (or smaller) subgroup defined with regard to the presence or absence of the characteristic under study (e.g., males, success, positive differences, etc.). If this number departs sufficiently from $\frac{1}{2}n$, the null hypothesis is rejected.

The power tables in this chapter (Tables 5.3.1–5.3.5) contain, in the v column, the number of observations in the larger portion of the sample necessary to attain the exact significance level (given in column a) for the sample size of the row in which it appears. For nondirectional (two-tailed) tests, **v** is simply the number in the larger portion; for directional (one-tailed) tests, it is assumed that the test has been oriented so that the predicted direction is the one in which the larger portion occurs, since no matter how extreme the departure from .50, if it is in the wrong direction in a one-tailed test, the result is not significant.

Except for the three values of **n** double-asterisked in Tables 5.3.1–5.3.5, all the values given for **v** are exactly the minimum number needed to reject the null hypothesis ($P = .50$, $g = 0$) at the exact significance criterion given in the next column (**a**) using the symmetrical binomial test. At $n = 250$, 350, and 450, the value **v** is that required by the normal (or equivalently chi square) approximation to the binomial.

Illustrative Examples

5.9 Consider the analysis of the data arising from the political science class project to forecast the result of a student government election using a sample of 100 voters at $a_2 \approx .05$. When the sample results are tallied, it is found that one of the two slates has garnered 57 ($= v_s$) of the 100 votes. The specifications for the significance test are

$$a_2 \approx .05, \quad n = 100, \quad v_s = 57.$$

In Table 5.3.5 for $a_2 \approx .05$ at row $n = 100$ it is first found that the nearest exact value to a_2 of .05 is at .057 (from column a_2). For significance at $a_2 = .057$, in the same row, it is found that the larger portion must contain $v = 60$ cases. Since 57 is less than 60, the departure from $P_s = .50$ is insufficient for rejection at $a_2 = .057$.

Let us consider the same situation from the perspective of problem 5.4, where it was finally decided, on the basis of a power analysis, that **n** should equal 194. Assume, instead, that the survey is accomplished with $n = 200$ voter respondents, at the $a_2 \approx .05$ level as before, and that one of the two slates has $v_s = 116$ adherents. The specifications for the test of significance now are:

$$a_2 \approx .05, \quad n = 200, \quad v_s = 116.$$

The same table (5.3.5 for $a_2 \approx .05$) is used for row $n = 200$, and now the exact a_2 value equals .056 (from column a_2). In the same row, the criterion for significance (at the $a_2 = .056$ level) is found in column **v** to be 114. Since 116 exceeds this (minimum necessary) value, the null hypothesis is rejected at the .056 level, and the class concludes that the slate in question has a majority of the voting population.

5.10   Reconsider the circumstances of example 5.2, where an experimental psychologist was studying the effect on litter pairs of an early impoverished environment (versus control) on aggressiveness. Assume that the experiment was carried out as planned, and that it was found that 17 ($= \mathbf{v}_s$) of the 24 E rats were judged more aggressive (in the predicted direction). Is this significantly different from the 12 expected on the null hypothesis? The specifications are

$$\mathbf{a}_1 \approx .05, \qquad \mathbf{n} = 24, \qquad \mathbf{v}_s = 17.$$

In Table 5.3.2. (for $\mathbf{a}_1 \approx .05$) for row $\mathbf{n} = 24$, he finds first that the nearest $\mathbf{a}_2$ exact value to .05 is (in column $\mathbf{a}_1$) .032, at which level he requires a minimum of 17 ($= \mathbf{v}$) pairs in which the E rat was judged the more aggressive. Since there are 17 ($= \mathbf{v}_s$) in this group, his results are significant, and he can reject the null hypothesis at $\mathbf{a}_1 = .032$ (see example 5.12 below).

5.11   The educational psychologist in example 5.3 was studying which of two frame sequences more effectively taught a unit of plane geometry. Using matched pairs of students, he found that 60 (of the original 150) pairs were made up of members one of whom had passed and the other of whom had failed the criterion problem. Assume, as originally specified in example 5.3, that the test was planned to be performed at the $\mathbf{a}_2 \approx .05$, and that it was found that the students in sequence A who passed the criterion problem while their matches failed numbered 35. The specifications for the significance test are

$$\mathbf{a}_2 \approx .05, \qquad \mathbf{n} = 60, \qquad \mathbf{v}_s = 35.$$

In Table 5.3.5 (for $\mathbf{a}_2 \approx .05$) for $\mathbf{n} = 60$, he finds first that the exact $\mathbf{a}_2$ value nearest .05 is .052, and for significance at that level he requires $\mathbf{v} = 38$. Since his observed $\mathbf{v}_s$ falls short of that value, he cannot reject the null hypothesis and conclude superiority for sequence A.

When this problem was revisited in example 5.6, the educational psychologist eventually decided that his needs would be better met by using the $\mathbf{a}_2 \approx .20$ level. Assume that, on the basis of power considerations, he uses an initial sample size that results in his having 96 pairs of subjects with differing outcomes on the criterion. Let us say that he finds that of these there are 59 for which those with sequence A passed (while their matches on B failed). Does this lead to rejection of the $\mathbf{P} = .50$ null hypothesis? The test specifications are

$$\mathbf{a}_2 \approx .20, \qquad \mathbf{n} = 96, \qquad \mathbf{v}_s = 59.$$

Although there is no power table headed ". . . at $\mathbf{a}_2 \approx .20$," the values for $\mathbf{v}$ are the same as those given for $\mathbf{a}_1 \approx .10$. Accordingly, in Table 5.3.3

for row $n = 96$, he finds in column a_1 that a test is available at $a_1 = .092$. He can treat it as providing a test at $2a_1 = .184 = a_2$. At this level, if the larger portion has $v = 55$ or more cases of the 96, he can conclude that the frame sequence of that portion is superior. Since sequence A superior pairs numbered 59, the null hypothesis is rejected and the superiority of sequence A affirmed at the .184 significance level.

5.12   In example 5.7, a psychiatrist was planning a study of the effects of LSD in a single patient on the productivity of psychoanalytic sessions by randomly assigning LSD or placebo to successive pairs of sessions. His planning specifications ($a_1 = .05$, $g = .30$, power $= .90$) led to the determination that he required $n = 23$ pairs of sessions. Assume that he has now performed the experiment as planned and finds that his judges have decided that in 16 of the paired sessions, the session preceded by LSD was more productive than the one preceded by placebo. Does this warrant rejecting the null hypothesis? The specifications are

$$a_1 \approx .05, \qquad n = 23, \qquad v_s = 16.$$

In Table 5.3.2 for $a_1 \approx .05$ and row $n = 23$, he finds that $v = 16$ (for exact $a_1 = .047$). In other words, when the population $P = .50$, he will obtain a 16:7 (or more extreme) break in the predicted prediction .047 of the time in random sampling. Since his v_s is included in the critical region (i.e., 16–23 out of 23), he rejects the null and concludes that *for this patient*, LSD leads to more productive sessions than placebo.

Note that his sample proportion is $16/23 = .70$, which is less than the .80 he hypothesized in the alternative hypothesis, yet this result led to a proper rejection of the null hypothesis. This can occur whenever the power planned for $> .50$. This makes it clear that the rejection of the null hypothesis ($P = .50$) does not carry the implication that the alternate hypothesis ($P = .80$ or $g = .30$) is necessarily true. His sample value of .70 is not consistent with $P = .50$ (at $a_1 = .047$), but is consistent with many values of P, including in this instance .80.

6

Differences between Proportions

6.1 INTRODUCTION AND USE

This chapter is concerned with the testing of hypotheses concerning differences between independent population proportions (**P**). Chapter 5 was devoted to a frequently occurring special case of this issue, namely, the difference between a population proportion and .50. In the present chapter, other cases are considered: the difference between two independent population **P**'s when a random sample is available from each, and the difference between a population **P** and any specified hypothetical value.

A proportion is a special case of an arithmetic mean, one in which the measurement scale has only two possible values, zero for the absence of a characteristic and one for its presence. Thus, one can describe a population as having a proportion of males of .62, or, with equal validity (if not equal stylistic grace), as having a mean "male-ness" of .62, the same value necessarily coming about when one scores each male 1, each nonmale 0, and finds the mean. It follows, then, that the same kinds of inferential issues arise for this special kind of mean as arise for means in general.

When one considers a difference between independent population proportions it becomes apparent that one can just as well think of the issue in terms of a relationship between two variables. Thus, if the **P** of Republicans in a given population above a certain income level is .30 and the **P** of Democrats above that level is .20, it is a matter of convenience or habit of thought whether this is viewed as a difference between Republicans and Democrats in income or as a relationship between political affiliation and income. It is apparent, then, that differences between proportions (as, indeed, between means) can be viewed in correlational terms.

R. HILDENBRAND

It is possible to approach the testing of hypotheses about proportions by different statistical techniques, including the classical normal curve test using a "critical ratio" applied directly to the proportions (Edwards, 1960, pp. 51–53; Guilford, 1965, pp. 185–187; Blalock, 1960, pp. 176–178), by a chi-square contingency test (see Chapter 7 and references), by a special case of the hypergeometric probability distribution ("Fisher's Exact Method") for 2×2 tables (McNemar, 1962, pp. 236–239; Owen, 1962, pp. 479–496), or by means of a normal curve test applied to the arcsine transformation of the proportions. Despite its unfamiliarity, it is the last of these alternatives that provides the basis for the approach of this chapter because of certain advantages it has, particularly from the viewpoint of power analysis. However, the results from using any of these procedures will be the same to a close approximation, particularly when samples are not small.

The types of tests on proportions which the methods of this chapter facilitate are organized into cases, according to the specific hypothesis and sample(s) employed:

Case 0. $\mathbf{P}_s$ values from equal size samples to test $\mathbf{P}_1 = \mathbf{P}_2$.

Case 1. The same hypothesis, but $\mathbf{n}_1 \neq \mathbf{n}_2$.

Case 2. One sample drawn from a population to test $\mathbf{P} = \mathbf{c}$.

6.2 THE ARCSINE TRANSFORMATION AND THE EFFECT SIZE INDEX: h

$\mathbf{P}_s$ shares with the product moment $\mathbf{r}_s$ the difficulty that the standard deviation of the sampling distributions depend upon their population parameters, which are unknown. A consequence of this is that the detectability of a difference in magnitude between either population $\mathbf{P}$'s or $\mathbf{r}$'s is not a simple function of the difference. This problem and its resolution for differences in $\mathbf{r}$'s was discussed in Section 4.2 (*q.v.*). The same problem with $\mathbf{P}$'s has a similar resolution.

If we were to define $\mathbf{j} = \mathbf{P}_1 - \mathbf{P}_2$, and try to use $\mathbf{j}$ as our ES, we would soon discover that the detectability of some given value of $\mathbf{j}$, under given fixed conditions of $\mathbf{a}$ and $\mathbf{n}$, would *not* be constant, but would vary depending upon where along the scale of $\mathbf{P}$ between zero and one the value $\mathbf{j}$ occurred. Concretely, when

1. $\mathbf{P}_1 = .65$ and $\mathbf{P}_2 = .45$, $\mathbf{j} = .65 - .45 = .20$; and when

2. $\mathbf{P}_1 = .25$ and $\mathbf{P}_2 = .05$, $\mathbf{j} = .25 - .05 = .20$ also.

But for these two *equal* differences of $\mathbf{j} = .20$, given $\mathbf{a}_2 = .05$ and $\mathbf{n} = 46$ (for

Table 6.2.1

P_1 values as a function of P_2 and $h = \phi_1 - \phi_2$

P_2	.10	.20	.30	.40	.50	.60	.70	.80	.90	1.00	1.10	1.20
.05	07	10	13	17	21	25	30	34	39	44	49	54
.10	13	17	21	25	29	34	39	44	49	54	59	63
.15	19	23	27	32	36	41	46	51	56	61	66	71
.20	24	29	33	38	43	48	53	58	63	67	72	76
.25	29	34	39	44	49	54	59	64	68	73	77	81
.30	35	40	44	49	54	59	64	69	73	78	82	85
.35	40	45	50	55	60	65	69	74	78	82	86	89
.40	45	50	55	60	65	69	74	78	82	86	89	92
.45	50	55	60	65	69	74	78	82	86	89	92	95
.50	55	60	65	69	74	78	82	86	89	92	95	97
.55	60	65	69	74	78	82	86	89	92	95	97	98
.60	65	70	74	78	82	86	89	92	95	97	98	99
.65	70	74	78	82	86	89	92	95	97	98	99	*
.70	74	79	83	86	90	92	95	97	98	99	*	
.75	79	83	87	90	93	95	97	98	99	*		
.80	84	87	91	93	96	97	99	*	*			
.85	88	91	94	96	98	99	*					
.90	93	95	97	99	*	*						
.95	97	98	99	*								

* Values below this point are greater than .995.

example), the power to detect the first difference (.65 − .45) is .48, while the power for the second (.25 − .05) is .82. Thus, **P** does not provide a scale of equal units of detectability, hence the difference between **P**'s is not an appropriate ES index.

As was the case with **r**, a transformation of **P** provides a solution to the problem. When **P**'s are transformed by the relationship[1]

(6.2.1) $$\phi = 2 \arcsin \sqrt{\mathbf{P}},$$

equal differences between ϕ's are equally detectable. Thus, we define as the ES index for a difference in proportions

(6.2.2) $$\mathbf{h} = \phi_1 - \phi_2 \qquad \text{(directional)}$$
$$= |\phi_1 - \phi_2| \qquad \text{(nondirectional)}.$$

[1] The use of the symbol ϕ for the arcsin transformation should not be confused with its use elsewhere in this book to represent the fourfold point product-moment correlation coefficient.

Thus, unlike $P_1 - P_2$, $\phi_1 - \phi_2 = h$ gives values whose detectability does *not* depend on whether the ϕ's (and hence the **P**'s) fall around the middle or on one side of their possible range. The power and sample size tables in this chapter provide values for $h = .10$ (.10) 1.20.

Tables 6.2.1 and 6.2.2 provide the necessary conversion of $P_1 - P_2$ to $\phi_1 - \phi_2 = h$ values. Table 6.2.1 gives **h** values as a function of $P_1 - P_2$; Table 6.2.2 is a **P** to ϕ transformation table.

Table 6.2.1 is likely to be more convenient for use in power analysis, and when the tabled **h** values are sufficient. It provides direct conversion of $P_1 - P_2$ to $\phi_1 - \phi_2 = h$ values for tabled **h**. Taking $P_1 > P_2$, locate at the left P_2, the smaller **P**, and read horizontally to P_1, the larger. When P_1 is found, determine the heading of the column which is **h**, the difference between the arcsine transformations of the **P**'s, that is, $\phi_1 - \phi_2$. For example, with **P**'s of .35 ($= P_2$) and .50 ($= P_1$), the table provides the difference **h** between their respective ϕ values, as follows: Find in the first column $P_2 = .35$ and read across to $P_1 = .50$; then read up to the head of that column, where you find $h = .30$.

Since one cannot have both convenient multiples of .10 for **h** and simultaneously convenient multiples of .05 for both P_1 and P_2, the use of Table 6.2.1 may require interpolation in **h**. Thus, for $P_2 = .25$ and $P_1 = .50$, values in the row for $P_2 = .25$ indicate that $h = .50$ for $P_1 = .49$ and $h = .60$ for $P_1 = .54$. Linear interpolation gives the approximate value of $h = .52$.

Alternatively, for exact values of **h**, $P_1 = .50$ and $P_2 = .25$ may be located in Table 6.2.2 and their respective ϕ values found: $\phi_1 = 1.571$, $\phi_2 = 1.047$. Then, $h = 1.571 - 1.047 = .524$. Note that with the resulting nontabled **h** value, interpolation would be required in order to use it in the power tables (but not for sample size determination[2]).

Table 6.2.2 will also be useful for finding h_s when the power tables are used for significance testing, as described in Section 6.5.

In practice, the need to use nontabled values of **h** in power and sample size determination will not arise frequently. This is because one rarely has so highly specified an alternate hypothesis in terms of P_1 and P_2 that one must find power or sample size for a value of **h** which is not tabled. A looser specification of the $P_1 - P_2$ difference permits the use of the nearest tabled value of **h** in Table 6.2.1 and the later tables in this chapter. Indeed, the even looser procedure of defining **h** as "small," "medium," or "large," with the operational definitions proposed below, will suffice for most purposes.

---

[2] As will be seen below, determining **n** from the sample size Table (4.4.1) requires no interpolation. For nontabled values of **h**, formula (6.4.1) is used.

Table 6.2.2

Transformations of Proportion (P) to ϕ**

P	ϕ	P	ϕ	P	ϕ	P	ϕ
.00	.000*	.25	1.047	.50	1.571	.75	2.094
.01	.200	.26	1.070	.51	1.591	.76	2.118
.02	.284	.27	1.093	.52	1.611	.77	2.141
.03	.348	.28	1.115	.53	1.631	.78	2.165
.04	.403	.29	1.137	.54	1.651	.79	2.190
.05	.451	.30	1.159	.55	1.671	.80	2.214
.06	.495	.31	1.181	.56	1.691	.81	2.240
.07	.536	.32	1.203	.57	1.711	.82	2.265
.08	.574	.33	1.224	.58	1.731	.83	2.292
.09	.609	.34	1.245	.59	1.752	.84	2.319
.10	.644	.35	1.266	.60	1.772	.85	2.346
.11	.676	.36	1.287	.61	1.793	.86	2.375
.12	.707	.37	1.308	.62	1.813	.87	2.404
.13	.738	.38	1.328	.63	1.834	.88	2.434
.14	.767	.39	1.349	.64	1.855	.89	2.465
.15	.795	.40	1.369	.65	1.875	.90	2.498
.16	.823	.41	1.390	.66	1.897	.91	2.532
.17	.850	.42	1.410	.67	1.918	.92	2.568
.18	.876	.43	1.430	.68	1.939	.93	2.606
.19	.902	.44	1.451	.69	1.961	.94	2.647
.20	.927	.45	1.471	.70	1.982	.95	2.691
.21	.952	.46	1.491	.71	2.004	.96	2.739
.22	.976	.47	1.511	.72	2.026	.97	2.793
.23	1.000	.48	1.531	.73	2.049	.98	2.858
.24	1.024	.49	1.551	.74	2.071	.99	2.941
							1.00	3.142*

*For observed $P_s = 0$, $\phi_0 = 2$ arcsin $1/4n$;
  for observed $P_s = 1$, $\phi_1 = 3.142 - \phi_0$ (Owen, 1962, p. 293).
**This table is abridged from Table 9.9 in Owen, D. B., *Handbook of Statistical Tables.* Reading, Mass.: Addison–Wesley, 1962. Reproduced with the permission of the publisher. (Courtesy of the U.S. Atomic Energy Commission.)

6.2.1   "SMALL," "MEDIUM," AND "LARGE" DIFFERENCES BETWEEN PROPORTIONS. To provide the investigator with a frame of reference for the appraisal of differences between proportions, we define the adjectives "small," "medium," and "large" in terms of specific values of **h** at these levels to serve as conventions, as has been done with each type of statistical test discussed in this handbook. As before, the reader is counseled to avoid the use of these conventions, if he can, in favor of exact values provided by theory or experience in the specific area in which he is working.

As noted above, in working with **h**, we use an index of ES which provides units which are equal in detectability, rather than equal in units of raw differences in proportion (i.e., $j = P_1 - P_2$). This means that for any given value of **h**, the value of **j** varies depending on whether **j** occurs symmetrically about .50 as a midpoint between P_1 and P_2, where it is at its largest, or toward either tail (P_2 near zero or P_1 near one), where it is at its smallest. If we restrict ourselves to the part of the **P** scale between .05 and .95, the range of **j** is tolerably small. Thus, we do not have to pay a large price in consistency of interpretation of **h** in terms of $P_1 - P_2 = j$ for the convenience of using an equal power unit. In the description of each conventional level of ES which follows, the range of **j** values for each value of **h** will be described.

SMALL EFFECT SIZE: **h** = .20. A small difference between proportions is defined as a difference between their arcsine transformation values of .20. The following pairs of **P**'s illustrate this amount of difference: .05, .10; .20, .29; .40, .50; .60, .70; .80, .87; .90, .95 (Table 6.2.1). The (P_1, P_2) pairs yielding any value of **h** are symmetric about **P** = .50 (where $\phi = 1.571$); also, **j** is largest when P_1 and P_2 are symmetrical about .50. Thus, for **h** = .20, **j** reaches its maximum of .100 when the **P**s are .45 and .55. The minimum value of **j** is not useful, since it approaches zero as P_1 approaches one or P_2 approaches zero. If we stay within a **P** range .05–.95, the minimum value of **j** is .052. Summarizing then, a small difference between proportions, **h** = .20, means a raw difference **j** which varies from .05 near either extreme to .10 around the middle of the **P** scale. As can be seen from the values of **P** given above, and from Table 6.2.2, between .20 and .80, **j** equals .09 or .10 when **h** = .20.

As has already been noted, a difference between populations 1 and 2 in the proportions having attribute **X** can alternatively be viewed as a relationship between population membership (1 versus 2) and having–not having **X**. This relationship can be indexed by the product-moment correlation coefficient **r**, which, when applied to dichotomous variables, is frequently called the phi or four-fold point correlation coefficient. When the two populations are equally numerous, the value of this **r** implied by **h** = .20 varies narrowly from .095 (for **P**'s of .05–.10 or .90–.95) to .100 (for **P**'s of

.45–.55).[3] This is quite consistent with the definition of a small **r** given in Section 3.2.

In summary, a small difference in proportions is a difference of about .10 (down to .05 near the extremes) and is equivalent to an **r** of about .10.

MEDIUM EFFECT SIZE: **h** = .50. With **h** = .50 taken to define a medium ES, we find (from Table 6.2.1) the following pairs of **P**'s illustrating this amount of difference: .05, .21; .20, .43; .40, .65; .60, .82; .80, .96. The difference **j** reaches its maximum of .248 for **P** values of .376 and .624. Within a restricted .05–.95 scale for **P**, the minimum value of **j** is .160 (**P**'s of .050 and .210 or .790 and .950). Over a broad range of midscale values, say between .20 and .80, a medium difference between proportions is a **j** of .23 to .25.

Expressed in terms of **r**, this is equivalent to a value of .238 to .248. This is lower than our operational definition of a medium ES for **r** in general, which was .30, but quite consistent with the more relevant point biserial **r** or η (see Sections 3.2, 8.2).

Thus, a medium difference in proportions is a raw difference of about .20 to .25 over most of the scale and is equivalent to an **r** between population and attribute of about .25.

LARGE EFFECT SIZE: **h** = .80. A large difference in proportions is operationally defined as one which yields **h** = $\phi_1 - \phi_2$ = .80. Pairs of **P**'s illustrative of this degree of difference are: .05, .34; .20, .58; .40, .78; .60, .92; .80, .996. The maximum difference is .390 and occurs for **P**'s of .305 and .695. For **P**'s between .05 and .95, the smallest difference is .293 (for **P**'s of .050 and .343 or .657 and .950). Over a wide range of midscale values (**P**'s between .12 and .88), a large difference between proportions is .35 to .39.

Again, when this difference in proportions is translated into a fourfold product moment **r**, the value ranges between .37 and .39. Note, again, that this value is smaller than the ES for a large **r** defined in Section 3.2, which was .50.

Thus, a large ES in differences between proportions is defined as being about .35 to .39, and implying an **r** between population membership and presence–absence of the attribute of about .37–.39.

6.3 POWER TABLES

When the significance criterion, ES, and sample size are specified, the tables in this section can be used to determine power values. Thus, they will receive their major use after a research is performed, or at least after

---

[3] The equality of the maximum **j** for a given value of **h** with the **r** for this maximum (both .100 here) is no accident. For *any* value of **h**, this equality holds. When two proportions are symmetrical about .50, their difference equals the fourfold point **r**.

Table 6.3.1

Power of Normal Curve Test of $P_1 = P_2$
via Arcsine Transformation at $a_1 = .01$

n	h_c						h						
		.10	.20	.30	.40	.50	.60	.70	.80	.90	1.00	1.10	1.20
10	1.040	02	03	05	08	11	16	22	30	38	46	55	64
11	.992	02	03	05	08	12	18	25	33	41	51	60	69
12	.950	02	03	06	09	14	20	27	36	45	55	64	73
13	.912	02	03	06	10	15	21	29	39	49	59	68	77
14	.879	02	04	06	10	16	23	32	42	52	63	72	80
15	.849	02	04	07	11	17	25	34	45	56	66	75	83
16	.823	02	04	07	12	18	26	36	47	59	69	78	86
17	.798	02	04	07	12	19	28	39	50	62	72	81	88
18	.775	02	04	08	13	20	30	41	53	65	75	83	90
19	.755	02	04	08	14	22	32	43	56	67	77	86	91
20	.736	02	05	08	14	23	33	46	58	70	80	88	93
21	.718	02	05	09	15	24	35	48	60	72	82	89	94
22	.701	02	05	09	16	25	37	50	63	75	84	91	95
23	.686	02	05	10	17	26	39	52	65	77	86	92	96
24	.672	02	05	10	17	28	40	54	67	79	87	93	97
25	.658	02	05	10	18	29	42	56	69	80	89	94	97
26	.645	02	05	11	19	30	44	58	71	82	90	95	98
27	.633	03	06	11	20	31	45	60	73	84	91	96	98
28	.622	03	06	11	20	32	47	62	75	85	92	96	98
29	.611	03	06	12	21	34	48	63	76	86	93	97	99
30	.601	03	06	12	22	35	50	65	78	88	94	97	99
31	.591	03	06	13	23	36	51	67	79	89	95	98	99
32	.582	03	06	13	23	37	53	68	81	90	95	98	99
33	.573	03	07	13	24	38	54	70	82	91	96	98	99
34	.564	03	07	14	25	40	56	71	83	92	96	99	*
35	.556	03	07	14	26	41	57	73	85	92	97	99	
36	.548	03	07	15	26	42	59	74	86	93	97	99	
37	.541	03	07	15	27	43	60	75	87	94	98	99	
38	.534	03	07	15	28	44	61	77	88	94	98	99	
39	.527	03	07	16	29	45	63	78	89	95	98	99	
40	.520	03	08	16	30	46	64	79	89	96	98	*	
42	.508	03	08	17	31	49	66	81	91	96	99		
44	.496	03	08	18	33	51	69	83	92	97	99		
46	.485	03	09	19	34	53	71	85	93	98	99		
48	.475	03	09	20	36	55	73	86	94	98	99		

6 DIFFERENCES BETWEEN PROPORTIONS

Table 6.3.1 *(continued)*

							h						
n	h_c	.10	.20	.30	.40	.50	.60	.70	.80	.90	1.00	1.10	1.20
50	.465	03	09	20	37	57	75	88	95	99	*	*	*
52	.456	03	10	21	39	59	77	89	96	99			
54	.448	04	10	22	40	61	79	91	97	99			
56	.440	04	10	23	42	63	80	92	97	99			
58	.432	04	11	24	43	64	82	93	98	99			
60	.425	04	11	25	45	66	83	93	98	*			
64	.411	04	12	26	47	69	86	95	99				
68	.399	04	12	28	50	72	88	96	99				
72	.388	04	13	30	53	75	90	97	99				
76	.377	04	14	32	56	78	91	98	*				
80	.368	05	14	33	58	80	93	98					
84	.359	05	15	35	60	82	94	99					
88	.351	05	16	37	63	84	95	99					
92	.343	05	17	39	65	86	96	99					
96	.336	05	17	40	67	87	97	99					
100	.329	05	18	42	69	89	97	*					
120	.300	06	22	50	78	94	99						
140	.278	07	26	57	85	97	*						
160	.260	08	30	64	89	98							
180	.245	08	33	70	93	99							
200	.233	09	37	75	95	*							
250	.208	11	46	85	98								
300	.190	14	55	91	99								
350	.176	16	63	95	*								
400	.165	18	69	97									
450	.155	20	75	99									
500	.147	23	80	99									
600	.134	28	87	*									
700	.124	32	92										
800	.116	37	95										
900	.110	42	97										
1000	.104	46	98										

* Power values below this point are greater than .995.

Table 6.3.2

Power of Normal Curve Test of $P_1 = P_2$
via Arcsine Transformation at $a_1 = .05$

n	h_c	.10	.20	.30	.40	.50	.60	.70	.80	.90	1.00	1.10	1.20
10	.736	08	12	17	23	30	38	47	56	64	72	79	85
11	.701	08	12	17	24	32	41	50	59	68	76	83	88
12	.672	08	12	18	25	34	43	53	62	71	79	85	90
13	.645	08	13	19	27	36	45	56	65	74	82	88	92
14	.622	08	13	20	28	37	48	58	68	77	84	90	94
15	.601	09	14	21	29	39	50	61	71	79	86	91	95
16	.582	09	14	21	30	41	52	63	73	82	88	93	96
17	.564	09	14	22	32	43	54	65	75	84	90	94	97
18	.548	09	15	23	33	44	56	68	77	85	91	95	97
19	.534	09	15	24	34	46	58	70	79	87	92	96	98
20	.520	09	16	24	35	47	60	72	81	89	94	97	98
21	.508	09	16	25	36	49	62	73	83	90	94	97	99
22	.496	09	16	26	38	51	64	75	84	91	95	98	99
23	.485	10	17	27	39	52	65	77	86	92	96	98	99
24	.475	10	17	27	40	53	67	78	87	93	97	98	99
25	.465	10	17	28	41	55	68	80	88	94	97	99	*
26	.456	10	18	29	42	56	70	81	89	95	98	99	
27	.448	10	18	29	43	58	71	82	90	95	98	99	
28	.440	10	18	30	44	59	73	84	91	96	98	99	
29	.432	10	19	31	45	60	74	85	92	96	98	99	
30	.425	10	19	31	46	61	75	86	93	97	99	*	
31	.418	11	20	32	47	63	76	87	93	97	99		
32	.411	11	20	33	48	64	77	88	94	97	99		
33	.405	11	20	33	49	65	79	88	95	98	99		
34	.399	11	21	34	50	66	80	89	95	98	99		
35	.393	11	21	35	51	67	81	90	96	98	99		
36	.388	11	21	35	52	68	82	91	96	99	*		
37	.382	11	22	36	53	69	83	91	96	99			
38	.377	11	22	37	54	70	83	92	97	99			
39	.372	12	22	37	55	71	84	93	97	99			
40	.368	12	23	38	56	72	85	93	97	99			
42	.359	12	23	39	57	74	87	94	98	99			
44	.351	12	24	41	59	76	88	95	98	*			
46	.343	12	25	42	61	77	89	96	99				
48	.336	13	25	43	62	79	90	96	99				

Table 6.3.2 *(continued)*

							h					
n	h_c	.10	.20	.30	.40	.50	.60	.70	.80	.90	1.00	1.10	1.20
50	.329	13	26	44	64	80	91	97	99	*	*	*	*
52	.323	13	27	45	65	82	92	97	99				
54	.317	13	27	47	67	83	93	98	99				
56	.311	13	28	48	68	84	94	98	*				
58	.305	14	28	49	69	85	94	98					
60	.300	14	29	50	71	86	95	99					
64	.291	14	30	52	73	88	96	99					
68	.282	14	32	54	75	90	97	99					
72	.274	15	33	56	77	91	97	99					
76	.267	15	34	58	79	92	98	*					
80	.260	16	35	60	81	94	98						
84	.254	16	36	62	83	94	99						
88	.248	16	38	63	84	95	99						
92	.243	17	39	65	86	96	99						
96	.237	17	40	67	87	97	99						
100	.233	17	41	68	88	97	*						
120	.212	19	46	75	93	99							
140	.197	21	51	81	96	99							
160	.184	23	56	85	97	*							
180	.173	24	60	89	98								
200	.164	26	64	91	99								
250	.147	30	72	96	*								
300	.134	34	79	98									
350	.124	38	84	99									
400	.116	41	88	*									
450	.110	44	91										
500	.104	47	94										
600	.095	53	97										
700	.088	59	98										
800	.082	64	99										
900	.078	68	*										
1000	.074	72											

* Power values below this point are greater than .995.

Table 6.3.3

Power of Normal Curve Test of $P_1 = P_2$
via Arcsine Transformation at $a_1 = .10$

n	h_c						h						
		.10	.20	.30	.40	.50	.60	.70	.80	.90	1.00	1.10	1.20
10	.573	15	20	27	35	44	52	61	69	77	83	88	92
11	.547	15	21	28	37	46	55	64	72	80	86	90	94
12	.523	15	21	29	38	48	57	67	75	82	88	92	95
13	.503	15	22	30	40	50	60	69	78	84	90	94	96
14	.484	15	23	31	41	52	62	72	80	86	91	95	97
15	.468	16	23	32	43	53	64	74	82	88	93	96	98
16	.453	16	24	33	44	55	66	76	84	90	94	97	98
17	.440	16	24	34	45	57	68	78	85	91	95	97	99
18	.427	16	25	35	47	59	70	79	87	92	96	98	99
19	.416	17	25	36	48	60	71	81	88	93	96	98	99
20	.405	17	26	37	49	62	73	82	89	94	97	99	99
21	.396	17	26	38	51	63	75	84	90	95	97	99	*
22	.386	17	27	39	52	65	76	85	91	96	98	99	
23	.378	17	27	40	53	66	77	86	92	96	98	99	
24	.370	17	28	40	54	67	79	87	93	97	99	99	
25	.362	18	28	41	55	69	80	88	94	97	99	*	
26	.355	18	29	42	56	70	81	89	95	98	99		
27	.349	18	29	43	57	71	82	90	95	98	99		
28	.342	18	30	44	59	72	83	91	96	98	99		
29	.337	18	30	44	60	73	84	92	96	98	99		
30	.331	19	31	45	61	74	85	92	97	99	*		
31	.326	19	31	46	62	75	86	93	97	99			
32	.320	19	32	47	62	76	87	94	97	99			
33	.316	19	32	47	63	77	88	94	98	99			
34	.311	19	32	48	64	78	88	95	98	99			
35	.306	19	33	49	65	79	89	95	98	99			
36	.302	20	33	50	66	80	90	95	98	99			
37	.298	20	34	50	67	81	90	96	98	*			
38	.294	20	34	51	68	82	91	96	99				
39	.290	20	35	52	69	82	91	96	99				
40	.287	20	35	52	69	83	92	97	99				
42	.280	21	36	54	71	84	93	97	99				
44	.273	21	37	55	72	86	94	98	99				
46	.267	21	37	56	74	87	94	98	99				
48	.262	21	38	57	75	88	95	98	*				

Table 6.3.3 *(continued)*

n	h_c	.10	.20	.30	.40	.50	.60	.70	.80	.90	1.00	1.10	1.20
									h				
50	.256	22	39	59	76	89	96	99	*	*	*	*	*
52	.251	22	40	60	78	90	96	99					
54	.247	22	40	61	79	91	97	99					
56	.242	23	41	62	80	91	97	99					
58	.238	23	42	63	81	92	97	99					
60	.234	23	43	64	82	93	98	99					
64	.227	24	44	66	84	94	98	*					
68	.220	24	45	68	85	95	99						
72	.214	25	47	70	87	96	99						
76	.208	25	48	71	88	96	99						
80	.203	26	49	73	89	97	99						
84	.198	26	51	75	91	97	*						
88	.193	27	52	76	91	98							
92	.189	27	53	77	92	98							
96	.185	28	54	79	93	99							
100	.181	28	55	80	94	99							
120	.165	31	61	85	97	*							
140	.153	33	65	89	98								
160	.143	35	69	92	99								
180	.135	37	73	94	99								
200	.128	39	76	96	*								
250	.115	44	83	98									
300	.105	48	88	99									
350	.097	52	91	*									
400	.091	55	94										
450	.085	59	96										
500	.081	62	97										
600	.074	67	99										
700	.069	72	99										
800	.064	76	*										
900	.060	80											
1000	.057	83											

* Power values below this point are greater than .995.

Table 6.3.4

Power of Normal Curve Test of $P_1 = P_2$
via ArcsineTransformation at $a_2 = .01$

							h						
n	h_c	.10	.20	.30	.40	.50	.60	.70	.80	.90	1.00	1.10	1.20
10	1.152	01	02	03	05	07	11	16	22	29	37	45	54
11	1.098	01	02	03	05	08	12	18	24	32	41	50	59
12	1.052	01	02	03	06	09	13	19	27	36	45	55	64
13	1.010	01	02	03	06	10	15	21	30	39	49	59	69
14	.973	01	02	04	06	11	16	23	32	42	53	63	73
15	.940	01	02	04	07	11	18	26	35	46	56	67	76
16	.911	01	02	04	07	12	19	28	38	49	60	70	79
17	.884	01	02	04	08	13	20	30	40	52	63	74	82
18	.859	01	02	05	08	14	22	32	43	55	66	77	85
19	.836	01	03	05	09	15	23	34	45	58	69	79	87
20	.815	01	03	05	09	16	25	36	48	61	72	82	89
21	.795	01	03	05	10	17	26	38	51	63	75	84	91
22	.777	01	03	06	11	18	28	40	53	66	77	86	92
23	.760	01	03	06	11	19	29	42	55	68	79	88	93
24	.744	01	03	06	12	20	31	44	58	71	81	89	94
25	.728	01	03	06	12	21	32	46	60	73	83	91	95
26	.714	02	03	07	13	22	34	48	62	75	85	92	96
27	.701	02	03	07	13	23	36	50	64	77	86	93	97
28	.688	02	03	07	14	24	37	52	66	79	88	94	97
29	.676	02	04	08	15	25	39	54	68	80	89	95	98
30	.665	02	04	08	15	26	40	55	70	82	90	95	98
31	.654	02	04	08	16	27	42	57	72	83	91	96	98
32	.644	02	04	08	16	28	43	59	73	85	92	97	99
33	.634	02	04	09	17	29	44	61	75	86	93	97	99
34	.625	02	04	09	18	30	46	62	77	87	94	97	99
35	.616	02	04	09	18	31	47	64	78	88	95	98	99
36	.607	02	04	10	19	32	49	65	79	89	95	98	99
37	.599	02	04	10	20	34	50	67	81	90	96	98	*
38	.591	02	04	10	20	35	52	68	82	91	96	99	
39	.583	02	05	11	21	36	53	70	83	92	97	99	
40	.576	02	05	11	22	37	54	71	84	93	97	99	
42	.562	02	05	11	23	39	57	74	86	94	98	99	
44	.549	02	05	12	24	41	59	76	88	95	98	*	
46	.537	02	05	13	26	43	62	78	90	96	99		
48	.526	02	06	13	27	45	64	80	91	97	99		

Table 6.3.4 *(continued)*

n	h_c	.10	.20	.30	.40	.50	.60	.70	.80	.90	1.00	1.10	1.20
50	.515	02	06	14	28	47	66	82	92	97	99	*	*
52	.505	02	06	15	30	49	69	84	93	98	99		
54	.496	02	06	15	31	51	71	86	94	98	*		
56	.487	02	06	16	32	53	73	87	95	99			
58	.478	02	07	17	34	55	74	88	96	99			
60	.470	02	07	18	35	56	76	90	96	99			
64	.455	02	07	19	38	60	79	92	97	99			
68	.442	02	08	20	40	63	82	93	98	*			
72	.429	02	08	22	43	66	85	95	99				
76	.418	03	09	23	46	69	87	96	99				
80	.407	03	09	25	48	72	89	97	99				
84	.397	03	10	26	51	75	91	98	*				
88	.388	03	11	28	53	77	92	98					
92	.380	03	11	29	55	79	93	99					
96	.372	03	12	31	58	81	94	99					
100	.364	03	12	33	60	83	95	99					
120	.333	04	15	40	70	90	98	*					
140	.308	04	18	47	78	95	99						
160	.288	05	22	54	84	97	*						
180	.272	05	25	61	89	98							
200	.258	06	28	66	92	99							
250	.230	07	37	78	97	*							
300	.210	09	45	86	99								
350	.195	11	53	92	*								
400	.182	12	60	95									
450	.172	14	66	97									
500	.163	16	72	98									
600	.149	20	81	*									
700	.138	24	88										
800	.129	28	92										
900	.121	32	95										
1000	.115	37	97										

* Power values below this point are greater than .995.

Table 6.3.5

Power of Normal Curve Test of $P_1 = P_2$
via ArcsineTransformation at $a_2 = .05$

n	h_c	.10	.20	.30	.40	.50	.60	.70	.80	.90	1.00	1.10	1.20
10	.877	06	07	10	15	20	27	35	43	52	61	69	77
11	.836	06	08	11	16	22	29	38	47	56	65	73	80
12	.800	06	08	11	17	23	31	40	50	60	69	77	84
13	.769	06	08	12	17	25	33	43	53	63	72	80	86
14	.741	06	08	12	18	26	36	46	56	66	75	83	89
15	.716	06	09	13	19	28	38	48	59	69	78	85	91
16	.693	06	09	14	20	29	40	51	62	72	81	88	92
17	.672	06	09	14	21	31	42	53	65	75	83	89	94
18	.653	06	09	15	22	32	44	56	67	77	85	91	95
19	.636	06	09	15	23	34	46	58	69	79	87	92	96
20	.620	06	10	16	24	35	48	60	72	81	89	94	97
21	.605	06	10	16	25	37	49	62	74	83	90	95	97
22	.591	06	10	17	26	38	51	64	76	85	91	95	98
23	.578	06	10	17	27	39	53	66	77	86	92	96	98
24	.566	06	11	18	28	41	55	68	79	88	93	97	99
25	.554	06	11	19	29	42	56	70	81	89	94	97	99
26	.544	07	11	19	30	44	58	71	82	90	95	98	99
27	.533	07	11	20	31	45	60	73	84	91	96	98	99
28	.524	07	12	20	32	46	61	75	85	92	96	98	99
29	.515	07	12	21	33	48	63	76	86	93	97	99	*
30	.506	07	12	21	34	49	64	77	87	94	97	99	
31	.498	07	12	22	35	50	66	79	88	94	98	99	
32	.490	07	13	22	36	52	67	80	89	95	98	99	
33	.483	07	13	23	37	53	69	81	90	96	98	99	
34	.475	07	13	23	38	54	70	82	91	96	98	99	
35	.469	07	13	24	39	55	71	83	92	96	99	*	
36	.462	07	14	24	40	56	72	84	92	97	99		
37	.456	07	14	25	41	58	73	85	93	97	99		
38	.450	07	14	26	41	59	74	86	94	98	99		
39	.444	07	14	26	42	60	75	87	94	98	99		
40	.438	07	15	27	43	61	77	88	95	98	99		
42	.428	07	15	28	45	63	79	89	96	98	*		
44	.418	08	16	29	47	65	80	91	96	99			
46	.409	08	16	30	48	67	82	92	97	99			
48	.400	08	17	31	50	69	84	93	97	99			

Table 6.3.5 (continued)

n	h_c	.10	.20	.30	.40	.50	.60	.70	.80	.90	1.00	1.10	1.20
50	.392	08	17	32	52	71	85	94	98	99	*	*	*
52	.384	08	18	33	53	72	86	95	98	*			
54	.377	08	18	34	55	74	88	95	99				
56	.370	08	18	35	56	75	89	96	99				
58	.364	08	19	37	58	77	90	96	99				
60	.358	09	19	38	59	78	91	97	99				
64	.346	09	20	40	62	81	92	98	99				
68	.336	09	21	42	65	83	94	98	*				
72	.327	09	22	44	67	85	95	99					
76	.318	09	23	46	69	87	96	99					
80	.310	10	24	48	72	89	97	99					
84	.302	10	25	49	74	90	97	*					
88	.295	10	26	51	76	91	98						
92	.289	10	27	53	77	92	98						
96	.283	11	28	55	79	93	99						
100	.277	11	29	56	81	94	99						
120	.253	12	34	64	87	97	*						
140	.234	14	39	71	92	99							
160	.219	16	43	77	95	99							
180	.207	16	48	81	97	*							
200	.196	17	52	85	98								
250	.175	20	61	92	99								
300	.160	23	69	96	*								
350	.148	26	75	98									
400	.139	29	81	99									
450	.131	32	85	99									
500	.124	35	89	*									
600	.113	41	93										
700	.105	46	96										
800	.098	52	98										
900	.092	56	99										
1000	.088	61	99										

* Power values below this point are greater than .995.

Table 6.3.6

Power of Normal Curve Test of $P_1 = P_2$
via Arcsine Transformation at $a_2 = .10$

							h						
n	h_c	.10	.20	.30	.40	.50	.60	.70	.80	.90	1.00	1.10	1.20
10	.736	11	13	18	23	30	38	47	56	64	72	79	85
11	.701	11	14	18	24	32	41	50	59	68	76	83	88
12	.672	11	14	19	26	34	43	53	62	71	79	85	90
13	.645	11	14	20	27	36	45	56	65	74	82	88	92
14	.622	11	15	20	28	38	48	58	68	77	84	90	94
15	.601	11	15	21	29	39	50	61	71	79	86	91	95
16	.582	11	15	22	31	41	52	63	73	82	88	93	96
17	.564	11	16	23	32	43	54	65	75	84	90	94	97
18	.548	12	16	23	33	44	56	68	77	85	91	95	97
19	.534	12	16	24	34	46	58	70	79	87	92	96	98
20	.520	12	17	25	35	48	60	72	81	89	94	97	98
21	.508	12	17	25	37	49	62	73	83	90	94	97	99
22	.496	12	17	26	38	51	64	75	84	91	95	98	99
23	.485	12	18	27	39	52	65	77	86	92	96	98	99
24	.475	12	18	28	40	54	67	78	87	93	97	98	99
25	.465	12	18	28	41	55	68	80	88	94	97	99	*
26	.456	12	19	29	42	56	70	81	89	95	98	99	
27	.448	12	19	30	43	58	71	82	90	95	98	99	
28	.440	12	19	30	44	59	73	84	91	96	98	99	
29	.432	12	20	31	45	60	74	85	92	96	98	99	
30	.425	13	20	32	46	61	75	86	93	97	99	*	
31	.418	13	20	32	47	63	76	87	93	97	99		
32	.411	13	21	33	48	64	77	88	94	97	99		
33	.405	13	21	34	49	65	79	88	95	98	99		
34	.399	13	21	34	50	66	80	89	95	98	99		
35	.393	13	22	35	51	67	81	90	96	98	99		
36	.388	13	22	36	52	68	82	91	96	99	*		
37	.382	13	22	36	53	69	83	91	96	99			
38	.377	13	23	37	54	70	83	92	97	99			
39	.372	13	23	38	55	71	84	93	97	99			
40	.368	13	23	38	56	72	85	93	97	99			
42	.359	14	24	39	57	74	87	94	98	99			
44	.351	14	24	41	59	76	88	95	98	*			
46	.343	14	25	42	61	77	89	96	99				
48	.336	14	26	43	62	79	90	96	99				

Table 6.3.6 *(continued)*

							h						
n	h_c	.10	.20	.30	.40	.50	.60	.70	.80	.90	1.00	1.10	1.20
50	.329	14	26	44	64	80	91	97	99	*	*	*	*
52	.323	14	27	45	65	82	92	97	99				
54	.317	15	28	47	67	83	93	98	99				
56	.311	15	28	48	68	84	94	98	*				
58	.305	15	29	49	69	85	94	98					
60	.300	15	29	50	71	86	95	99					
64	.291	15	31	52	73	88	96	99					
68	.282	16	32	54	75	90	97	99					
72	.274	16	33	56	77	91	97	99					
76	.267	16	34	58	79	92	98	*					
80	.260	17	35	60	81	94	98						
84	.254	17	37	62	83	94	99						
88	.248	17	38	64	84	95	99						
92	.243	18	39	65	86	96	99						
96	.237	18	40	67	87	97	99						
100	.233	18	41	68	88	97	*						
120	.212	20	46	75	93	99							
140	.197	22	51	81	96	99							
160	.184	23	56	85	97	*							
180	.173	25	60	89	98								
200	.164	26	64	91	99								
250	.147	30	72	96	*								
300	.134	34	79	98									
350	.124	38	84	99									
400	.116	41	88	*									
450	.110	44	91										
500	.104	48	94										
600	.095	54	97										
700	.088	59	98										
800	.082	64	99										
900	.078	68	*										
1000	.074	72											

* Power values below this point are greater than .995.

it is planned. They can, of course, also be used in research planning by varying **n**, ES or **a**, or all three to see how their variation affects power.

6.3.1   CASE 0: $n_1 = n_2$. The power tables of this chapter are designed to yield directly power values for the normal curve test of the difference between **P**'s of two independent samples of equal size (via the arcsine transformation). This is designated Case 0. Other cases are described and illustrated in succeeding sections. Tables are entered with **a**, **h**, and **n**.

1. Significance Criterion, **a**. Six tables are provided for the following values of **a**: $a_1 = .01,, .05, .10$ and $a_2 = .01, .05,$ and $.10$, where the subscripts refer to one- and two-tailed tests. since power at a_1 is to a close approximation equal to power at $a_2 = 2a_1$ for power greater than (say) .10, the tables can also be used for power at $a_2 = .02$, $a_2 = .20$, $a_1 = .005$, and $a_1 = .025$.

2. Effect Size, ES. This is the difference between arcsine-transformed **P**'s, i.e., $\phi_1 - \phi_2 = h$, whose properties are described in Section 6.2. Table 6.2.1 facilitates the conversion of P_1, P_2 pairs into **h** values. The tables provide for $h = .10 (.10)$ 1.20. Conventional or operational definitions of ES have been offered, as follows:

small: $h = .20$,

medium: $h = .50$,

large: $h = .80$.

3. Sample Size, **n**. This is the size of each of the two samples whose proportions are being compared. Provision is made for $n = 10$ (1) 40 (2) 60 (4) 100 (20) 200 (50) 500 (100) 1000.

The values in the table are the power of the test times 100, i.e., the percent of tests carried out under the given conditions which will result in the rejection of the null hypothesis. They are rounded to the nearest unit and are accurate to within ± 1 as tabulated.

Illustrative Examples

6.1   A social psychologist is interested in the cross-cultural generalizability of the finding in the United States that first-born and only child *S*s (A) more frequently than later-born *S*s (B) prefer waiting with others to waiting alone while anticipating an anxiety provoking experience. In a non-Western culture, he performs a replicating experiment for which he obtains the cooperation of 80 *S*'s of each birth order type, 160 in all. The prior work in the U.S. suggests that about two-thirds of the A's prefer waiting "together" while only about half of the B's do. On the expectation of a difference of similar magnitude in the other culture, even though both **P**'s might rise or fall under his particular conditions, he posits an ES of about the same size, namely $h = .30$ (actually, $h = \phi_{.67} - \phi_{.50} = 1.918 - 1.571 = .347$ from Table 6.2.2). He plans a directional test of H_0: $P_A = P_B$ at $a_1 = .05$. What is the power of the test? The specification summary is

$$a_1 = .05, \qquad h = .30, \qquad n_A = n_B = n = 80.$$

In Table 6.3.2 for $a_1 = .05$, column $h = .30$, and row $n = 80$, he finds power $= .60$. Thus, he works with only $3 : 2$ odds of obtaining a significant $(a_1 = .05)$ result if the populations in the new culture have proportions whose ϕ's differ by .30 in favor of the A sample. Note that $h = .30$ when the following pairs of proportions are compared: .10 and .21, .25 and .39, .40 and .55, .60 and .78, .75 and .87, .90 and .97, as well as .50 and .65, the values approximated by the original experiments.

On the reasonable assumption that the psychologist finds the power value of .60 unsatisfactorily low, he would need to change his plans, either by increasing **n** or by increasing **a**, preferably the former. This assumes, of course, that the experiment has not yet been run. If it has, and his results were nonsignificant, he could not readily conclude that the U.S. finding did not generalize, since even if **h** were .30 in the new culture, his **b** risk was much too large $(1 - .60 = .40)$ for such a conclusion. If, on the other hand, the results *were* significant, although he can conclude that $P_A > P_B$, he cannot conclude that the population difference in terms of **h** *was* .30 (although his results may be consistent with **h** being .30, and, of course, other values).

6.2 A clinical psychologist plans a research in which patients, upon admission to a mental hospital, are randomly assigned to two admission wards of different treatment atmospheres, one "custodial–authoritarian" (C), the other "therapeutic–democratic" (T). Among other criteria, he plans six months after admission, to compare the proportions of each group which have been discharged. The issue, then, is the effect of the atmosphere of the initial ward placement on length of stay in the hospital. The hospital admits about 50 patients a month, and he plans to assign randomly to C and T conditions for a four-month period, yielding two samples of about 100 cases each. He reviews Table 6.2.1 and decides that the ES he expects is given by $h = .40$, since the pairs of proportions which differ by this amount around the middle of the scale of **P** (where from experience he expects his results to lie) are .40 and .60, .45 and .65, .50 and .69, and .55 and .74. The test will be performed at $a_2 = .05$. He wishes to assess the power of the eventual test of the significance of the difference between P_C and P_T. In summary, his specifications are

$$a_2 = .05, \qquad h = .40, \qquad n_C = n_T = n = 100.$$

To find the power of this test, use Table 6.3.5 (for $a_2 = .05$) with column $h = .40$, row $n = 100$; power is .81. He thus has about four chances in five of concluding (at the .05 level) that the atmosphere difference has consequence to length of stay *if* the difference in proportions amounts to $h = .40$. If either (*a*) he wishes a better probability than .81 under these specifications, or (*b*) he wants to assure high power if the difference in proportions were smaller, say $h = .30$, he might consider running his experiment longer in order to get more S's. If he can run a fifth month so that he has a total of about 250 Ss, under condition (*a*) above his specifications are:

$$a_2 = .05, \quad h = .40, \quad n_C = n_T = n = 125.$$

In Table 6.3.5, again for column $h = .40$, and roughly interpolating between the rows $n = 120$ and $n = 140$, we find power with this larger n to be about .88 (i.e., one-quarter of the way between .87 and .92), a better than 7:1 chance of rejecting the null hypothesis if $h = .40$. Or, assuming the (*b*) condition, the specifications become

$$a_2 = .05, \quad h = .30, \quad n_C = n_T = n = 125.$$

When we move to the left one column in Table 6.3.5, i.e., to $h = .30$, roughly interpolating again between the rows $n = 120$ and $n = 140$, we find power to be about .59 (i.e., one-quarter of the way between .56 and .64). This value may well give him pause. If h is as small as .30, he would have to run about seven months (so that $n = 180$) to get power of .81 at $a_2 = .05$.

6.3.2 CASE 1: $n_1 \neq n_2$. The tables will yield valid power values for tests on differences between population proportions when samples of different sizes are drawn. In such cases, find the harmonic mean of n_1 and n_2, i.e.,

$$(6.3.1) \qquad\qquad n' = \frac{2n_1 n_2}{n_1 + n_2}$$

and use the n column of the power table for n'. The results of this procedure are exact,[4] provided that neither n is very small (< 10).

Illustrative Example

6.3 In example 6.1 we described a cross-cultural research on the experimental hypothesis that first-born and only children (A) have a preference for waiting with others rather than alone relative to the later born (B) while anticipating an experience that is contemplated with anxiety. There, we posited that the social psychologist obtained the cooperation of 80 Ss of

---

[4] That is, as exact as the Case 0 value, generally within ± 1 as tabulated.

each birth-order type. It was found there that if $h = .30$, the probability of finding a difference significant at $a_1 = .05$ was $.60$. That example was somewhat artificial, in that in canvassing people to volunteer for the experiment, it is likely that the number of first and only born volunteers would not equal the number of later born volunteers, since there are more of the latter in most populations, particularly in a non-Western culture. If, for example, 80 A's and 245 B's volunteered, it would be a mistake to accept only 80 of the B's in order to keep the sample n's equal. The mistake lies in the loss of power through reduced total n. What is the power of the test using all the volunteers? Keeping the other conditions the same, the specifications are

$$a_1 = .05, \qquad h = .30, \qquad n_A = 80 \neq 245 = n_B.$$

With unequal n's, one finds [from (6.3.1)]

$$n' = \frac{2(80)(245)}{80 + 245} = 120.6.$$

Using Table 6.3.2 for $a_1 = .05$, as before, and column $h = .30$, but now row $n = 120$, one finds that power $= .75$, in contrast with the value of $.60$ obtained for $n_A = n_B = 80$.

6.4   A proposition derivable from psychoanalytic theory holds that the incidence of homosexuality should be higher in female paranoid schizophrenics (P) than in females bearing other psychiatric diagnoses (O). A clinical psychologist has records available to him for 85 P's and 450 O's. On the expectation that the difference in relative incidence or proportion of cases in which homosexuality is found in the case records of the two populations is "medium," i.e., $h = .50$, what is the power of a (directional) test of $H_0 \colon P_P \leq P_O$ at $a_1 = .01$? The specifications are

$$a_1 = .01, \qquad h = .50, \qquad n_P = 85 \neq 450 = n_O.$$

For unequal n's, first find [from formula (6.3.1)]

$$n' = \frac{2(85)(450)}{85 + 450} = 143.0.$$

Using Table 6.3.1 (for $a_1 = .01$) for column $h = .50$, row $n = 140$, one finds power $= .97$.

The psychologist formulated his test as directional, since the theory's prediction was not merely that there would be a difference, but that $P_P > P_O$. Theories normally do predict the direction of differences. However, if, in fact, it turned out that the sample proportions differed in the direction *opposite* to prediction, no conclusion could be drawn no matter how great the difference. (See Section 1.2 and Cohen, 1965, pp. 106–111.) It is instructive to inquire here what the power would be if a nondirectional test, which permits conclusions in either direction, were performed. The specifications are to be otherwise held constant, i.e.,

$$\mathbf{a}_2 = .01, \qquad \mathbf{h} = .50, \qquad \mathbf{n}' = 143.$$

In Table 6.3.4 (for $\mathbf{a}_2 = .01$) for column $\mathbf{h} = .50$, row $\mathbf{n} = 140$, we find power $= .95$, in contrast to the $\mathbf{a}_1 = .01$ power value of .97. The clinical psychologist might well decide that the loss in power is trivial, and that it is worth formulating the problem in nondirectional (two-tailed) terms to make possible the converse conclusion.[5]

6.3.3   CASE 2: ONE SAMPLE OF $\mathbf{n}$ OBSERVATIONS TO TEST $\mathbf{P} = \mathbf{c}$. Thus far we have been considering the power of the test of the difference between proportions of two independent samples, where the null hypothesis is $\mathbf{P}_1 = \mathbf{P}_2$. Essentially the same test procedure can be used to test the departure of the $\mathbf{P}$ in a single population from some specified value $\mathbf{c}$. $\mathbf{H}_0$ for the one-sample test is $\mathbf{P} = \mathbf{c}$. The test is employed when, given a random sample of $\mathbf{n}$ cases, the investigator's purpose is to determine whether the data are consonant with the hypothesis that the population $\mathbf{P}$ is .62 or .90 or any other value. It is thus the general case of which the test that $\mathbf{P} = .50$ of the preceding chapter is a special case.[6]

Although the special case $\mathbf{P} = \mathbf{c} = .50$ occurs quite widely in behavioral science (including particularly the "Sign Test"), the case of $\mathbf{P} = \mathbf{c} \neq .50$ is not as frequently found. Increasingly, however, the use of mathematical models provides ever stronger and more precise hypotheses, which are frequently cast in a form which predicts values of $\mathbf{P}$ not generally equal to .50. The rejection or affirmation of such hypotheses may proceed by use of the tables provided in this chapter.

For Case 2 we define the ES as for the other cases, that is, as the difference between arcsine-transformed $\mathbf{P}$'s. However, in formula (6.2.2), $\mathbf{P}_2 \rightarrow \phi_2$ is an estimable population parameter. Here it is a constant, so that for Case 2

$$(6.3.2) \qquad \mathbf{h}_2' = \phi_1 - \phi_c \qquad \text{(directional)}$$

$$= |\phi_1 - \phi_c| \qquad \text{(nondirectional)},$$

where $\phi_1 =$ the arcsine transformation of $\mathbf{P}_1$ as before, and

$\phi_c =$ the arcsine transformation of $\mathbf{c}$.

---

[5] It should be noted that the smallness of the power difference is due to the fact that the power values are close to 1.00.

[6] As in the case where $\mathbf{H}_0$: $\mathbf{P} = .50$, the test of $\mathbf{H}_0$: $\mathbf{P} = \mathbf{c}$ can be performed exactly by means of tables for the binomial distribution. The present procedure, however, requires no additional tables and provides an excellent approximation unless $\mathbf{n}$ is quite small.

There is no conceptual change in the ES; h_2' is the difference between the (alternate) population value P_1 and the value specified by the null hypothesis, c, expressed in units of the arcsine transformation of formula (6.2.1). and Table 6.2.2. The interpretation of h_2' proceeds exactly as described in Section 6.2 with regard to Table 6.2.1 and the operational definition of small, medium, and large ES.

The power and sample size tables, however, cannot be used directly with h_2' since they are constructed for Case 0, where there are *two* sample statistics *each* of which contributes sampling error variance for a total of $2/n$. Here, there is only one sample contributing sampling error variance, yielding half the amount, $1/n$. This is simply allowed for by finding

$$(6.3.3) \qquad h = h_2' \sqrt{2} = 1.414\,h_2'.$$

The value h is sought in the tables, while h_2' is the ES index which is interpreted.

If h_2' is chosen as a convenient multiple of .10, h will in general not be such a multiple. Thus, the proposed operational definitions of ES for h_2' of .20, .50, and .80 become, for table entry, .28, .71, and 1.13. Linear interpolation between columns will provide values which are sufficiently close (within .01 or .02) for most purposes.

Illustrative Example

6.5 A mathematical model predicts that a certain response will occur in (H_0: $P_1 = c =$) .40 of the animals subjected to a certain set of conditions. An experimental psychologist plans to test this model using $n = 64$ animals, using as his significance criterion $a_2 = .05$. Assuming that the model is incorrect, and that the population rate is actually .50, what would be the power of this test?

The ES is found directly from Table 6.2.1, where, from .40 (column P_2) to .50 amounts to a difference in ϕ's of .20. This value is for h_2'. For entry into the power table, we require [from (6.3.3)], $h = h_2' \sqrt{2} = .20 \sqrt{2} = .28$. Thus, the specifications are

$$a_2 = .05, \qquad h = .28, \qquad n = 60.$$

In Table 6.3.5 (for $a_2 = .05$), row $n = 60$, for column $h = .20$, power is .19 and for $h = .30$, power is .38. Interpolating linearly between these values, we approximate the power as $.19 + (.38 - .19)(.28 - .20)/(.30 - .20) = .34$. Thus, even if a discrepancy of .50–.40 in the parameter existed, the experiment as planned would have only about one chance in three of detecting it. It is apparent that if this experimental plan is followed, and the result is a nonsignificant departure of the sample **P** value, the psychologist would be making an error if he concluded that the results were confirmatory of the model. Our alternate hypothetical value of .50 would likely be considered a large discrepancy in this context, and failing to reject the model when there was only a one-third chance of doing so, given a large true departure from it, can hardly be considered confirmatory.

The above results hold whether the test is to be performed by means of the arcsine transformation (as described in Section 6.5), or the exact binomial, or the approximations to the latter provided by either the normal curve test using proportions or the equivalent χ^2 "goodness of fit" test on frequencies.

6.4 Sample Size Tables

The tables in this section list the significance criterion, the ES to be detected, and the *desired power*. One then can find the necessary sample size. Their primary utility lies in the planning of experiments to provide a basis for the decision as to the sample size to use.

6.4.1 Case 0: $n_1 = n_2$. The use of the sample size tables is first described for the application for which they were optimally designed, Case 0, where they yield the sample size, **n**, for each of two independent samples whose populations **P**'s are to be compared. The description of their use in two other cases follows this subsection. Tables give values for **a, h,** and desired power:

1. Significance Criterion, **a.** The same **a** values are provided as in the power tables by means of a table for each of the following: $a_1 = .01$ $(a_2 = .02)$, $a_1 = .05$ $(a_2 = .10)$, $a_1 = .10$ $(a_2 = .20)$, $a_2 = .01$ $(a_1 = .005)$, and $a_2 = .05$ $(a_1 = .025)$.

2. Effect Size. **h** is defined and interpreted as above [formula (6.2.2)] and used as in the power tables. The same provision is made: $h = .10$ $(.10)$ 1.20.

To find **n** for a value of **h** not tabled, substitute in

$$(6.4.1) \qquad n = \frac{n_{.10}}{100h^2},$$

where $n_{.10}$ is the necessary sample size for the given **a** and desired power at $h = .10$ (read from the table) and **h** is the nontabled ES. Round to the nearest integer.

3. Desired Power. Provision is made for desired power values of .25, .50, .60, 2/3, .70 (.05) .95, .99 (See Section 2.4.1 for a discussion of the basis for the selection of these values, and the proposal that power = .80 serve as a convention in the absence of another basis for a choice.

Table 6.4.1

n to detect h = $\phi_1 - \phi_2$ via Arcsine Transformation

| Power | \multicolumn{12}{c}{$a_1 = .01\ (a_2 = .02)$} |
| | \multicolumn{12}{c}{h} |
	.10	.20	.30	.40	.50	.60	.70	.80	.90	1.00	1.10	1.20
.25	546	136	61	34	22	15	11	9	7	5	5	4
.50	1082	271	120	68	43	30	22	17	13	11	9	8
.60	1331	333	148	83	53	37	27	21	16	13	11	9
2/3	1520	380	169	95	61	42	31	24	19	15	13	11
.70	1625	406	181	102	65	45	33	25	20	16	13	11
.75	1801	450	200	113	72	50	37	28	22	18	15	13
.80	2007	502	223	125	80	56	41	31	25	20	17	14
.85	2262	565	251	141	90	63	46	35	28	23	19	16
.90	2603	651	289	163	104	72	53	41	32	26	22	18
.95	3154	789	350	197	126	88	64	49	39	32	26	22
.99	4330	1082	481	271	173	120	88	68	53	43	36	30

| Power | \multicolumn{12}{c}{$a_1 = .05\ (a_2 = .10)$} |
| | \multicolumn{12}{c}{h} |
	.10	.20	.30	.40	.50	.60	.70	.80	.90	1.00	1.10	1.20
.25	188	47	21	12	8	5	4	3	2	2	2	1
.50	541	135	60	34	22	15	11	8	7	5	4	4
.60	721	180	80	45	29	20	15	11	9	7	6	5
2/3	862	215	96	54	34	24	18	13	11	9	7	6
.70	941	235	105	59	38	26	19	15	12	9	8	7
.75	1076	269	120	67	43	30	22	17	13	11	9	7
.80	1237	309	137	77	49	34	25	19	15	12	10	9
.85	1438	359	160	90	58	40	29	22	18	14	12	10
.90	1713	428	190	107	69	48	35	27	21	17	14	12
.95	2164	541	240	135	87	60	44	34	27	22	18	15
.99	3154	789	350	197	126	88	64	49	39	32	26	22

| Power | \multicolumn{12}{c}{$a_1 = .10\ (a_2 = .20)$} |
| | \multicolumn{12}{c}{h} |
	.10	.20	.30	.40	.50	.60	.70	.80	.90	1.00	1.10	1.20
.25	74	18	8	5	3	2	2	1	1	1	1	1
.50	328	82	36	21	13	9	7	5	4	3	3	2
.60	471	118	52	29	19	13	10	7	6	5	4	3
2/3	586	147	65	37	23	16	12	9	7	6	5	4
.70	652	163	72	41	26	18	13	10	8	7	5	5
.75	765	191	85	48	31	21	16	12	9	8	6	5
.80	902	225	100	56	36	25	18	14	11	9	7	6
.85	1075	269	119	67	43	30	22	17	13	11	9	7
.90	1314	328	146	82	53	36	27	21	16	13	11	9
.95	1713	428	190	107	69	48	35	27	21	17	14	12
.99	2603	651	289	163	104	72	53	41	32	26	22	18

Table 6.4.1 *(continued)*

$$a_2 = .01 \ (a_1 = .005)$$
h

Power	.10	.20	.30	.40	.50	.60	.70	.80	.90	1.00	1.10	1.20
.25	723	181	80	45	29	20	15	11	9	7	6	5
.50	1327	332	147	83	53	37	27	21	16	13	11	9
.60	1601	400	178	100	64	44	33	25	20	16	13	11
2/3	1808	452	201	113	72	50	37	28	22	18	15	13
.70	1922	481	214	120	77	53	39	30	24	19	16	13
.75	2113	528	235	132	85	59	43	33	26	21	17	15
.80	2336	584	260	146	93	65	48	36	29	23	19	16
.85	2610	652	290	163	104	72	53	41	32	26	22	18
.90	2976	744	331	186	119	83	61	46	37	30	25	21
.95	3563	891	396	223	143	99	73	56	44	36	29	25
.99	4806	1202	534	300	192	134	98	75	59	48	40	33

$$a_2 = .05 \ (a_1 = .025)$$
h

Power	.10	.20	.30	.40	.50	.60	.70	.80	.90	1.00	1.10	1.20
.25	330	83	37	21	13	9	7	5	4	3	3	2
.50	768	192	85	48	31	21	16	12	9	8	6	5
.60	980	245	109	61	39	27	20	15	12	10	8	7
2/3	1143	286	127	71	46	32	23	18	14	11	9	8
.70	1234	309	137	77	49	34	25	19	15	12	10	9
.75	1388	347	154	87	56	39	28	22	17	14	11	10
.80	1570	392	174	98	63	44	32	25	19	16	13	11
.85	1796	449	200	112	72	50	37	28	22	18	15	12
.90	2101	525	233	131	84	58	43	33	26	21	17	15
.95	2599	650	289	162	104	72	53	41	32	26	21	18
.99	3674	919	408	230	147	102	75	57	45	37	30	26

The Case 0 procedure involves finding (*a*) the table for the significance criterion (**a**) being used, then finding (*b*) the difference in arcsine-transformed **P**'s (**h**) along the horizontal stub and (*c*) the desired power along the vertical stub. This gives **n**, the necessary size for *each* sample to detect **h** at the **a** significance level with the desired power.

Illustrative Example

6.6   Consider again the research in example 6.1, where there is described a crosscultural test of the experimental hypothesis that, in circumstances which arouse anxiety, *S*s who were first-born or only children more frequently prefer to wait with others than do *S*s who were later born. It was found there that if the population proportions differed by $h = .30$, a test of the null hypothesis at $a_1 = .05$ using samples of 80 cases in each group, would have only a .60 probability of rejection (power). If power of .80 is desired, what sample sizes should be used? The specifications are

$$a_1 = .05, \qquad h = .30, \qquad \text{power} = .80.$$

Table 6.4.1 for $a_1 = .05$, column $h = .30$, and row power $= .80$ yields $n = 137$. The social psychologist would thus need samples of 137 each of the two kinds of Ss in order to have a probability of .80 of rejecting the null hypothesis if the population P's differed by $h = .30$.

6.4.2   CASE 1: $n_1 \neq n_2$. Although in manipulative experiments one does not ordinarily plan to use samples of unequal size (since the equal n condition is optimal), unequal n's can occur in planning when a sample proportion is already available for one population or when the size of one sample is necessarily fixed by other circumstances. In such an eventuality, the investigator is free to set the size of only one of the two samples. With one sample size fixed at n_F, the problem is to determine the necessary size of the sample whose size is at the investigator's disposal (n_U). Table 6.4.1 is used as in Case 0 with a, h, and desired power, and n is determined. To find n_U, substitute the fixed sample size (n_F) and the n read from Table 6.4.1 in

$$(6.4.2) \qquad\qquad n_U = \frac{n\, n_F}{2n_F - n}.$$

(See Section 2.4.2 when denominator is zero negative.)

Illustrative Example

6.7   A psychopharmacologist plans to study the efficacy of a new drug for first psychiatric admissions bearing a given admission diagnosis. He wishes to compare the discharge rate four months from admission of patients treated with this drug (E) with that of patients currently treated by other means (C). He wishes to detect with power of .90 a small difference, in either direction from the rate for C patients, accepting the proposed convention of a small difference of $h = .20$. He plans the test at the $a_2 = .01$ criterion. From past records of $n_F = 1600$ patients bearing the diagnosis, he has available a sample P_C. His specifications summary is

$$a_2 = .01, \qquad h = .20, \qquad \text{power} = .90.$$

In the section of Table 6.4.1. for $a_2 = .01$, column $h = .20$, and row power $= .90$, he finds $n = 744$. Thus, his specifications are met by two samples,

each of 744 cases. But he already has one sample of $n_F = 1600$ cases for the
C group. To find how many patients he requires in the E group, he substitutes
in formula (6.4.2) to find

$$n_U = \frac{744(1600)}{2(1600) - 744} = 485 \text{ cases.}$$

Thus, the availability of a sample of $n_F = 1600$ cases makes it possible
for him to satisfy his specifications (attain power of .90 to detect $h = .20$
at $a_2 = .01$) with a sample for the new drug of 485 cases.

6.4.3 CASE 2: ONE SAMPLE OF n OBSERVATIONS TO TEST $P = c$. In
using the n tables for the one-sample test, the only departure from Case 0
is that which was discussed for the use of the power tables for Case 2, namely
the proper value of h to use the tables (see Section 6.3.3). Briefly, to test
with a single sample the null hypothesis that a population P has some
specified value, i.e., H_0: $P = c$, and the ES is indexed in the usual way,
as a difference between arcsine transformed values of the alternate, P_1,
and c, namely $h_2' = \phi_1 - \phi_2$, entry into the n tables is made with $h = h_2' \sqrt{2}$.
If, as is probable, the resultant h is not tabled, recourse is taken to formula
(6.4.1).

Illustrative Example

6.8 Return to example 6.5, where an experimental psychologist was
testing a derivation from a mathematical model that a population response
rate was $P = .40$. With a test to be performed at $a_2 = .05$, given that the true
parameter differs from .40 by $ES = h_2' = .20$, how large a sample of animals
does he need to attain power of .95? He sets this high power requirement
because he wishes to interpret *non*significance as confirmatory of the model.

Since there is only one sample P yielding sampling error, as described in
Section 6.3.3, for the table entry he requires [formula (6.4.1)] $h = h_2' \sqrt{2} = .20 \sqrt{2} = .2828$. Thus, the specifications are

$$a_2 = .05, \quad h = .2828, \quad \text{power} = .95.$$

Since $h = .2828$ is not tabled, he follows the procedure described in
Section 6.4.1. Use the part of Table 6.4.1 for $a_2 = .05$, row power $= .95$,
and column $h = .10$ to find $n_{.10} = 2599$. Then substitute $n_{.10} = 2599$ and
$h = .2828$ in formula (6.4.1) for the required n:

$$n = \frac{2599}{100(.2828)^2} = 325.$$

Thus, if $P = .50$, a one-sample test of H_0: $P = .40$ performed at the $a_2 = .05$ level, in order to have .95 probability of rejection of H_0, must have sample $n = 325$. (This is much larger than the $n = 60$ experiment originally posited, but a nonsignificant result from the latter would have been inconclusive.)

6.5 THE USE OF THE TABLES FOR SIGNIFICANCE TESTING

6.5.1 GENERAL INTRODUCTION. As a convenience to the researcher, provision has been made in the power tables to facilitate significance testing. Power analysis is primarily relevant to the planning of experiments and thus with the alternate-hypothetical ES. Once the experiment is performed and the data are in, attention turns to the assessment of the null hypothesis in the light of the sample data.

For significance testing, we redefine our ES index, h, so that its elements are observed sample statistics rather than hypothetical population parameters, and call it h_s. For Cases 0 and 1, where the P's of two independent samples are being compared, the sample P_s values are transformed by the arcsine function, and

(6.5.1) $h_s = \phi_{s_1} - \phi_{s_2}$ (directional)

                        $= |\phi_{s_1} - \phi_{s_2}|$ (nondirectional).

Thus, h_s is simply the difference in sample ϕ values. It is related to the unit normal curve deviate (or "critical ratio") x, by

(6.5.2) $$h_s = x \sqrt{\frac{n_1 + n_2}{n_1 n_2}},$$

(6.5.3) $$x = h_s \sqrt{\frac{n_1 n_2}{n_1 + n_2}}.$$

These formulas are stated generally, so that the sample n's need not be equal. They simplify for the Case 0 condition of equal n (see below).

The value of h_s necessary for significance is called h_c, i.e., the criterion value of h_s. The second column of the power tables 6.3, headed h_c, carries these values as a function of n. Using these values, the normal curve deviate x need not be computed. One simply finds the sample difference in arcsine transformed ϕ's using Table 6.2.2, and compares it with the tabled h_c value for his sample size. If the obtained h_s value equals or exceeds h_c, his obtained difference is significant at the a level for that table; otherwise, it is not.

6.5.2 SIGNIFICANCE TESTING IN CASE 0, $n_1 = n_2 = n$. When the sample sizes are equal, the relationship between h_s and the normal deviate x are simplified:

$$(6.5.4) \qquad h_s = x \sqrt{\frac{2}{n}},$$

$$(6.5.5) \qquad x = h_s \sqrt{\frac{n}{2}}.$$

[Formula (6.5.4) was used for the computation of the tables, q_c values, x being taken as the normal curve deviate for the a criterion.]

Use of the h_c values in Case 0 is straightforward: the investigator looks up the arcsine $P = \phi$ values for the two P_s's in Table 6.2.2, finds their difference, h_s, and enters the appropriate power table depending on a, in the row for his n ($= n_1 = n_2$), and checks whether his h_s value equals or exceeds the tabled h_c value.

Illustrative Example

6.9 Reconsider the research described in example 6.2, where a clinical psychologist was planning a study to compare the relative treatment effectiveness of two ward atmospheres (T and C) by comparing the proportions of 100 cases originally admitted to each ward who are discharged within six months. Now assume that the experiment is performed as planned and the sample proportions discharged turn out to be .41 for the C condition and .57 for the T condition. Is this difference significant at the planned $a_2 = .05$ level? First, he looks up the ϕ transformation of these P_s's in Table 6.2.2, and finds them to be respectively, 1.390 and 1.711. Thus, $h_s = |1.711 - 1.390| = .321$. Therefore, the specifications are:

$$a_2 = .05, \qquad n = 100, \qquad h_s = .321.$$

In Table 6.3.5 (for $a_2 = .05$) for row $n = 100$, he finds under h_c the value .277. Since his h_s value exceeds h_c, his observed difference is significant. This determination may be sufficient for his purposes, but if he wants the exact normal deviate value, x, he can substitute in formula (6.5.5) and find $x = .321 \sqrt{100/2} = 2.27$.

6.5.3 SIGNIFICANCE TESTING IN CASE 1, $n_1 \neq n_2$. Inequality of sample sizes in significance testing using the tabled h_c values requires only finding the harmonic mean of the two n's, n', as described in Section 6.3.2 [formula (6.3.1)]:

$$n' = \frac{2n_1 n_2}{n_1 + n_2}.$$

The Tables 6.3 are applied, using n' for n. The procedure is otherwise exactly the same as for Case 0.

If the normal curve deviate value x is desired, it is found using formula (6.5.3), or, if n' has already been found, more simply by substituting n' for n in formula (6.5.5).

Illustrative Example

6.10   Example 6.3, which in turn referred to example 6.1, described a cross-cultural test of the experimental hypothesis that, under anxiety conditions, first-born and only children (A) more frequently than later-born (B) prefer to wait with others. As revised in example 6.3, sample sizes of $n_A = 80$ and $n_B = 245$ are available for a test at $a_1 = .05$. Assume now that when the experiment is run, he finds the sample proportions preferring to wait with others to be $56/80 = .70$ for the A sample and $159/245 = .65$ for the B sample. Since the difference is in the predicted direction $(P_A > P_B)$, the test proceeds. The P_s's are transformed to ϕ's by finding in Table 6.2.2 the values respectively of 1.982 and 1.875. Their difference, $h_s = 1.982 - 1.875 = .107$, is found. For use in the table, find n' from formula (6.3.1) (as in example 6.3):

$$n' = \frac{2(80)(245)}{80 + 245} = 120.6.$$

The specifications for significance testing of the sample difference are:

$$a_1 = .05, \qquad n' = 120.6, \qquad h_s = .107.$$

Table 6.3.2 (for $a_1 = .05$) for row $n = 120$ and column h_c yields .212 Since h_s is smaller than the criterion h_c, the difference is not significant at $a_1 = .05$.[7] Thus, the research provides no warrant for concluding the generalizability of the United States finding to this culture.

6.5.4   SIGNIFICANCE TESTING IN CASE 2: ONE SAMPLE, H_0: $P = c$. When the null hypothesis takes the form: "For a population from which a sample of n observations is randomly drawn, the P having a given characteristic equals c," an adjustment must be made of the tabled h_c value. This is because the tables were constructed for Case 0 conditions and hence allow for

---

[7] When n' is not tabulated, and intermediate h_c values are desired, linear interpolation will usually provide an adequate approximation. If greater accuracy is desired, either h_c or x can be solved by using formulas (6.5.2) and (6.5.3).

sampling error variance of two P_s's, while in Case 2 there is only one. The proper criterion for one sample tests of $P = c$ is

(6.5.6) $$h_c' = h_c \sqrt{\tfrac{1}{2}} = .707 h_c ,$$

where h_c is the tabulated value for n.

As for the observed h_s value for Case 2, we follow the principle expressed in (6.5.1) and simply define h_s' as we defined h_2' [formula (6.3.2)], merely substituting the sample value of ϕ_s for the population parameter ϕ_1:

(6.5.7) $$h_s' = \phi_s - \phi_c \qquad \text{(directional)}$$

$$= |\phi_s - \phi_c| \qquad \text{(nondirectional)}.$$

The prime is used to denote a one-sample test. The relationships between h_s' and the normal deviate x for the case are now

(6.5.8) $$h_s' = x \sqrt{\frac{1}{n}} ,$$

(6.5.9) $$x = h_s' \sqrt{n}.$$

Formula (6.5.9) can be used if the exact normal deviate ("critical ratio") is desired, e.g., for reporting results for publication.

Illustrative Example

6.11 Assume that the experimental psychologist of example 6.5, following the power analysis described therein, actually performs the experiment to test H_0: $P = .40$, but uses instead the more liberal rejection criterion of $a_2 = .20$ and a larger sample size of $n = 100$, both of these changes in specifications serving to make it easier to detect departures from, and hence reject, the model. (The reader can determine as an exercise that, if in fact, $P = .50$, then power is now approximately .75.) Given these new conditions, he finds that the sample proportion of animals giving the response is $47/100 = .47$. Can he conclude from this result that the null hypothesis is false, i.e., that the value predicted by the mathematical model, .40, is incorrect?

He finds the arcsine transformations of these two values from Table 6.2.2 to be 1.511 (for .47) and 1.369 (for .40), and their difference [formula (6.5.7)] $h_s' = |1.511 - 1.369| = .142$. This is the sample ES. His specifications, then, are

$$a_2 = .20, \qquad n = 100, \qquad h_s' = .142.$$

Table 6.3.3 (for $a_1 = .10$, but used here for $a_2 = .20$), with row $n = 100$ and column h_c, gives the value .181. This would be the criterion for a two-sample test where each $n = 100$. For this one-sample case, he goes on to find [formula (6.5.6)] $h_c' = .181\sqrt{\frac{1}{2}} = (.707)(.181) = .128$. This is the relevant criterion value, and since the sample $h_s' = .142$ exceeds it, the null hypothesis of $P = c = .40$ is rejected. The experiment, thus, casts serious doubt on the validity of the model.

If he wishes to determine the exact normal deviate value x which would result from this test, he finds [formula (6.5.9)] $x = .142\sqrt{100} = 1.42$.

7

Chi-Square Tests for Goodness of Fit and Contingency Tables

7.1 INTRODUCTION AND USE

This chapter is concerned with the most frequent application of the chi-square (χ^2) distribution in behavioral science applications, namely to sets of frequencies or proportions. Two types of circumstances may be distinguished:

1. Case 0: Goodness of Fit Tests. Here a single array of categories of sample frequencies or proportions is tested against a prespecified set which comprise the null hypothesis (*cf.*, McNemar, 1962, pp. 209–212, 231–236; Edwards, 1960, pp. 63–65; Hays, 1963, pp. 578–588).

2. Case 1: Contingency Tests. Here observed frequencies are each classified simultaneously by means of two different variables or principles of classification, i.e., in a two-way table. The joint frequencies are tested against a null hypothesis which specifies no association between the two bases of classification (see the following: McNemar, 1962, pp. 219–231; Edwards, 1960, pp. 65–73; Blalock, 1960, pp. 212–221).

The chi-square test on frequencies is quite general in its applicability to problems in data analysis in behavioral science, in both manipulative experiments and survey analysis. It is particularly appropriate with variables expressed as nominal scales or unordered categories, e.g., religion, marital status, experimental condition, etc.

When used for frequency comparisons, the chi-square test is a nonparametric test, since it compares entire distributions rather than parameters (means, variances) of distributions. Thus, other than the need to avoid very small hypothetical frequencies (*see* Guilford, 1965, pp. 237–238), the test is relatively free of constraining assumptions.

In the following section, the two types of tests will be described in greater detail in the context of the ES index.

7.2 THE EFFECT SIZE INDEX: e

We require for an ES index a "pure" number which increases with the degree of discrepancy between the distribution specified by the alternate hypothesis and that which represents the null hypothesis. We achieve "pureness" here by working with *relative* frequencies, i.e., proportions. In both cases, there are "cells"; categories in Case 0 and joint categories in Case 1. For each cell, there are two population proportions, one given by the null hypothesis, the other by the alternate. The ES index, **e**, measures the discrepancy between these paired proportions over the cells in the following way:

$$(7.2.1) \qquad\qquad \mathbf{e} = \sum_{i\,=\,1}^{m} \frac{(\mathbf{P}_{1i} - \mathbf{P}_{0i})^2}{\mathbf{P}_{0i}},$$

where $\mathbf{P}_{0i} =$ the proportion in cell **i** posited by the null hypothesis,

$\quad\ \mathbf{P}_{1i} =$ the proportion in cell **i** posited by the alternate hypothesis and reflects the effect for that cell, and

$\quad\ \mathbf{m} =$ the number of cells.

Thus, for each cell, the difference between the two hypothetical **P**'s is squared and divided by the null-specified $\mathbf{P}_0$; the resulting values are then added over the cells.

Note the identity in structure of formula (7.2.1) with that of the standard computing formula for χ^2 with frequencies; in **e**, proportions are used in place of frequencies (for generality), and the population values replace the sample values.[1] Indeed, if the *sample* proportions are used in the formula in place of the $\mathbf{P}_{1i}$'s, and the resulting $\mathbf{e}'$ multiplied by **n**, the total sample size, the result is the sample χ^2 value.

e varies from zero, when the paired **P**'s in all cells are equal and hence there is no effect and the null hypothesis is true, to an upper limit which depends on the nature of the problem, as is detailed below.

The structure of χ^2 tests on distributions (hence **e**) is "naturally" nondirectional. Only when there is $\mathbf{u} = 1$ degree of freedom in χ^2, are there only two directions in which discrepancies between null and alternate can occur. With more than 1 **df**, departures can occur in many directions. The results

---

[1] The technically oriented reader will note that **e** is simply the noncentrality parameter, lambda, divided by the total sample size.

of all these departures from the null are included in the upper tail rejection region, and, as normally used, χ^2 tests do not discriminate among these and are therefore nondirectional. The tests will be so treated here.

7.2.1 CASE 0: **e** AND GOODNESS OF FIT. The null hypothesis for goodness of fit tests is simply:

$$\mathbf{H}_0: \mathbf{P}_{01}, \mathbf{P}_{02}, \mathbf{P}_{03}, \ldots, \mathbf{P}_{0m}, \quad \left(\sum_{i=1}^{m} \mathbf{P}_{0i} = 1\right),$$

i.e., a specified distribution of proportions in **m** cells, summing to unity. A population of independent observations is posited as falling into **m** mutually exclusive and exhaustive classes with a specified proportion in each.

The source of such null-hypothetical distributions varies in different behavioral science applications. One common example is a test of the hypothesis that a population is normally distributed on a continuous variable **X**. Then, $\mathbf{H}_0$ is the array of proportions in successive step intervals of **X** which would accord with the form of the normal distribution (Guilford, 1965, pp. 243–247; McNemar, 1962, pp. 231–235). For **m** = 9 intervals, the successive $\mathbf{P}_{0i}$ values might be: $\mathbf{H}_0$: .020, .051, .118, .195, .232, .195, .118, .051, .020.

In some areas of behavioral science, a strong theory may yield predicted distributions of populations over relevant classes, or cells. For example, a behavioral geneticist may be enabled by Mendelian theory to predict the ratio of four behavior types resulting from cross-breeding to be 1:3:3:9. The theory would be expressed in proportions in the $\mathbf{H}_0$: .0625, .1875, .1875, .5625 (Edwards, 1960, pp. 63–65).

Another source of $\mathbf{H}_0$ might be an empirical distribution determined for the population in the past, as in census data. A contemporary sample could be tested against such an $\mathbf{H}_0$ in a study of social or economic change (Hays, 1963, pp. 580–584).

The logical structure of many experiments, e.g., those resulting in decisions or the expression of preference among **m** alternatives, suggests a null hypothesis of equiprobability: $\mathbf{H}_0: \mathbf{P}_{01} = \mathbf{P}_{02} = \mathbf{P}_{03} = \ldots = \mathbf{P}_{0m} = 1/\mathbf{m}$. Thus, a study of consumer preference among **m** = 4 advertising displays would posit $\mathbf{H}_{0i}$ $\mathbf{P}_{01} = .25$ for **i** = 1, 2, 3, 4.

The test for equiprobability can be seen as a generalization of the test $\mathbf{H}_0: \mathbf{P} = .50$ to which Chapter 5 was devoted. In the present context, the test of Chapter 5 is the test for equiprobability when **m** = 2.

Furthermore, the Case 0 circumstance for χ^2 tests of frequencies for **m** = 2 is an alternative procedure to the Chapter 6, Case 2 test that the proportion of a population having a given characteristic equals some specified value **c**. In present terms, the same hypothesis is stated as H_0: $P_{01} = c$, $P_{02} = 1 - c$.

By whichever of the above relevant approaches an H_0 set of P_{0i}'s is established, the alternative hypothesis is expressed by a paired set of P_{1i}'s and the departure or ES defined by **e** of formula (7.2.1). It is clear that with no departure, the numerator of each cell's contribution is zero, hence **e** = 0 when there is no effect, i.e., the null hypothesis is true. In general, the maximum value of **e** in Case 0 applications is infinity. This occurs when the null hypothesis specifies that for any given cell, $P_0 = 0$. If zero values for the P_{0i} are ruled out as inadmissible, **e** can become as large as we like by defining any P_0 value as very small (relative to its fixed paired P_1 value).

For the special circumstances of equiprobability in **m** cells, the maximum value of **e** is **m** − 1. Thus, for the **m** = 4 advertising displays, the maximum possible value of **e**, which occurs when all respondents prefer one display, is 4 − 1 = 3.

Despite the general upper limit of infinity, in practice, for sample sizes large enough to yield valid results with the χ^2 test, it is not generally necessary to make provision for **e** greater than .80 (a long way, indeed, from infinity!).

In Case 0 tests, in general, the degrees of freedom (**u**) for χ^2 is simply **m** − 1. An exception to this rule occurs where additional degrees of freedom are "lost" because of additional parameter estimation. In the normal curve fitting test, for example, where the sample yields estimates of the mean and standard deviation, each estimate costs an additional degree of freedom, so that **u** = **m** − 3. In the other examples given above, **u** is always **m** − 1.

In a later section, operationally defined values of **e** for "small," "medium," and "large" ES will be offered.

7.2.2 CASE 1: **e** AND CONTINGENCY TESTS. The most frequent application of χ^2 in behavioral science is to what are variously called "contingency," "independence," or "association" tests. They can also be viewed as tests of the equality of two or more distributions over a set of two or more categories.

Consider a circumstance where there are two variables or classification schemes, each made up of mutually exclusive and exhaustive categories. Call one of the variables **R**, made up of **r** ≥ 2 categories, and the other **K**, made up of **k** ≥ 2 categories. If all the members of a population are simultaneously characterized with regard to their category assignment on **R** and **K**, the results can be expressed in a two-way table of dimension **r** × **k**, with **rk** cells. In each cell, we can write the proportion of observations in the population which it contains. From such a table, one can determine whether

R is associated with (or contingent upon, or not independent of) **K** in the population, or, equivalently, whether the **r** subpopulations on the **R** variable have differing distributions over the **k** categories of **K**.[2]

For concreteness, consider the cross-classification Table (7.2.1) in which a population has been jointly characterized with regard to sex = **R** (**r** = 2) and political preference = **K** (**k** = 3). Note that the marginal (i.e., total) distribution for sex is .60, .40 and that for political preference .45, .45, .10.

TABLE 7.2.1

P₁ VALUES IN A JOINT DISTRIBUTION OF SEX AND
POLITICAL PREFERENCE

	Dem.	Rep.	Ind.	Sex marginal
Men	.22	.35	.03	.60
Women	.23	.10	.07	.40
Preference marginal	.45	.45	.10	1.00

Note that although the marginal ratio of men to women is .60: .40 or 3:2, the ratio for Republicans is 3.5:1, and the Democrats are made up about equally of men and women (i.e., 1:1). Similarly, one might note that although there are equal marginal proportions of Democrats and Republicans, there are more Republicans than Democrats among the men and the preference is reversed among the women. This inequality of ratios within a column (or row) of the table with the column (or row) marginal ratios constitutes evidence that **R** and **K** are not independent of each other, or that they are associated.

A formal way to describe this association proceeds by asking the question, "Given the two marginal distributions in this population, what cell values would constitute independence (or no association)?" This is readily found for each cell by multiplying its row marginal proportion by its column marginal proportion. Consider the proportion of men-Democrats which would evidence no association: Since .60 of the population are men, and .45 of the population are Democrats, the condition of no association would lead us to expect (.60)(.45) = .27 of the population being men-Democrats. The other no-association cell proportions are similarly computed and are given in Table 7.2.2. Note that this operation has resulted in within row (or column) ratios being equal to the row (or column) marginal ratios. In the

[2] **R** and **K** can be interchanged; the relationships are symmetrical.

TABLE 7.2.2

P_0 (No Association) Values in a Joint Distribution
of Sex and Political Preference

	Dem.	Rep.	Ind.	Sex marginal
Men	.27	.27	.06	.60
Women	.18	.18	.04	.40
Preference marginal	.45	.45	.10	1.00

circumstance described in Table 7.2.2, in contrast to that in Table 7.2.1, given the knowledge of a person's sex, one can make no better a guess as to political preference than doing so without such knowledge. The converse is also true, since the association is symmetric.

Although the above has been described in terms of association between **R** and **K**, it could also be understood as an inquiry into whether the different **R** groups (the two sexes) have the same proportional distribution over the various categories of **K** (political preference). In Table 7.2.1, they clearly do not, while in the no-association condition described in Table 7.2.2, they do.[3]

In the analysis of contingency tables, the null hypothesis conventionally tested is that of no association. Thus, for the issue of association between sex and political preference, the null hypothesis is represented by the P_0 values in the cells of Table 7.2.2. Small departures from these values would represent weak association (or dependence), large departures strong association. The degree of departure or ES index is given by **e**, as defined in formula (7.2.1). It is applied in **r** × **k** contingency tables in the same way as in goodness of fit tests. Each of the **rk** = **m** cells has a null-hypothetical P_0 value given by the product of the marginal proportions (such as in Table 7.2.2) and an alternate-hypothetical P_1 value reflecting the association posited (as in Table 7.2.1). For the problem considered, using the values in these tables,

$$e = \sum_{i=1}^{rk=6} \frac{(P_{1i} - P_{0i})^2}{P_{0i}} = \frac{(.22 - .27)^2}{.27} + \frac{(.35 - .27)^2}{.27} + \cdots + \frac{(.07 - .04)^2}{.04}$$

$$= .0093 + .0237 + .0150 + .0139 + .0356 + .0225$$

$$= .1200.$$

[3] Again we note that **R** and **K** can be interchanged.

Thus $e = .12$ indexes the amount of departure from no association, or the degree of association between sex and political preference in this population. Equivalently it can be understood as indexing the difference between men and women in their distribution over political preference.

In Case 1 tests, the number of degrees of freedom associated with the χ^2 for an $r \times k$ contingency table is given by

$$(7.2.2) \qquad u = (r - 1)(k - 1).$$

For the 2×3 table under consideration, $u = (2 - 1)(3 - 1) = (1)(2) = 2$. Because the marginals of both rows and columns are fixed, it is *not* the number of cells less one, as in Case 0.[4]

In contingency tables, the maximum value of e depends upon r, k, and the marginal conditions. If r and k are assigned so that r is not larger than k (this will be assumed throughout) and no restriction is put on the marginals, maximum e is $r - 1$. Thus, in the example, no P_1 values can be written which yield e greater than $2 - 1 = 1$. If for both marginals, the classes have equal proportions, i.e., $1/r$ for one set and $1/k$ for the other, maximum $e = r(r - 1)/k$.

e AND OTHER MEASURES OF ASSOCIATION. Although e is a useful ES index in the power analysis of contingency tables, as a measure of association it lacks familiarity and convenience. As noted above, its maximum is $r - 1$; hence e varies with the size of the smaller of the table's two dimensions.

There are several indices of association for $r \times k$ contingency tables which are familiar to behavioral scientists and which are simply related to e. These will be briefly described, and formulas relating them to e will be given. In Table 7.2.3, for the convenience of the reader, the equivalent values for these other indices are given for the values of e provided in the power and sample size tables in this chapter. The formulas and table make possible indexing ES in terms of these other measures.

Contingency Coefficient, **C.** The most widely used measure of association in contingency tables is **C**, Pearson's coefficient of contingency (McNemar, 1962, pp. 198–202; Guilford, 1965, pp. 338–339). The relationship among **C**, χ^2, and e is given by

$$(7.2.3) \qquad C = \sqrt{\frac{\chi^2}{\chi^2 + n}} = \sqrt{\frac{e}{e + 1}}.$$

---

[4] For example, note that in Table 7.2.1, after one has specified the 2 ($=u$) values .22 and .35, all the other cell values are determined by the requirement that they sum to the row and column totals.

(The first expression gives the *sample* C value, the second that of the population.)

For the population data of Table 7.2.1, for example, where $e = .12$, the C value equals $\sqrt{.12/(.12 + 1)} = \sqrt{.12/1.12} = .33$.

To express e in terms of C,

(7.2.4)
$$e = \frac{C^2}{1 - C^2}.$$

$C = 0$ when $e = 0$, indicating no association. The maximum value of C is not 1, but increases towards 1, as maximum e increases. We have seen that maximum e equals $r - 1$. Therefore, substituting in (7.2.3), maximum $C = \sqrt{(r - 1)/r}$. For example, a $2 \times k$ table ($k \geq 2$) has a maximum C of $\sqrt{(2 - 1)/2} = \sqrt{\frac{1}{2}} = .71$, while a $5 \times k$ table ($k \geq 5$) has a maximum C of $\sqrt{(5 - 1)/5} = \sqrt{4/5} = .89$. This varying upper limit dependency on r is generally considered a deficiency in the measure, becoming particularly awkward when one wishes to compare C values coming from tables of different size.

TABLE 7.2.3

EQUIVALENTS OF e IN TERMS OF C, ϕ, AND ϕ'

				ϕ'		
e	C	r = 2*	3	4	5	6
.05	.218	.224	.158	.129	.112	.100
.10	.302	.316	.224	.183	.158	.141
.20	.408	.447	.316	.258	.224	.200
.30	.480	.548	.387	.316	.274	.245
.40	.535	.632	.447	.365	.316	.283
.50	.577	.707	.500	.408	.354	.316
.60	.612	.775	.548	.447	.387	.346
.70	.642	.837	.592	.483	.418	.374
.80	.667	.894	.632	.516	.447	.400

* This column gives the equivalents in terms of ϕ, the product-moment correlation coefficient for the fourfold (2×2) table.

Note the relationship between e and C in Table 7.2.3. As e increases, C increases, but with progressively smaller increments.

ϕ, *The Fourfold Point Correlation Coefficient*. Among contingency tables, the most frequently analyzed in behavioral science is the 2×2 table. In 2×2 tables, one can conceive of each of the R and K dichotomous dimensions as scaled 0 for one category and 1 for the other (or any other distinct values) and compute a product-moment correlation coefficient between the two dimensions. In such circumstances the correlation coefficient[5] is called ϕ (see McNemar, 1962, pp. 197–198; Guilford, 1965, pp. 333–338). Its relationship to **e** is simple:

$$(7.2.5) \qquad \phi = \sqrt{\frac{\overline{\chi^2}}{n}} = \sqrt{\overline{e}}.$$

(The first expression is the *sample* ϕ value, the second that of the population.)

Squaring and transposing, we obtain

$$(7.2.6) \qquad e = \phi^2.$$

Since ϕ is a bonafide product moment correlation coefficient, ϕ^2 is interpretable as the proportion of variance (PV) shared by the two variables **R** and **K** (see Chapter 3; also Chapters 2, 4, 6). Thus, for the 2×2 table, **e** gives directly the PV shared by the two dichotomies.

The equivalent ϕ for tabled **e** values are given in Table 7.2.3 (in the column headed **r** = 2 under ϕ').

Cramér's ϕ'. A useful generalization of ϕ for contingency tables of any dimensionality is provided by Cramér's statistic ϕ' (Hays, 1963, pp. 605–606; Blalock, 1960, p. 230);

$$(7.2.7) \qquad \phi' = \sqrt{\frac{\chi^2}{n(r-1)}} = \sqrt{\frac{e}{r-1}},$$

where **r** is, as before, not greater than **k**. (Again, the first expression gives the sample value and the second the population value.) **e** in terms of ϕ' and **r** is given by

$$(7.2.8) \qquad e = \phi'^2(r-1).$$

Naturally, ϕ' cannot be interpreted as a product-moment correlation, since neither **R** nor **K** is, in general, metric or even ordered. But it does have a range between zero and a uniform upper limit of one. The latter is true because, as we have seen, the upper limit of **e** in a contingency table is **r** − 1.

That ϕ' is a generalization of ϕ can be seen when we note that for a 2×2 table, **r** = 2; formula (7.2.7) then gives for $\phi' \sqrt{e/(2-1)} = \sqrt{e}$ (= ϕ). This is why the ϕ equivalents of Table 7.2.3 are given under ϕ' for **r** = 2. The latter is more general, since it applies not only to 2×2 tables but to

---

[5] Not to be confused with the same symbol, ϕ, to indicate the arcsine transformation of **P** in Chapter 6.

$2 \times k$ tables. For example, for the association between sex and political preference in Table 7.2.1, a 2×3 table, $\phi' = \sqrt{.12/(2-1)} = \sqrt{.12} = .346$.

7.2.3 "SMALL," "MEDIUM," AND "LARGE" e VALUES. Since e is not a familiar index, it becomes particularly important to have some guide to its magnitude for the purpose of power analysis or the estimation of necessary sample size or both. The best guide here, as always, is the development of some sense of magnitude *ad hoc*, for a particular problem or a particular field. Since it is a function of proportions, the investigator should generally be able to express the size of the effect he wishes to be able to detect by writing a set of alternate-hypothetical proportions for either Case 0 or Case 1, and, with the null-hypothetical proportions, compute e. Some experimentation along these lines should provide one with a "feel" for e.

As in the other chapters, values of e for "small," "medium," and "large" ES are offered to serve as conventions for these qualitative adjectives. Their use requires particular caution, since, apart from their possible inaptness in any given substantive context, what is subjectively the "same" degree of departure (Case 0) or degree of association (Case 1) may yield varying e as the size of **r**, **k**, or **u** (degrees of freedom) changes, and conversely. Note, for example, in Table 7.2.3, that for constant e, ϕ' decreases as **r** increases. The investigator is best advised to use the conventional definitions as a general frame of reference for ES and not to take them too literally.

SMALL EFFECT SIZE: $e = .05$. For Case 0 goodness of fit applications, $e = .05$ for the following H_0, H_1 pairs, where in each instance H_0 posits equiprobability for the **m** cells, and the H_1 values are placed at equal intervals and symmetrically about $1/\mathbf{m}$:

$\mathbf{m} = 3$ H_0: .333 .333 .333
H_1: .242 .333 .425

$\mathbf{m} = 4$ H_0: .250 .250 .250 .250
H_1: .175 .225 .275 .325

$\mathbf{m} = 5$ H_0: .200 .200 .200 .200 .200
H_1: .137 .168 .200 .232 .263

$\mathbf{m} = 10$ H_0: .100 .100 .100 .100 .100 .100 .100 .100 .100 .100
H_1: .065 .073 .081 .088 .096 .104 .112 .119 .127 .135

The illustration of Case 1 instances of $e = .05$ would demand the presentation of several cumbersome contingency tables. Instead, attention is called to Table 7.2.3, where equivalents of $e = .05$ for **C**, ϕ, and ϕ' are given. Note that what is defined as a small degree of association implies a **C** of .218, and for a 2×2 table, a ϕ of .224. For larger tables, Cramér's ϕ' decreases, so that when the smaller dimension (of **r** categories) is 6, $\phi' = .100$.

MEDIUM EFFECT SIZE: $e = .10$. To illustrate a medium ES in Case 0 applications, the following H_0, H_1 pairs are presented in all of which $e = .10$:

$m = 3$ H_0: .333 .333 .333
         H_1: .204 .333 .462

$m = 4$ H_0: .250 .250 .250 .250
         H_1: .144 .215 .285 .356

$m = 5$ H_0: .200 .200 .200 .200 .200
         H_1: .111 .155 .200 .245 .289

$m = 10$ H_0: .100 .100 .100. 100 .100 .100 .100 .100 .100 .100
          H_1: .050 .061 .072 .083 .094 .106 .117 .128 .139 .150

For contingency tables (Case 1) we note, as before, the equivalences from Table 7.2.3. Equivalent to $e = .10$ are $C = .302$ and the fourfold $\phi = .316$. For ϕ' in larger tables, constant $e = .10$ implies diminishing values, e.g., $\phi' = .141$ for $r = 6$.

The P_1 values relating sex to political preference of Table 7.2.1 yielded an $e = .12$, slightly above our operational definition of a medium effect.

LARGE EFFECT SIZE: $e = .20$. As before, we here illustrate the large ES for Case 0 by a series of H_0, H_1 pairs for each of which $e = .20$:

$m = 3$ H_0: .333 .333 .333
         H_1: .150 .333 .516

$m = 4$ H_0: .250 .250 .250 .250
         H_1: .100 .200 .300 .400

$m = 5$ H_0: .200 .200 .200 .200 .200
         H_1: .074 .137 .200 .263 .326

$m = 10$ H_0: .100 .100 .100 .100 .100 .100 .100 .100 .100 .100
          H_1: .030 .045 .061 .077 .092 .108 .123 .139 .154 .170

For contingency tables, a large degree of association as defined here implies $C = .408$ and for the 2×2 table, $\phi = .447$ (Table 7.2.3). For larger tables, the ϕ' values decrease with constant $e = .20$ as r increases, e.g., for $r = 6$, $\phi' = .200$.

SOME FURTHER COMMENTS ON ES AND e. The Case 0 illustrations above were all for H_1 of an equally spaced departure from an H_0 of equiprobability. This was done for the sake of simplicity, but should not mislead the reader. *Any* full set of proportions can be tested as an H_0, and e will index the departure of *any* H_1 from it. Thus, when we define $e = .10$ as a medium departure of H_1 from H_0 or ES, any discrepancy yielding

$e = .10$ is so defined. For example, for $m = 4$, the following H_0, H_1 pair also represents an ES of $e = .10$, and their detectability by means of a χ^2 test is the same as for the $m = 4$ illustration above:

$$H_0: \quad .250 \quad .250 \quad .250 \quad .250$$
$$H_1: \quad .387 \quad .204 \quad .204 \quad .204$$

This is an $e = .10$ departure from equiprobability in which the effect is concentrated in the first category, the remainder being equiprobable.

The following pair illustrates yet another $e = .10$ departure from equiprobability for $m = 4$, one in which the effect is divided equally between the first two categories, and between the last two:

$$H_0: \quad .250 \quad .250 \quad .250 \quad .250$$
$$H_1: \quad .329 \quad .329 \quad .171 \quad .171$$

Since the departure from H_0 may occur in many ways, and since H_0 may itself occasionally represent other than an equiprobable distribution, clearly any given value of e may arise from a multiplicity of patterns of discrepancies. It is the size of e which is important. An investigator may specify an H_0 appropriate to his purpose, and posit an H_1 which he believes to be the true state of nature. He then obtains some specific e, say .10. He may be wrong about the specific H_1 set of P_1 values he has posited, but the power (or sample size) he determines from the tables for $e = .10$ will hold for *any* H_1 which yields $e = .10$. Thus, however they may have come about, his inference can be viewed as testing $H_0: e = 0$ against $H_1: e = .10$.

We reiterate a word of caution about the use of constant e values to define a given level of departure, such as the operational definitions of "small," "medium," and "large" ES as applied to Case 1 contingency tests. It was noted several times above that constant e implies a decreasing value for ϕ' as table size (specifically r) increases (see Table 7.2.3).[6] If an investigator thinks of amount of association in terms of ϕ', then clearly he cannot use the operational definitions suggested above, or any other pegged to a constant e. Thus, for example, if he is prepared to define a "large" amount of association as a $\phi' = .40$, this implies varying e depending on r: it would be $e = .16$ for a $2 \times k$ table, $e = .32$ for a $3 \times k$ table, $\cdots e = .80$ for a $6 \times k$ table [formula (7.2.8) and Table 7.2.3].

7.3 POWER TABLES

The power tables for this section are given on pages 221–241; the text follows on page 242.

---

[6] This is also true for a measure of association not discussed here, Tschuprow's T (Blalock, 1960, pp. 229–230). The remarks about ϕ in this context hold also for T.

Table 7.3.1

Power of X^2 at a = .01, u = 1

				e					
n	.05	.10	.20	.30	.40	.50	.60	.70	.80
25	07	16	37	56	72	83	90	95	97
30	09	20	45	66	81	90	95	98	99
35	11	24	53	75	88	95	98	99	*
40	12	28	60	81	92	97	99	*	
45	14	32	66	86	95	99	*		
50	16	37	72	90	97	99			
60	20	45	81	95	99	*			
70	24	53	88	98	99				
80	28	60	92	99	*				
90	32	66	95	*					
100	37	72	97						
120	45	81	99						
140	53	88	*						
160	60	92							
180	66	95							
200	72	97							
250	83	99							
300	90	*							
350	95								
400	97								
500	99								
600	*								

Table 7.3.2

Power of X^2 at a = .01, u = 2

				e					
n	.05	.10	.20	.30	.40	.50	.60	.70	.80
25	05	11	27	45	61	74	84	90	94
30	06	14	35	55	72	84	91	95	98
35	07	17	42	64	80	90	95	98	99
40	08	20	49	72	87	94	98	99	*
45	10	24	55	79	91	97	99	*	
50	11	27	61	84	94	98	99		
60	14	35	72	91	98	99	*		
70	17	42	80	95	99	*			
80	20	49	87	98	*				
90	24	55	91	99					
100	27	61	94	99					
120	35	72	98	*					
140	42	80	99						
160	49	87	*						
180	55	91							
200	61	94							
250	74	98							
300	84	99							
350	90	*							
400	94								
500	98								
600	99								
700	*								

* Power values below this point are greater than .995.

Table 7.3.3

Power of χ^2 at $a = .01$, $u = 3$

n	.05	.10	.20	.30	.40	.50	.60	.70	.80
25	04	09	22	38	54	68	78	86	91
30	05	11	29	48	65	78	87	93	96
35	06	14	35	57	74	86	93	97	98
40	07	16	42	65	82	91	96	98	99
45	08	19	48	72	87	95	98	99	*
50	09	22	54	78	91	97	99	*	
60	11	29	65	87	96	99	*		
70	14	35	74	93	98	*			
80	16	42	82	96	99				
90	19	48	87	98	*				
100	22	54	91	99					
120	29	65	96	*					
140	35	74	98						
160	42	82	99						
180	48	87	*						
200	54	91							
250	68	97							
300	78	99							
350	86	*							
400	91								
500	97								
600	99								
700	*								

Table 7.3.4

Power of χ^2 at $a = .01$, $u = 4$

n	.05	.10	.20	.30	.40	.50	.60	.70	.80
25	04	07	19	34	49	62	74	82	89
30	04	09	25	43	60	74	84	90	95
35	05	12	31	52	69	82	90	95	98
40	06	14	37	60	77	89	95	98	99
45	07	16	43	67	84	93	97	99	*
50	07	19	49	74	89	96	98	*	
60	09	25	60	84	95	98	*		
70	12	31	69	90	98	*			
80	14	37	77	95	99				
90	16	43	84	97	*				
100	19	49	89	98					
120	25	60	95	*					
140	31	69	98						
160	37	77	99						
180	43	84	*						
200	49	89							
250	62	95							
300	74	98							
350	82	*							
400	89								
500	96								
600	98								
700	*								

* Power values below this point are greater than .995.

Table 7.3.6

Power of χ^2 at a = .01, u = 6

n	.05	.10	.20	.30	.40	.50	.60	.70	.80
						e			
25	03	06	15	27	41	54	66	76	83
30	03	07	19	35	51	66	77	86	91
35	04	09	24	43	61	76	86	92	96
40	05	11	30	51	70	83	91	96	98
45	05	13	35	59	77	89	95	98	99
50	06	15	41	66	83	93	97	99	*
60	07	19	51	77	91	97	99	*	
70	09	24	61	86	96	99	*		
80	11	30	70	91	98	*			
90	13	35	77	95	99				
100	15	41	83	97	*				
120	19	51	91	99					
140	24	61	96	*					
160	30	70	98						
180	35	77	99						
200	41	83	*						
250	54	93							
300	66	97							
350	76	99							
400	83	*							
500	93								
600	97								
700	99								
800	*								

Table 7.3.5

Power of χ^2 at a = .01, u = 5

n	.05	.10	.20	.30	.40	.50	.60	.70	.80
						e			
25	03	06	17	30	44	57	70	79	86
30	04	08	22	38	55	70	80	88	93
35	04	10	27	47	65	79	88	94	97
40	05	12	33	55	74	86	93	97	99
45	06	14	38	63	80	91	96	98	99
50	06	17	44	70	86	94	98	99	*
60	08	22	55	80	93	98	99	*	
70	10	27	65	88	97	99	*		
80	12	33	74	93	99	*			
90	14	38	80	96	99				
100	17	44	86	98	*				
120	22	55	93	99					
140	27	65	97	*					
160	33	74	99						
180	38	80	99						
200	44	86	*						
250	57	94							
300	70	98							
350	79	99							
400	86	*							
500	94								
600	98								
700	99								
800	*								

* Power values below this point are greater than .995.

Table 7.3.8

Power of X^2 at $a = .01$, $u = 8$

n	.05	.10	.20	.30	.40	.50	.60	.70	.80
25	03	05	12	23	35	47	59	70	78
30	03	06	16	30	45	59	72	81	88
35	03	07	20	37	55	70	81	89	94
40	04	09	25	45	64	78	88	94	97
45	04	11	30	52	72	85	93	97	99
50	05	12	35	59	78	90	96	98	99
60	06	16	45	72	88	96	99	*	
70	07	20	55	81	94	98	*		
80	09	25	64	88	97	99			
90	11	30	72	93	99	*			
100	12	35	78	96	99				
120	16	45	88	99	*				
140	20	55	94	*					
160	25	64	97						
180	30	72	99						
200	35	78	99						
250	47	90	*						
300	59	96							
350	70	98							
400	78	99							
500	90	*							
600	96								
700	98								
800	99								
900	*								

Table 7.3.7

Power of X^2 at $a = .01$, $u = 7$

n	.05	.10	.20	.30	.40	.50	.60	.70	.80
25	03	05	13	25	37	50	62	73	81
30	03	07	18	32	48	62	74	83	90
35	04	08	22	40	58	72	83	90	95
40	04	10	27	48	67	81	90	95	98
45	05	12	32	55	74	87	94	97	99
50	05	13	37	62	81	91	96	99	*
60	07	18	48	74	90	96	99	*	
70	08	22	58	83	95	99	*		
80	10	27	67	90	98	*			
90	12	32	74	94	99				
100	13	37	81	96	*				
120	18	48	90	99					
140	22	58	95	*					
160	27	67	98						
180	32	74	99						
200	37	81	*						
250	50	91							
300	62	96							
350	72	99							
400	81	*							
500	91								
600	96								
700	99								
800	*								

* Power values below this point are greater than .995.

Table 7.3.9

Power of X^2 at a = .01, u = 9

n	.05	.10	.20	.30	.40	.50	.60	.70	.80
25	02	05	11	21	33	45	57	67	76
30	03	06	15	28	42	57	69	79	86
35	03	07	19	35	52	67	79	87	93
40	04	08	23	42	61	76	86	93	96
45	04	10	28	50	69	83	91	96	98
50	05	11	33	57	76	88	95	98	99
60	06	15	42	69	86	95	98	99	*
70	07	19	52	79	93	98	99	*	
80	08	23	61	86	96	99	*		
90	10	28	69	91	98	*			
100	11	33	76	95	99				
120	15	42	86	98	*				
140	19	52	93	99					
160	23	61	96	*					
180	28	69	98						
200	33	76	99						
250	45	88	*						
300	57	95							
350	67	98							
400	76	99							
500	88	*							
600	95								
700	98								
800	99								
900	*								

Table 7.3.10

Power of X^2 at a = .01, u = 10

n	.05	.10	.20	.30	.40	.50	.60	.70	.80
25	02	04	11	20	31	42	54	64	74
30	03	05	14	26	40	54	66	77	84
35	03	06	18	33	49	65	77	86	91
40	03	08	22	40	58	74	84	91	96
45	04	09	26	47	66	81	90	95	98
50	04	11	31	54	74	87	94	97	99
60	05	14	40	66	84	94	98	99	*
70	06	18	49	77	91	97	99	*	
80	08	22	58	84	96	99	*		
90	09	26	66	90	98	*			
100	11	31	74	94	99				
120	14	40	84	98	*				
140	18	49	91	99					
160	22	58	96	*					
180	26	66	98						
200	31	74	99						
250	42	87	*						
300	54	94							
350	65	97							
400	74	99							
500	87	*							
600	94								
700	97								
800	99								
900	*								

* Power values below this point are greater than .995.

Table 7.3.11

Power of χ^2 at a = .01, u = 12

n	.05	.10	.20	.30	.40	.50	.60	.70	.80
25	02	04	09	17	27	38	49	60	69
30	02	05	12	23	36	49	62	73	81
35	03	06	16	29	45	60	73	82	89
40	03	07	19	36	54	69	81	89	94
45	03	08	23	43	62	77	87	94	97
50	04	09	27	49	69	83	92	96	99
60	05	12	36	62	81	92	97	99	*
70	06	16	45	73	89	96	99	*	
80	07	19	54	81	94	99	*		
90	08	23	62	87	97	99			
100	09	27	69	92	99	*			
120	12	36	81	97	*				
140	16	45	89	99					
160	19	54	94	*					
180	23	62	97						
200	27	69	99	*					
250	38	83	*						
300	49	92							
350	60	96							
400	69	99							
500	83	*							
600	92								
700	96								
800	99								
900	99								
1000	*								

Table 7.3.12

Power of χ^2 at a = .01, u = 16

n	.05	.10	.20	.30	.40	.50	.60	.70	.80
25	02	03	08	14	22	32	42	52	62
30	02	04	10	19	30	42	54	65	75
35	02	05	13	24	38	52	65	76	84
40	03	06	16	30	46	62	75	84	91
45	03	07	19	36	54	70	82	90	95
50	03	08	22	42	62	77	88	94	97
60	04	10	30	54	75	88	95	98	99
70	05	13	38	65	84	94	98	99	*
80	06	16	46	75	91	97	99	*	
90	07	19	54	82	95	99	*		
100	08	22	62	88	97	*			
120	10	30	75	95	99				
140	13	38	84	98	*				
160	16	46	91	99					
180	19	54	95	*					
200	22	62	97						
250	32	77	*						
300	42	88							
350	52	94							
400	62	97							
500	77	*							
600	88								
700	94								
800	97								
900	99								
1000	*								

* Power values below this point are greater than .995.

Table 7.3.14

Power of X^2 at $a = .01$, $u = 24$

n	.05	.10	.20	.30	.40	.50	.60	.70	.80
25	02	03	06	10	17	24	33	42	51
30	02	03	07	14	22	33	43	54	64
35	02	04	09	18	29	42	54	65	75
40	02	04	12	22	36	51	64	75	84
45	02	05	14	27	43	59	73	83	90
50	03	06	17	33	51	67	80	89	94
60	03	07	22	43	64	80	90	95	98
70	04	09	29	54	75	89	95	98	*
80	04	12	36	64	84	94	98	*	
90	05	14	43	73	90	97	99		
100	06	17	51	80	94	99	*		
120	07	22	64	90	98	*			
140	09	29	75	95	*				
160	12	36	84	98					
180	14	43	90	99					
200	17	51	94	*					
250	24	67	99						
300	33	80	*						
350	42	89							
400	51	94							
500	67	99							
600	80	*							
700	89								
800	94								
900	97								
1000	99								

Table 7.3.13

Power of X^2 at $a = .01$, $u = 20$

n	.05	.10	.20	.30	.40	.50	.60	.70	.80
25	02	03	07	12	19	28	37	46	56
30	02	04	08	16	26	37	48	59	69
35	02	04	11	21	33	46	59	71	80
40	02	05	13	26	41	56	69	80	87
45	03	06	16	31	48	64	77	87	92
50	03	07	19	37	56	72	84	91	96
60	04	08	26	48	69	84	92	97	99
70	04	11	33	59	80	91	97	99	*
80	05	13	41	69	87	96	99	*	
90	06	16	48	77	92	98	*		
100	07	19	56	84	96	99			
120	08	26	69	92	99	*			
140	11	33	80	97	*				
160	13	41	87	99					
180	16	48	92	*					
200	19	56	96						
250	28	72	99						
300	37	84	*						
350	46	91							
400	56	96							
500	72	99							
600	84	*							
700	91								
800	96								
900	98								
1000	99								

* Power values below this point are greater than .995.

Table 7.3.15

Power of χ^2 at a = .05, u = 1

n	.05	.10	.20	.30	.40	.50	.60	.70	.80
25	20	35	61	78	89	94	97	99	99
30	23	41	69	85	93	97	99	*	*
35	26	46	75	90	96	99	*		
40	29	52	81	93	98	99			
45	32	56	85	96	99	*			
50	35	61	89	97	99	*			
60	41	69	93	99	*				
70	46	75	96	*					
80	52	81	98						
90	56	85	99						
100	61	89	99						
120	69	93	*						
140	75	96							
160	81	98							
180	85	99							
200	89	99							
250	94	*							
300	97								
350	99								
400	99								
500	*								

Table 7.3.16

Power of χ^2 at a = .05, u = 2

n	.05	.10	.20	.30	.40	.50	.60	.70	.80
25	16	27	50	69	82	90	94	97	99
30	18	32	58	77	88	94	97	99	*
35	20	37	66	83	93	97	99	*	
40	23	42	72	88	96	99	*		
45	25	46	77	92	97	99			
50	27	50	82	94	99	*			
60	32	58	88	97	*				
70	37	66	93	99					
80	42	72	96	*					
90	46	77	97						
100	50	82	99						
120	58	88	*						
140	66	93							
160	72	96							
180	77	97							
200	82	99							
250	90	*							
300	94								
350	97								
400	99								
500	*								

* Power values below this point are greater than .995.

Table 7.3.18

Power of χ^2 at a = .05, u = 4

					e				
n	.05	.10	.20	.30	.40	.50	.60	.70	.80
25	12	21	40	57	72	82	89	94	96
30	14	24	47	66	80	89	94	97	99
35	15	28	54	74	87	94	97	99	*
40	17	32	60	80	91	96	99	*	
45	19	36	66	85	94	98	99		
50	21	40	72	89	96	99	*		
60	24	47	80	94	99	*			
70	28	54	87	97	*				
80	32	60	91	99					
90	36	66	94	99					
100	40	72	96	*					
120	47	80	99						
140	54	87	*						
160	60	91							
180	66	94							
200	72	96							
250	82	99							
300	89	*							
350	94								
400	96								
500	99								
600	*								

Table 7.3.17

Power of χ^2 at a = .05, u = 3

					e				
n	.05	.10	.20	.30	.40	.50	.60	.70	.80
25	13	23	44	62	76	86	92	95	98
30	15	27	52	71	84	92	96	98	99
35	17	32	59	78	90	95	98	99	*
40	19	36	65	84	93	98	99	*	
45	21	40	71	88	96	99	*		
50	23	44	76	92	98	99			
60	27	52	84	96	99	*			
70	32	59	90	98	*				
80	36	65	93	99					
90	40	71	96	*					
100	44	76	98						
120	52	84	99						
140	59	90	*						
160	65	93							
180	71	96							
200	76	98							
250	86	99							
300	92	*							
350	95								
400	98								
500	99								
600	*								

* Power values below this point are greater than .995.

Table 7.3.19

Power of X^2 at $a = .05$, $u = 5$

n	e								
	.05	.10	.20	.30	.40	.50	.60	.70	.80
25	11	19	36	53	68	79	87	92	95
30	13	22	43	62	77	87	93	96	98
35	14	26	50	70	84	92	96	98	99
40	16	29	56	77	89	95	98	99	*
45	17	33	62	82	93	97	99	*	
50	19	36	68	87	95	98	*		
60	22	43	77	93	98	*			
70	26	50	84	96	99	*			
80	29	56	89	98	*				
90	33	62	93	99					
100	36	68	95	*					
120	43	77	98						
140	50	84	99						
160	56	89	*						
180	62	93							
200	68	95							
250	79	98							
300	87	*							
350	92								
400	95								
500	98								
600	*								

Table 7.3.20

Power of X^2 at $a = .05$, $u = 6$

n	e								
	.05	.10	.20	.30	.40	.50	.60	.70	.80
25	11	18	34	50	64	76	84	90	94
30	12	21	40	59	74	84	91	95	97
35	13	24	47	67	81	90	95	98	99
40	15	27	53	74	87	94	97	99	*
45	16	30	59	80	91	96	99	*	
50	18	34	64	84	94	98	99		
60	21	40	74	91	97	99	*		
70	24	47	81	95	99	*			
80	27	53	87	97	*				
90	30	59	91	99					
100	34	64	94	99					
120	40	74	97	*					
140	47	81	99						
160	53	87	*						
180	59	91							
200	64	94							
250	76	98							
300	84	99							
350	90	*							
400	94								
500	98								
600	99								
700	*								

* Power values below this point are greater than .995.

Table 7.3.22

Power of χ^2 at a = .05, u = 8

n	.05	.10	.20	.30	.40	.50	.60	.70	.80
25	10	16	30	45	59	71	80	87	92
30	11	18	36	53	68	80	88	93	96
35	12	21	42	61	77	87	93	96	98
40	13	24	48	68	83	92	96	98	99
45	14	27	53	75	88	95	98	99	*
50	16	30	59	80	92	97	99	*	
60	18	36	68	88	96	99	*		
70	21	42	77	93	98	*			
80	24	48	83	96	99				
90	27	53	88	98	*				
100	30	59	92	99					
120	36	68	96	*					
140	42	77	98						
160	48	83	99						
180	53	88	*						
200	59	92							
250	71	97							
300	80	99							
350	87	*							
400	92								
500	97								
600	99								
700	*								

Table 7.3.21

Power of χ^2 at a = .05, u = 7

n	.05	.10	.20	.30	.40	.50	.60	.70	.80
25	10	16	31	47	61	73	82	88	93
30	11	19	38	56	71	82	89	94	97
35	13	22	44	64	79	88	94	97	99
40	14	25	50	71	85	93	97	99	99
45	15	28	56	77	89	96	98	99	*
50	16	31	61	82	93	97	99	*	
60	19	38	71	89	97	99	*		
70	22	44	79	94	99	*			
80	25	50	85	97	99				
90	28	56	89	98	*				
100	31	61	93	99					
120	38	71	97	*					
140	44	79	99						
160	50	85	99						
180	56	89	*						
200	61	93							
250	73	97							
300	82	99							
350	88	*							
400	93								
500	97								
600	99								
700	*								

* Power values below this point are greater than .995.

Table 7.3.24

Power of X^2 at $a = .05$, $u = 10$

n	.05	.10	.20	.30	.40	.50	.60	.70	.80
25	09	14	27	41	54	66	76	84	89
30	10	17	32	49	64	76	85	91	95
35	11	19	38	57	72	84	91	95	98
40	12	21	43	64	79	89	95	98	99
45	13	24	49	70	85	93	97	99	*
50	14	27	54	76	89	96	98	99	*
60	17	32	64	85	95	98	*		
70	19	38	72	91	98	99	*		
80	21	43	79	95	99	*			
90	24	49	85	97	*				
100	27	54	89	98	*				
120	32	64	95	*					
140	38	72	98	*					
160	43	79	99	*					
180	49	85	*						
200	54	89							
250	66	96							
300	76	98							
350	84	99							
400	89	*							
500	96								
600	98								
700	99								
800	*								

Table 7.3.23

Power of X^2 at $a = .05$, $u = 9$

n	.05	.10	.20	.30	.40	.50	.60	.70	.80
25	09	15	28	43	56	68	78	85	90
30	10	17	34	51	66	78	86	92	95
35	11	20	40	59	74	85	92	96	98
40	13	23	45	66	81	90	95	98	99
45	14	25	51	72	86	94	97	99	*
50	15	28	56	78	90	96	99	*	
60	17	34	66	86	95	99	*		
70	20	40	74	92	98	*			
80	23	45	81	95	99	*			
90	25	51	86	97	*				
100	28	56	90	99	*				
120	34	66	95	*					
140	40	74	98	*					
160	45	81	99	*					
180	51	86	*						
200	56	90							
250	68	96							
300	78	99							
350	85	*							
400	90								
500	96								
600	99								
700	*								

* Power values below this point are greater than .995.

Table 7.3.25

Power of χ^2 at a = .05, u = 12

n	.05	.10	.20	.30	.40	.50	.60	.70	.80
25	09	13	25	38	50	62	72	80	87
30	10	15	30	45	60	72	82	89	93
35	10	18	35	53	69	80	89	94	97
40	11	20	40	60	76	87	93	97	98
45	12	22	45	67	82	91	96	98	99
50	13	25	50	72	87	94	98	99	*
60	15	30	60	82	93	98	99	*	
70	18	35	69	89	97	99	*		
80	20	40	76	93	98	*			
90	22	45	82	96	99				
100	25	50	87	98	*				
120	30	60	93	99					
140	35	69	97	*					
160	40	76	98						
180	45	82	99						
200	50	87	*						
250	62	94							
300	72	98							
350	80	99							
400	87	*							
500	94								
600	98								
700	99								
800	*								

Table 7.3.26

Power of χ^2 at a = .05, u = 16

n	.05	.10	.20	.30	.40	.50	.60	.70	.80
25	08	12	21	33	45	56	66	75	82
30	09	14	26	40	54	66	76	84	90
35	10	15	30	47	62	75	84	90	95
40	10	17	35	54	70	82	90	95	97
45	11	19	40	60	76	87	94	97	99
50	12	21	45	66	82	91	96	98	99
60	14	26	54	76	90	96	99	*	*
70	15	30	62	84	95	98	*		
80	17	35	70	90	97	99			
90	19	40	76	94	99	*			
100	21	45	82	96	99				
120	26	54	90	99	*				
140	30	62	95	*					
160	35	70	97						
180	40	76	99						
200	45	82	99						
250	56	91	*						
300	66	96							
350	75	98							
400	82	99							
500	91	*							
600	96								
700	98								
800	99								
900	*								

* Power values below this point are greater than .995.

Table 7.3.27

Power of χ^2 at a = .05, u = 20

n	.05	.10	.20	.30	.40	.50	.60	.70	.80
25	08	11	19	29	40	51	61	70	78
30	08	13	23	36	49	61	72	80	87
35	09	14	27	42	57	70	80	87	92
40	10	16	31	49	65	78	87	92	96
45	10	18	36	55	72	84	91	96	98
50	11	19	40	61	78	88	94	98	99
60	13	23	49	72	87	94	98	99	*
70	14	27	57	80	92	98	99	*	
80	16	31	65	87	96	99	*		
90	18	36	72	91	98	*			
100	19	40	78	94	99				
120	23	49	87	98	*				
140	27	57	92	99					
160	31	65	96	*					
180	36	72	98						
200	40	78	99						
250	51	88	*						
300	61	94							
350	70	98							
400	78	99							
500	88	*							
600	94								
700	98								
800	99								
900	*								

Table 7.3.28

Power of χ^2 at a = .05, u = 24

n	.05	.10	.20	.30	.40	.50	.60	.70	.80
25	07	10	18	27	37	47	57	66	74
30	08	12	21	33	45	57	67	76	83
35	09	13	25	39	53	66	76	84	90
40	09	15	29	45	60	74	83	90	94
45	10	16	33	51	67	80	89	94	97
50	10	18	37	57	74	85	92	96	98
60	12	21	45	67	83	92	97	99	*
70	13	25	53	76	90	96	99	*	
80	15	29	60	83	94	98	*		
90	16	33	67	89	97	99			
100	18	37	74	92	98	*			
120	21	45	83	97	*				
140	25	53	90	99					
160	29	60	94	*					
180	33	67	97						
200	37	74	98						
250	47	85	*						
300	57	92							
350	66	96							
400	74	98							
500	85	*							
600	92								
700	96								
800	98								
900	99								
1000	*								

* Power values below this point are greater than .995.

Table 7.3.29

Power of χ^2 at a = .10, u = 1

n	.05	.10	.20	.30	.40	.50	.60	.70	.80
25	30	48	72	86	94	97	99	99	*
30	34	54	79	91	97	99	*	*	
35	38	59	84	95	98	99			
40	41	64	88	97	99	*			
45	44	68	91	98	*				
50	48	72	94	99					
60	54	79	97	*					
70	59	84	98						
80	64	88	99						
90	68	91	*						
100	72	94							
120	79	97							
140	84	98							
160	88	99							
180	91	*							
200	94								
250	97								
300	99								
350	99								
400	*								

Table 7.3.30

Power of χ^2 at a = .10, u = 2

n	.05	.10	.20	.30	.40	.50	.60	.70	.80
25	25	39	63	79	89	94	97	99	99
30	28	44	70	85	93	97	99	*	*
35	31	49	76	90	96	99	*		
40	33	54	81	93	98	99			
45	36	59	85	96	99	*			
50	39	63	89	97	99				
60	44	70	93	99	*				
70	49	76	96	*					
80	54	81	98						
90	59	85	99						
100	63	89	99						
120	70	93	*						
140	76	96							
160	81	98							
180	85	99							
200	89	99							
250	94	*							
300	97								
350	99								
400	99								
500	*								

* Power values below this point are greater than .995.

Table 7.3.31

Power of χ^2 at a = .10, u = 3

n	.05	.10	.20	.30	.40	.50	.60	.70	.80
25	22	34	57	73	85	92	96	98	99
30	25	39	64	81	90	96	98	99	*
35	27	44	71	86	94	98	99	*	
40	30	48	76	90	97	99	*		
45	32	53	81	93	98	99			
50	34	57	85	96	99	*			
60	39	64	90	98	*				
70	44	71	94	99					
80	48	76	97	*					
90	53	81	98						
100	57	85	99						
120	64	90	*						
140	71	94							
160	76	97							
180	81	98							
200	85	99							
250	92	*							
300	96								
350	98								
400	99								
500	*								

Table 7.3.32

Power of χ^2 at a = .10, u = 4

n	.05	.10	.20	.30	.40	.50	.60	.70	.80
25	20	31	52	69	81	89	94	97	98
30	23	36	60	77	88	94	97	99	99
35	25	40	66	83	92	97	99	99	*
40	27	44	72	88	95	98	99	*	
45	29	48	77	91	97	99	*		
50	31	52	81	94	98	*			
60	36	60	88	97	99				
70	40	66	92	99	*				
80	44	72	95	99					
90	48	77	97	*					
100	52	81	98						
120	60	88	99						
140	66	92	*						
160	72	95							
180	77	97							
200	81	98							
250	89	*							
300	94								
350	97								
400	98								
500	*								

* Power values below this point are greater than .995.

Table 7.3.33

Power of χ^2 at a = .10, u = 5

n	.05	.10	.20	.30	.40	.50	.60	.70	.80
25	19	29	49	66	78	87	92	96	98
30	21	33	56	74	85	92	96	98	99
35	23	37	63	80	90	96	98	99	*
40	25	41	69	85	94	98	99	*	
45	27	45	74	89	96	99	*		
50	29	49	78	92	98	99			
60	33	56	85	96	99	*			
70	37	63	90	98	*				
80	41	69	94	99					
90	45	74	96	*					
100	49	78	98						
120	56	85	99						
140	63	90	*						
160	69	94							
180	74	96							
200	78	98							
250	87	99							
300	92	*							
350	96								
400	98								
500	99								
600	*								

Table 7.3.34

Power of χ^2 at a = .10, u = 6

n	.05	.10	.20	.30	.40	.50	.60	.70	.80
25	18	28	46	63	75	85	91	95	97
30	20	31	53	71	83	91	95	98	99
35	22	35	60	78	89	95	98	99	*
40	24	39	66	83	92	97	99	*	
45	26	43	71	87	95	98	99		
50	28	46	75	91	97	99	*		
60	31	53	83	95	99	*			
70	35	60	89	98	*				
80	39	66	92	99					
90	43	71	95	99					
100	46	75	97	*					
120	53	83	99						
140	60	89	*						
160	66	92							
180	71	95							
200	75	97							
250	85	99							
300	91	*							
350	95								
400	97								
500	99								
600	*								

* Power values below this point are greater than .995.

Table 7.3.35

Power of X^2 at a = .10, u = 7

n	.05	.10	.20	.30	.40	.50	.60	.70	.80
25	18	26	44	60	73	83	89	93	96
30	19	30	51	68	81	89	94	97	98
35	21	33	57	75	87	93	97	99	99
40	23	37	63	81	91	96	98	99	*
45	25	40	68	85	94	98	99	*	
50	26	44	73	89	96	99	*		
60	30	51	81	94	98	*			
70	33	57	87	97	99				
80	37	63	91	98	*				
90	40	68	94	99					
100	44	73	96	*					
120	51	81	98						
140	57	87	99						
160	63	91	*						
180	68	94							
200	73	96							
250	83	99							
300	89	*							
350	93								
400	96								
500	99								
600	*								

Table 7.3.36

Power of X^2 at a = .10, u = 8

n	.05	.10	.20	.30	.40	.50	.60	.70	.80
25	17	25	42	58	71	81	88	92	95
30	19	28	49	66	79	88	93	96	98
35	20	32	55	73	85	92	96	98	99
40	22	35	61	79	90	95	98	99	*
45	24	39	66	84	93	97	99	*	
50	25	42	71	88	95	98	*		
60	28	49	79	93	98	*			
70	32	55	85	96	99				
80	35	61	90	98	*				
90	39	66	93	99					
100	42	71	95	*					
120	49	79	98						
140	55	85	99						
160	61	90	*						
180	66	93							
200	71	95							
250	81	98							
300	88	*							
350	92								
400	95								
500	98								
600	*								

* Power values below this point are greater than .995.

Table 7.3.37

Power of χ^2 at a = .10, u = 9

n	.05	.10	.20	.30	.40	.50	.60	.70	.80
25	17	24	40	56	69	79	86	91	95
30	18	27	47	64	77	86	92	96	98
35	20	31	53	71	84	91	96	98	99
40	21	34	58	77	88	95	98	99	*
45	23	37	64	82	92	97	99	*	
50	24	40	69	86	95	98	99		
60	27	47	77	92	98	99	*		
70	31	53	84	96	99	*			
80	34	58	88	98	*				
90	37	64	92	99					
100	40	69	95	99					
120	47	77	98	*					
140	53	84	99						
160	58	88	*						
180	64	92							
200	69	95							
250	79	98							
300	86	99							
350	91	*							
400	95								
500	98								
600	99								
700	*								

Table 7.3.38

Power of χ^2 at a = .10, u = 10

n	.05	.10	.20	.30	.40	.50	.60	.70	.80
25	16	23	39	54	67	77	85	90	94
30	18	26	45	62	75	85	91	95	97
35	19	29	51	69	82	90	95	98	99
40	20	33	57	75	87	94	97	99	*
45	22	36	62	80	91	96	99	99	
50	23	39	67	85	94	98	99	*	
60	26	45	75	91	97	99	*		
70	29	51	82	95	99	*			
80	33	57	87	97	*				
90	36	62	91	99					
100	39	67	94	99					
120	45	75	97	*					
140	51	82	99						
160	57	87	*						
180	62	91							
200	67	94							
250	77	98							
300	85	99							
350	90	*							
400	94								
500	98								
600	99								
700	*								

* Power values below this point are greater than .995.

Table 7.3.39

Power of χ^2 at $a = .10$, $u = 12$

n	.05	.10	.20	.30	.40	.50	.60	.70	.80
25	16	22	36	51	63	74	82	88	92
30	17	25	42	58	72	82	89	94	96
35	18	28	48	66	79	88	94	97	98
40	19	31	53	72	85	92	96	98	99
45	21	33	58	77	89	95	98	99	*
50	22	36	63	82	92	97	99	*	
60	25	42	72	89	96	99	*		
70	28	48	79	94	98	*			
80	31	53	85	96	99	*			
90	33	58	89	98	*				
100	36	63	92	99					
120	42	72	96	*					
140	48	79	98						
160	53	85	99						
180	58	89	*						
200	63	92							
250	74	97							
300	82	99							
350	88	*							
400	92								
500	97								
600	99								
700	*								

Table 7.3.40

Power of χ^2 at $a = .10$, $u = 16$

n	.05	.10	.20	.30	.40	.50	.60	.70	.80
25	15	20	33	46	58	68	77	84	89
30	16	23	38	53	66	77	85	91	94
35	17	25	43	60	74	84	91	95	97
40	18	28	48	66	80	89	94	97	99
45	19	30	53	72	85	93	97	99	99
50	20	33	58	77	89	95	98	99	*
60	23	38	66	85	94	98	99	*	
70	25	43	74	91	97	99	*		
80	28	48	80	94	99	*			
90	30	53	85	97	*				
100	33	58	89	98					
120	38	66	94	99					
140	43	74	97	*					
160	48	80	99						
180	53	85	99						
200	58	89	*						
250	68	95							
300	77	98							
350	84	99							
400	89	*							
500	95								
600	98								
700	99								
800	*								

* Power values below this point are greater than .995.

Table 7.3.42

Power of χ^2 at $a = .10$, $u = 24$

n	.05	.10	.20	.30	.40	.50	.60	.70	.80
25	14	18	28	39	50	60	69	77	83
30	15	20	32	46	58	69	78	85	90
35	16	22	37	52	66	77	85	91	95
40	16	24	41	58	72	83	90	95	97
45	17	26	46	64	78	88	94	97	99
50	18	28	50	69	83	92	96	98	99
60	20	32	58	78	90	96	99	*	
70	22	37	66	85	95	98	*		
80	24	41	72	90	97	99			
90	26	46	78	94	99	*			
100	28	50	83	96	99				
120	32	58	90	99	*				
140	37	66	95	*					
160	41	72	97						
180	46	78	99						
200	50	83	99						
250	60	92	*						
300	69	96							
350	77	98							
400	83	99							
500	92	*							
600	96								
700	98								
800	99								
900	*								

Table 7.3.41

Power of χ^2 at $a = .10$, $u = 20$

n	.05	.10	.20	.30	.40	.50	.60	.70	.80
25	14	19	30	42	53	64	73	80	86
30	15	21	35	49	62	73	82	88	92
35	16	23	40	56	70	80	88	93	96
40	17	26	44	62	76	86	92	96	98
45	18	28	49	68	82	90	95	98	99
50	19	30	53	73	86	93	97	99	*
60	21	35	62	82	92	97	99	*	
70	23	40	70	88	96	99	*		
80	26	44	76	92	98	*			
90	28	49	82	95	99				
100	30	53	86	97	*				
120	35	62	92	99					
140	40	70	96	*					
160	44	76	98						
180	49	82	99						
200	53	86	*						
250	64	93							
300	73	97							
350	80	99							
400	86	*							
500	93	*							
600	97								
700	99								
800	*								

* Power values below this point are greater than .995.

The 42 tables in this section are used when an overall sample size **n** is specified together with the degrees of freedom (**u**), the significance criterion **a**, and the ES, **e**; the tables then yield power values. As throughout this handbook, power tables find their major use after an experiment has been performed. They can also be used in experimental planning by varying **n** (and/or ES, and/or **a**) to study the consequences to power of such alternatives.

Tables list values for **a, u, e,** and **n**:

1. Significance Criterion, **a**. Since χ^2 is naturally nondirectional (see above, Section 7.2), 14 tables (for varying **u**) are provided at each of the **a** levels .01, .05, and .10.

2. Degrees of Freedom, **u**. At each **a** level, a table is provided for each of the following 14 values of **u**: 1 (1) 10, 12 (4) 24. They have been selected so as to cover most problems involving χ^2 comparisons of proportions (or frequencies) likely to be encountered in practice. In particular, since for **r** × **k** contingency tables, **u** = (**r** − 1)(**k** − 1), the larger values of **u** (12, 16, 20, 24) were chosen so as to have many factors. Thus, tables whose **r** × **k** are 2 × 25, 3 × 13, 4 × 9, and 5 × 7 all have **u** = 24. When necessary, linear interpolation between **u** values in the 10–24 range will yield quite adequate approximations.

3. Effect Size, **e**. For either Case 0 or Case 1 applications, **e** as defined in formula (7.2.1) provides the ES index. Provision is made for finding nine values of **e**: .05, .10, (.10) .80. As a frame of reference for ES magnitude, conventional definitions have been offered above, as follows:

small: **e** = .05,
medium: **e** = .10,
large: **e** = .20.

4. Sample Size, **n**. This is the *total* number of cases in the comparison. Provision is made for **n** = 25 (5) 50 (10) 100 (20) 200 (50) 400 (100) 1000. Note that although all the tables begin at **n** = 25, for the Case 0 and Case 1 application of χ^2 of this chapter, samples of this size will yield tests of dubious validity as **u** increases. See Section 7.4 for discussion and references on this point.

The values in the body of the tables are the power times 100, i.e., the percent of tests carried out under the specified conditions which will result in the rejection of the null hypothesis. They are rounded to the nearest unit, and they are generally accurate to within ± 1 as tabled.

7.3.1 CASE 0: GOODNESS OF FIT TESTS. By way of review: In Case 0, the H_0 is a set of proportions (P_{0i}) in **m** categories which reflect no effect in a way appropriate to the problem. The H_1 is another set of proportions (P_{1i}) in the m categories which collectively reflect the effect. Each category contributes a value $(P_{1i} - P_{0i})^2/P_{0i}$ to a total, e, which indexes the ES. The u for a given problem is $m - 1$, unless there are further constraints due to parameter estimation, as, e.g., in fitting a normal distribution, where $u = m - 3$ (see Section 7.2.1 and references).

Illustrative Examples

7.1 A market researcher is seeking to determine the relative preference by consumers among four different package designs for a new product. He arranges to have a panel of 100 consumers each select the single design he prefers over the rest. He performs a χ^2 test at $a = .05$ on the preference distribution against a null hypothesis of equal preference, i.e.,

$$\begin{array}{ccccc} & A & B & C & D \\ H_0: & .25 & .25 & .25 & .25. \end{array}$$

What is the power of this test, if in fact, in the population, the actual distribution is

$$\begin{array}{ccccc} & A & B & C & D \\ H_1: & .3750 & .2083 & .2083 & .2083 & ? \end{array}$$

First, one finds e for this alternative [formula (7.2.1)]:

$$e = \frac{(.3750 - .2500)^2}{.2500} + \frac{3(.2083 - .2500)^2}{.2500} = .0833.$$

The degrees of freedom, u, for this application is $m - 1 = 3$, there being only one constraint on the freedom of the category P values to vary, namely the requirement that they sum to 1.00. Thus, the summary of his specifications is

$$a = .05, \quad u = 3, \quad e = .0833, \quad n = 100.$$

In Table 7.3.17 for $a = .05$ and $u = 3$ at row $n = 100$, we find power for column $e = .05$ to be .44 and for $e = .10$ to be .76. Linear interpolation yields (approximate) power of

$$.44 + \frac{(.0833 - .05)}{(.10 - .05)} (.76 - .44) = .44 + .22 = .66.$$

Thus, if H_1 is true, or for any other H_1 which yields an $e = .0833$, the market researcher has about a 2 in 3 chance of rejecting the null hypothesis of equal preference in the population among the four designs.

7.2 A psychometrician needs to determine whether a population distribution of scores on a psychological test under development is normal.

He secures a random sample of 200 Ss, and by methods described by Guilford (1965, pp. 243–247) and McNemar (1962, pp. 231–235), determines that for 9 step intervals of his score distribution, a normal distribution would have the following proportion in successive intervals:

$$H_0: \quad .020 \quad .051 \quad .118 \quad .195 \quad .232 \quad .195 \quad .118 \quad .051 \quad .020$$

After experimenting with several alternate population distributions, he concludes that he wishes to be able to detect a departure from normality of $e = .05$. Since the burden of "proof" of normality is his, he selects $a = .10$ as his significance criterion in order to be lenient in his rejection of the null hypothesis of normality. Under these conditions, what is the power of his χ^2 test for goodness of fit to normality?

To determine the u, consider that in the fitting of the normal distribution to his sample values, in addition to the usual constraint of summation of the proportions to 1.00, he has estimated from his sample two population parameters, the mean and standard deviation. Thus, his degrees of freedom are $u = m - 3 = 9 - 3 = 6$.

The specifications for the power of the χ^2 test are:

$$a = .10, \quad u = 6, \quad e = .05, \quad n = 200.$$

In Table 7.3.34 (for $a = .10$, $u = 6$) for column $e = .05$, row $n = 200$, he finds power $= .75$. Under the circumstances, he might consider that, given a departure of $e = .05$ from normality, a probability of rejection of normality of .75 might not be sufficient.

7.3.2 CASE 1: CONTINGENCY TESTS. In Case 1, we deal with a two-way table of variables R and K which has $rk = m$ cells, each containing a proportion of the population. The m null hypothetical proportions P_{0i} are those which reflect no association between R and K and are found as products of the marginal proportions, as in Table 7.2.2. The alternate-hypothetical proportions P_{0i} are another set which then necessarily reflect some association, of greater or lesser degree. The amount of association or departure from H_0 is found as in Case 0, i.e., each of the m cells contributes a value $(P_{1i} - P_{0i})^2/P_{0i}$ to a total e. The u for a given problem is $(r - 1)(k - 1)$. Such problems can be viewed equally as concerning association between R and K or as concerning differences among the r subpopulations in distributions over the k categories (or k subpopulations over the r categories).

Illustrative Examples

7.3 A political scientist is studying the relationship between sex and political preference (Democrat, Republican, Independent) for a certain population. Assume that he knows, or can estimate, the marginals, i.e., the proportions of men and women voters, and the proportions of each political preference in the population. He has available a sample of $n = 140$ voters for the χ^2 contingency test, which he performs at the $a = .01$ significance level. His null hypothesis is expressed by the P_{0i} in Table 7.2.2 above, which reflects no association between voter sex and political preference or, equivalently, no sex difference in political preference distribution. The degrees of freedom for the test, $u = (2 - 1)(3 - 1) = 2$. If the joint proportions in the population are the P_{1i} of Table 7.2.1, what is the power of the test? It has been shown above (Section 6.2) that the ES of the departure of the P_{1i} from the P_{0i} is $e = .12$. Then,

$$a = .01, \quad u = 2, \quad e = .12, \quad n = 140.$$

In Table 7.3.2 (for $a = .01$, $u = 2$;, he finds for row $n = 140$ the power for $e = .10$ to be .80 and for $e = .20$ to be .99. Linear interpolation gives the (approximate) power for $e = .12$ as

$$.80 + \frac{(.12 - .10)}{(.20 - .10)}(.99 - .80) = .84.$$

Thus, if the population proportions are as in Table 7.2.1, or for *any* other set of values yielding $e = .12$, the probability of rejecting the hypothesis of no association at $a = .01$ using 140 respondents is .84.

7.4 A clinical psychologist is studying the predictive validity of a new psychodiagnostic procedure administered to patients upon admission to a psychiatric hospital, using as a criterion final psychiatric diagnosis. Assume that 80 patients are classified into the diagnostic categories "brain damaged," "functional psychotic," and "psychoneurotic," both by the psychodiagnostic procedure and by the final diagnosis. The contingency table for assessing predictive validity will thus be a 3×3 table, with $u = (3 - 1)(3 - 1) = 4$. If the degree of association in the population is indexed by a Cramér ϕ' of .20, what is the power of a χ^2 test using $a = .05$ as the significance criterion?

To be used in the power tables, the ϕ' must be converted into its e equivalent. From formula (7.2.8), noting that $r (= k) = 3$, we find $e = (.20)^2(3 - 1) = .08$. The specifications, then, are:

$$a = .05, \quad u = 4, \quad e = .08, \quad n = 80.$$

In Table 7.3.18 (for $a = .05$, $u = 4$) for row $n = 80$, we find power at $e = .05$ to be .32 and at $e = .10$ to be .60. Interpolating linearly for $e = .08$, power is found to be approximately

$$.32 + \frac{(.08 - .05)}{(.10 - .05)}(.60 - .32) = .49.$$

Thus, at the level of association of $\phi' = .20$ posited for the population, it is a "toss-up" whether a contingency test significant at $a = .05$ will result with $n = 80$.

7.5 A community psychiatry research team undertakes an inquiry into the association between religious-ethnic group ($r = 5$) and type of diagnosis given ($k = 6$) in a statewide population of child clinic referrals. Data are available for $n = 400$ referrals. If the degree of association is small ($e = .05$; $C = .218$; $\phi' = .112$ from Table 7.2.3), what is the power of a χ^2 test performed at the .01 level? For this large table, u is equal to $(5 - 1)(6 - 1) = 20$. The specifications, in summary form, are

$$a = .01, \quad u = 20, \quad e = .05, \quad n = 400.$$

In Table 7.3.13 for $a = .01$ and $u = 20$, column $e = .05$, and row $n = 400$, we find power to be .56. Note that if the more lenient $a = .05$ criterion is used instead (Table 7.3.27), power is substantially higher, .78. If the actual association is "medium" ($e = .10$, and from Table 7.2.3, $C = .302$, $\phi' = .158$), at $a = .01$, power is .96 and at $a = .05$, power is .99.

7.4 SAMPLE SIZE TABLES

The sample size tables for this section are given on pages 247–261; the text follows on page 262.

Table 7.4.1

n to detect e by χ^2 at a = .01, u = 1, 2, 3

				u = 1					
				e					
Power	.05	.10	.20	.30	.40	.50	.60	.70	.80
.25	72	36	18	12	9	7	6	5	5
.50	133	66	33	22	17	13	11	9	8
.60	160	80	40	27	20	16	13	11	10
2/3	183	92	46	31	23	18	15	13	11
.70	192	96	48	32	24	19	16	14	12
.75	211	106	53	35	26	21	18	15	13
.80	234	117	58	39	29	23	19	17	15
.85	261	130	65	43	33	26	22	19	16
.90	298	149	74	50	37	30	25	21	19
.95	356	178	89	59	45	36	30	25	22
.99	481	240	120	80	60	48	40	34	30

				u = 2					
				e					
Power	.05	.10	.20	.30	.40	.50	.60	.70	.80
.25	93	47	23	16	12	9	8	7	6
.50	164	82	41	27	20	16	14	12	10
.60	195	98	49	32	24	20	16	14	12
2/3	221	110	55	37	28	22	18	16	14
.70	231	116	58	39	29	23	19	17	14
.75	253	126	63	42	32	25	21	18	16
.80	278	139	69	46	35	28	23	20	17
.85	308	154	77	51	39	31	26	22	19
.90	349	174	87	58	44	35	29	25	22
.95	413	206	103	69	52	41	34	29	26
.99	548	274	137	91	69	55	46	39	34

				u = 3					
				e					
Power	.05	.10	.20	.30	.40	.50	.60	.70	.80
.25	109	54	27	18	14	11	9	8	7
.50	186	93	47	31	23	19	16	13	12
.60	220	110	55	37	28	22	18	16	14
2/3	248	124	62	41	31	25	21	18	16
.70	259	130	65	43	32	26	22	19	16
.75	282	141	71	47	35	28	24	20	18
.80	309	155	77	51	39	31	26	22	19
.85	342	171	85	57	43	34	28	24	21
.90	385	192	96	64	48	38	32	27	24
.95	453	227	113	76	57	45	38	32	28
.99	597	298	149	99	75	60	50	43	37

Table 7.4.2

n to detect e by χ^2 at a = .01, u = 4, 5, 6

				u = 4				
				e				
Power	.05	.10	.20	.30	.40	.50	.60	.70	.80
.25	121	61	30	20	15	12	10	9	8
.50	205	102	51	34	26	20	17	15	13
.60	241	120	60	40	30	24	20	17	15
2/3	271	135	68	45	34	27	23	19	17
.70	282	141	71	47	35	28	24	20	18
.75	307	153	77	51	38	31	26	22	19
.80	335	167	84	56	42	33	28	24	21
.85	369	185	92	62	46	37	31	26	23
.90	415	207	104	69	52	41	35	30	26
.95	487	243	122	81	61	49	41	35	30
.99	636	318	159	106	79	64	53	45	40

				u = 5				
				e				
Power	.05	.10	.20	.30	.40	.50	.60	.70	.80
.25	132	66	33	22	17	13	11	9	8
.50	221	110	55	37	28	22	18	16	14
.60	259	129	65	43	32	26	22	18	16
2/3	290	145	72	48	36	29	24	21	18
.70	302	151	76	50	38	30	25	22	19
.75	328	164	82	55	41	33	27	23	20
.80	357	179	89	60	45	36	30	26	22
.85	393	197	98	66	49	39	33	28	25
.90	415	207	104	69	52	41	35	30	26
.95	515	258	129	86	64	52	43	37	32
.99	670	335	167	112	84	67	56	48	42

				u = 6				
				e				
Power	.05	.10	.20	.30	.40	.50	.60	.70	.80
.25	142	71	36	24	18	14	12	10	9
.50	235	118	59	39	29	24	20	17	15
.60	275	137	69	46	34	27	23	20	17
2/3	310	155	78	52	39	31	26	22	19
.70	320	160	80	53	40	32	27	23	20
.75	347	173	87	58	43	35	29	25	22
.80	377	189	94	63	47	38	31	27	24
.85	415	207	104	69	52	41	35	30	26
.90	464	232	116	77	58	46	39	33	29
.95	541	270	135	90	68	54	45	39	34
.99	700	350	175	117	88	70	58	50	44

Table 7.4.3

n to detect e by χ^2 at a = .01, u = 7, 8, 9

| | | | | | u = 7 | | | | |
| | | | | | e | | | | |
Power	.05	.10	.20	.30	.40	.50	.60	.70	.80
.25	152	76	38	25	19	15	13	11	9
.50	248	124	62	41	31	25	21	18	16
.60	289	145	72	48	36	29	24	21	18
2/3	320	160	80	53	40	32	27	23	20
.70	337	168	84	56	42	34	28	24	21
.75	364	182	91	61	46	36	30	26	23
.80	396	198	99	66	49	40	33	28	25
.85	434	217	109	72	54	43	36	31	27
.90	485	242	121	81	61	48	40	35	30
.95	564	282	141	94	71	56	47	40	35
.99	728	364	182	121	91	73	62	52	46

| | | | | | u = 8 | | | | |
| | | | | | e | | | | |
Power	.05	.10	.20	.30	.40	.50	.60	.70	.80
.25	160	80	40	27	20	16	13	11	10
.50	260	130	65	43	33	26	22	19	16
.60	303	152	76	51	38	30	25	22	19
2/3	335	167	84	56	42	33	28	24	21
.70	352	176	88	59	44	35	29	25	22
.75	380	190	95	63	48	38	32	27	24
.80	413	206	103	69	52	41	34	29	26
.85	452	226	113	75	57	45	38	32	28
.90	504	252	126	84	63	50	42	36	32
.95	586	293	146	98	73	59	49	42	37
.99	754	377	188	126	94	75	63	54	47

| | | | | | u = 9 | | | | |
| | | | | | e | | | | |
Power	.05	.10	.20	.30	.40	.50	.60	.70	.80
.25	168	84	42	28	21	17	14	12	10
.50	272	136	68	45	34	27	23	19	17
.60	316	158	79	53	39	32	26	23	20
2/3	348	174	87	58	44	35	29	25	22
.70	366	183	91	61	46	37	30	26	23
.75	395	198	99	66	49	40	33	28	25
.80	429	214	107	71	54	43	36	31	27
.85	469	235	117	78	59	47	39	33	29
.90	522	261	131	87	65	52	44	37	33
.95	606	303	152	101	76	61	56	43	38
.99	778	389	194	130	97	78	65	36	49

Table 7.4.4

n to detect e by X^2 at a = .01, u = 10, 12, 16

| | | | | u = 10 | | | | |
| | | | | e | | | | |
Power	.05	.10	.20	.30	.40	.50	.60	.70	.80
.25	175	88	44	29	22	18	15	13	11
.50	283	141	72	47	36	28	24	20	18
.60	328	164	82	55	41	33	27	23	20
2/3	361	181	90	60	45	36	30	26	23
.70	379	190	95	63	47	38	32	27	24
.75	409	205	102	68	51	41	34	29	26
.80	444	222	111	74	55	44	37	32	28
.85	485	243	121	81	61	49	40	35	30
.90	540	270	135	90	67	54	45	39	34
.95	625	313	156	104	78	63	52	45	39
.99	800	400	200	133	100	80	67	57	50

| | | | | u = 12 | | | | |
| | | | | e | | | | |
Power	.05	.10	.20	.30	.40	.50	.60	.70	.80
.25	189	95	47	32	24	19	16	14	12
.50	303	151	76	50	38	30	25	22	19
.60	350	175	81	58	44	35	29	25	22
2/3	385	193	96	64	48	39	32	27	24
.70	404	202	101	67	51	40	34	29	25
.75	435	218	109	73	54	44	36	31	27
.80	471	236	118	79	59	47	39	34	29
.85	515	257	129	86	64	51	43	37	32
.90	572	286	143	95	71	57	48	41	36
.95	660	330	165	110	83	66	55	47	41
.99	842	421	211	140	105	84	70	60	53

| | | | | u = 16 | | | | |
| | | | | e | | | | |
Power	.05	.10	.20	.30	.40	.50	.60	.70	.80
.25	214	107	54	36	27	21	18	15	13
.50	338	169	84	56	42	34	28	24	21
.60	390	195	97	65	49	39	32	28	24
2/3	427	214	107	71	53	43	36	31	27
.70	448	224	112	75	56	45	37	32	28
.75	482	241	120	80	60	48	40	34	30
.80	520	260	130	87	65	52	43	37	33
.85	567	283	142	94	71	57	47	40	35
.90	628	314	157	105	78	63	52	45	39
.95	723	361	181	120	90	72	60	52	45
.99	916	458	229	153	114	92	76	65	57

Table 7.4.5

n to detect e by X^2 at a = .01, u = 20, 24

Power	.05	.10	.20	.30	.40	.50	.60	.70	.80
					u = 20				
					e				
.25	236	118	59	39	30	24	20	17	15
.50	369	185	92	61	46	37	31	26	23
.60	424	212	106	71	53	42	35	30	27
2/3	465	232	116	77	58	46	39	33	29
.70	486	243	122	81	61	49	41	35	30
.75	522	261	131	87	65	52	44	37	33
.80	563	282	141	94	70	56	47	40	35
.85	613	306	153	102	77	61	51	44	38
.90	677	339	169	113	85	68	56	48	42
.95	777	389	194	130	97	78	65	56	49
.99	981	490	245	163	123	98	82	70	61

Power	.05	.10	.20	.30	.40	.50	.60	.70	.80
					u = 24				
					e				
.25	260	130	65	43	33	26	22	19	16
.50	397	199	99	66	50	40	33	28	25
.60	456	228	114	76	57	46	38	33	28
2/3	498	249	125	83	62	50	42	36	31
.70	521	261	130	87	65	52	43	37	33
.75	559	279	140	93	70	56	47	40	35
.80	602	301	151	100	75	60	55	43	38
.85	654	327	163	109	82	65	54	47	41
.90	721	361	180	120	90	72	60	52	45
.95	826	413	207	138	103	83	69	59	52
.99	1039	519	260	173	130	104	87	74	65

Table 7.4.6

n to detect e by χ^2 at a = .05, u = 1, 2, 3

					u = 1 e				
Power	.05	.10	.20	.30	.40	.50	.60	.70	.80
.25	33	16	8	5	4	3	3	2	2
.50	77	38	19	13	10	8	6	5	5
.60	98	49	24	16	12	10	8	7	6
2/3	114	57	29	19	14	11	10	8	7
.70	123	62	31	21	15	12	10	9	8
.75	139	69	35	23	17	14	12	10	9
.80	157	78	39	26	20	16	13	11	10
.85	180	90	45	30	22	18	15	13	11
.90	210	105	53	35	26	21	18	15	13
.95	260	130	65	43	32	26	22	19	16
.99	367	184	92	61	46	37	31	26	23

					u = 2 e				
Power	.05	.10	.20	.30	.40	.50	.60	.70	.80
.25	45	23	11	8	6	5	4	3	3
.50	99	50	25	17	12	10	8	7	6
.60	124	62	31	21	16	12	10	9	8
2/3	143	72	36	24	18	14	12	10	9
.70	154	77	39	26	19	15	13	11	10
.75	172	86	43	29	21	17	14	12	11
.80	193	96	48	32	24	19	16	14	12
.85	218	109	55	36	27	22	18	16	14
.90	253	127	63	42	32	25	21	18	16
.95	309	154	77	51	39	31	26	22	19
.99	428	214	107	71	53	43	36	31	27

					u = 3 e				
Power	.05	.10	.20	.30	.40	.50	.60	.70	.80
.25	54	27	14	9	7	5	5	4	3
.50	115	58	29	19	14	12	10	8	7
.60	143	72	36	24	18	14	12	10	9
2/3	164	82	41	27	21	16	14	12	10
.70	176	88	44	29	22	18	15	13	11
.75	195	98	49	33	24	20	16	14	12
.80	218	109	55	36	27	22	18	16	14
.85	246	123	62	41	31	25	21	18	15
.90	283	142	71	47	35	28	24	20	18
.95	343	172	86	57	43	34	29	25	21
.99	470	235	118	78	59	47	39	34	29

Table 7.4.7

n to detect e by χ^2 at a = .05, u = 4, 5, 6

				$u = 4$ e				
Power	.05	.10	.20	.30	.40	.50	.60	.70	.80
.25	62	31	15	10	8	6	5	4	4
.50	128	64	32	21	16	13	11	9	8
.60	158	79	40	26	20	16	13	11	10
2/3	181	91	45	30	23	18	15	13	11
.70	194	97	48	32	24	19	16	14	12
.75	214	107	54	36	27	21	18	15	13
.80	239	119	60	40	30	24	20	17	15
.85	268	134	67	45	34	27	22	19	17
.90	308	154	77	51	39	31	26	22	19
.95	371	186	93	62	46	37	31	27	23
.99	505	252	126	84	63	50	42	36	31

				$u = 5$ e				
Power	.05	.10	.20	.30	.40	.50	.60	.70	.80
.25	68	34	17	11	9	7	6	5	4
.50	140	70	35	23	17	14	12	10	9
.60	172	86	43	29	21	17	14	12	11
2/3	196	98	49	33	24	20	16	14	12
.70	209	105	52	35	26	21	17	15	13
.75	231	116	58	38	29	23	19	17	14
.80	257	128	64	43	32	26	21	18	16
.85	288	144	72	48	36	29	24	21	18
.90	329	165	82	55	41	33	27	24	21
.95	396	198	99	66	49	40	33	28	25
.99	535	267	134	89	67	54	45	38	33

				$u = 6$ e				
Power	.05	.10	.20	.30	.40	.50	.60	.70	.80
.25	74	37	18	12	9	7	6	5	5
.50	150	75	38	25	19	15	13	11	9
.60	184	92	46	31	23	18	15	13	11
2/3	209	104	52	35	26	21	17	15	13
.70	223	111	56	37	28	22	19	16	14
.75	246	123	61	41	30	25	20	18	15
.80	272	136	68	45	34	27	23	19	17
.85	305	153	76	51	38	31	25	22	19
.90	348	174	87	58	44	35	29	25	22
.95	417	209	104	70	52	42	35	30	26
.99	561	280	140	93	70	56	47	40	35

Table 7.4.8

n to detect e by χ^2 at a = .05, u = 7, 8, 9

	u = 7								
	e								
Power	.05	.10	.20	.30	.40	.50	.60	.70	.80
.25	79	40	20	13	10	8	7	6	5
.50	159	80	40	27	20	16	13	11	10
.60	195	97	49	32	24	19	16	14	12
2/3	221	110	55	37	28	22	18	16	14
.70	235	118	59	39	29	24	20	17	15
.75	259	130	65	43	32	26	22	19	16
.80	287	144	72	48	36	29	24	21	18
.85	321	160	80	53	40	32	27	23	20
.90	366	183	91	61	46	37	30	26	23
.95	437	218	109	73	55	44	36	31	27
.99	585	292	146	97	73	58	49	42	37

	u = 8								
	e								
Power	.05	.10	.20	.30	.40	.50	.60	.70	.80
.25	84	42	21	14	11	8	7	6	5
.50	168	84	42	28	21	17	14	12	11
.60	205	102	51	34	26	20	17	15	13
2/3	232	116	58	39	29	23	19	17	15
.70	247	123	62	41	31	25	21	18	15
.75	272	136	68	45	34	27	23	19	17
.80	300	150	75	50	38	30	25	21	19
.85	335	168	84	56	42	34	28	24	21
.90	382	191	95	64	48	38	32	27	24
.95	455	227	114	76	57	45	38	33	28
.99	607	304	152	101	76	61	51	43	38

	u = 9								
	e								
Power	.05	.10	.20	.30	.40	.50	.60	.70	.80
.25	96	48	24	16	12	10	8	7	6
.50	176	88	44	29	22	18	15	13	11
.60	214	107	54	36	27	21	18	15	13
2/3	242	121	61	40	30	24	20	17	15
.70	258	129	64	43	32	26	21	18	16
.75	283	142	71	47	35	28	24	20	18
.80	313	156	78	52	39	31	26	22	20
.85	349	174	87	58	44	35	29	25	22
.90	397	198	99	66	50	40	33	28	25
.95	472	236	118	79	59	47	39	34	29
.99	628	314	157	105	78	63	52	45	39

Table 7.4.9

n to detect e by χ^2 at a = .05, u = 10, 12, 16

| Power | | | | u = 10 | | | | |
| | | | | e | | | | |
Power	.05	.10	.20	.30	.40	.50	.60	.70	.80
.25	93	47	23	16	12	9	8	7	6
.50	184	92	46	31	23	18	15	13	11
.60	223	112	56	37	28	22	19	16	14
2/3	252	126	63	42	32	25	21	18	16
.70	268	134	67	45	34	27	22	19	17
.75	294	147	74	49	37	29	25	21	18
.80	325	162	81	54	42	32	27	23	21
.85	362	181	90	60	45	36	30	26	23
.90	411	205	103	68	51	41	34	29	26
.95	488	244	122	81	61	49	41	35	30
.99	647	324	162	108	81	65	54	46	40

| Power | | | | u = 12 | | | | |
| | | | | e | | | | |
Power	.05	.10	.20	.30	.40	.50	.60	.70	.80
.25	102	51	25	17	13	10	8	7	6
.50	198	99	50	33	25	20	17	14	12
.60	240	120	60	40	30	24	20	17	15
2/3	270	135	68	45	34	27	23	19	17
.70	287	144	72	48	36	29	24	21	18
.75	315	157	79	52	39	31	26	22	20
.80	347	173	87	58	43	35	29	25	22
.85	386	193	96	64	48	39	32	28	24
.90	437	218	109	73	55	44	36	31	27
.95	517	259	129	86	65	52	43	37	32
.99	683	342	171	114	85	68	57	49	43

| Power | | | | u = 16 | | | | |
| | | | | e | | | | |
Power	.05	.10	.20	.30	.40	.50	.60	.70	.80
.25	116	58	29	19	15	12	10	8	7
.50	223	112	56	37	28	22	19	16	14
.60	269	134	67	45	34	27	22	19	17
2/3	302	151	76	50	38	30	25	22	19
.70	321	160	80	53	40	32	27	23	20
.75	351	175	88	58	44	35	29	25	22
.80	385	193	96	64	48	39	32	28	24
.85	427	214	107	71	53	43	36	31	27
.90	482	241	121	80	60	48	40	34	30
.95	569	285	142	95	71	57	47	41	36
.99	747	373	187	.24	93	75	62	53	47

Table 7.4.10

n to detect e by χ^2 at a = .05, u = 20, 24

Power	.05	.10	.20	.30	.40	.50	.60	.70	.80
					u = 20				
					e				
.25	129	65	32	22	16	13	11	9	8
.50	245	123	61	41	31	25	20	18	15
.60	294	147	74	49	37	29	25	21	18
2/3	330	165	83	55	41	33	28	24	21
.70	350	175	87	58	44	35	29	25	22
.75	382	191	96	64	48	38	32	27	24
.80	419	210	105	70	52	42	35	30	26
.85	464	232	116	77	58	46	39	33	29
.90	523	261	131	87	65	52	44	37	33
.95	614	307	154	102	77	61	51	44	38
.99	802	401	200	134	100	80	67	57	50

Power	.05	.10	.20	.30	.40	.50	.60	.70	.80
					u = 24				
					e				
.25	141	70	35	23	18	14	12	10	9
.50	265	133	66	44	33	27	22	19	16
.60	317	159	79	53	40	32	26	23	20
2/3	356	178	89	59	44	36	30	25	22
.70	376	188	94	63	47	38	31	27	24
.75	411	205	103	68	51	41	34	29	26
.80	450	225	112	75	56	45	37	32	28
.85	497	248	124	83	62	50	41	35	31
.90	559	279	140	93	70	56	47	40	35
.95	655	328	164	109	82	66	55	47	41
.99	852	426	213	142	106	85	71	61	53

Table 7.4.11

n to detect e by χ^2 at a = .10, u = 1, 2, 3

					u = 1				
					e				
Power	.05	.10	.20	.30	.40	.50	.60	.70	.80
.25	18	9	5	3	2	2	2	1	1
.50	54	27	14	9	7	5	5	4	3
.60	72	36	18	12	9	7	6	5	5
2/3	86	43	22	14	11	9	7	6	5
.70	94	47	24	16	12	9	8	7	6
.75	108	54	27	18	13	11	9	8	7
.80	124	62	31	21	15	12	10	9	8
.85	144	72	36	24	18	14	12	10	9
.90	171	86	43	29	21	17	14	12	11
.95	216	108	54	36	27	22	18	15	14
.99	315	158	79	53	39	32	26	23	20

					u = 2				
					e				
Power	.05	.10	.20	.30	.40	.50	.60	.70	.80
.25	25	13	6	4	3	3	2	2	2
.50	71	36	18	12	9	7	6	5	4
.60	93	47	23	16	12	9	8	7	6
2/3	110	55	28	18	14	11	9	8	7
.70	119	60	30	20	15	12	10	9	7
.75	135	68	34	23	17	14	11	10	8
.80	154	77	39	26	19	15	13	11	10
.85	178	89	44	30	22	18	15	13	11
.90	209	105	52	35	26	21	17	15	13
.95	260	130	65	43	33	26	22	19	16
.99	371	186	93	62	46	37	31	27	23

					u = 3				
					e				
Power	.05	.10	.20	.30	.40	.50	.60	.70	.80
.25	31	15	8	5	4	3	3	2	2
.50	84	42	21	14	10	8	7	6	5
.60	108	54	27	18	14	11	9	8	7
2/3	127	64	32	21	16	13	11	9	8
.70	138	69	34	23	17	14	11	10	9
.75	155	78	39	26	19	16	13	11	10
.80	176	88	44	29	22	18	15	13	11
.85	202	101	50	34	25	20	17	14	13
.90	236	118	59	39	29	24	20	17	15
.95	291	146	73	49	36	29	24	21	18
.99	410	205	103	68	51	41	34	29	26

Table 7.4.12

n to detect e by χ^2 at a = .10, u = 4, 5, 6

	u = 4 e								
Power	.05	.10	.20	.30	.40	.50	.60	.70	.80
.25	36	18	9	6	4	4	3	3	2
.50	94	47	23	16	12	9	8	7	6
.60	121	60	30	20	15	12	10	9	8
2/3	141	71	35	24	18	14	12	10	9
.70	153	76	38	25	19	15	13	11	10
.75	171	86	43	29	21	17	14	12	11
.80	194	97	48	32	24	19	16	14	12
.85	221	110	55	37	28	22	18	16	14
.90	258	129	64	43	36	26	21	18	18
.95	317	158	79	53	40	32	26	23	20
.99	442	221	110	74	55	44	37	32	28

	u = 5 e								
Power	.05	.10	.20	.30	.40	.50	.60	.70	.80
.25	40	20	10	7	5	4	3	3	2
.50	103	51	26	17	13	10	9	7	6
.60	132	66	33	22	16	13	11	9	8
2/3	153	77	38	26	19	15	13	11	10
.70	165	83	41	28	21	17	14	12	10
.75	185	93	46	31	23	19	15	13	12
.80	209	104	52	35	26	21	17	15	13
.85	238	119	59	40	30	24	20	17	15
.90	276	138	69	46	35	28	23	20	17
.95	338	169	85	56	42	34	28	24	21
.99	469	234	117	78	59	47	39	33	29

	u = 6 e								
Power	.05	.10	.20	.30	.40	.50	.60	.70	.80
.25	43	22	11	7	5	4	4	3	3
.50	111	55	28	18	14	11	9	8	7
.60	141	71	35	24	18	14	12	10	9
2/3	164	82	41	27	21	15	14	12	10
.70	177	88	44	29	22	18	15	13	11
.75	198	99	49	33	25	20	16	14	12
.80	223	111	56	37	28	22	19	16	14
.85	253	126	63	42	32	25	21	18	16
.90	293	147	73	49	37	29	24	21	18
.95	357	179	89	60	45	36	30	26	22
.99	493	246	123	82	62	49	41	35	31

Table 7.4.13

n to detect e by X^2 at a = .10, u = 7, 8, 9

| | | | | u = 7 | | | | |
| | | | | e | | | | |
Power	.05	.10	.20	.30	.40	.50	.60	.70	.80
.25	47	23	12	8	6	5	4	3	3
.50	118	59	29	20	15	12	10	8	7
.60	150	75	37	25	19	15	12	11	9
2/3	174	87	44	29	22	17	15	12	11
.70	187	94	47	31	23	19	16	13	12
.75	209	105	52	35	26	21	17	15	13
.80	235	118	59	39	29	24	20	17	15
.85	266	133	67	44	33	27	22	19	17
.90	308	154	77	51	39	31	26	22	19
.95	375	187	94	62	47	37	31	27	23
.99	515	257	129	86	64	51	43	37	32

| | | | | u = 8 | | | | |
| | | | | e | | | | |
Power	.05	.10	.20	.30	.40	.50	.60	.70	.80
.25	50	25	12	8	6	5	4	4	3
.50	125	62	31	21	16	12	10	9	8
.60	158	79	40	26	20	16	13	11	10
2/3	183	92	46	31	23	18	15	13	11
.70	197	98	49	33	25	20	16	14	12
.75	220	110	55	37	27	22	18	16	14
.80	246	123	62	41	31	25	21	18	15
.85	279	140	70	47	35	28	23	20	17
.90	322	161	81	54	40	32	27	23	20
.95	391	196	98	65	49	39	33	28	24
.99	535	268	134	89	67	54	45	38	33

| | | | | u = 9 | | | | |
| | | | | e | | | | |
Power	.05	.10	.20	.30	.40	.50	.60	.70	.80
.25	52	26	13	9	6	5	4	4	3
.50	131	66	33	22	16	13	11	9	8
.60	166	83	41	28	21	17	14	12	10
2/3	192	96	48	32	24	19	16	14	12
.70	206	103	52	34	26	21	17	15	13
.75	230	115	57	38	29	23	19	16	14
.80	257	129	64	43	32	26	21	18	16
.85	291	145	73	48	36	29	24	21	18
.90	335	168	84	56	42	34	28	24	21
.95	406	203	102	68	51	41	34	29	25
.99	554	277	138	92	69	55	46	40	35

Table 7.4.14

n to detect e by χ^2 at a = .10, u = 10, 12, 16

Power	.05	.10	.20	.30	.40	.50	.60	.70	.80
				u = 10					
				e					
.25	54	27	14	9	7	5	5	4	3
.50	137	68	34	23	17	14	11	10	9
.60	173	86	43	29	22	17	14	12	11
2/3	200	100	50	33	25	20	17	14	12
.70	215	107	54	36	27	21	18	15	13
.75	239	119	60	40	30	24	20	17	15
.80	267	134	67	45	33	27	22	19	17
.85	302	151	75	50	38	30	25	22	19
.90	348	174	87	58	43	35	29	25	22
.95	420	210	105	70	53	42	35	30	26
.99	572	286	143	95	71	57	48	41	36

Power	.05	.10	.20	.30	.40	.50	.60	.70	.80
				u = 12					
				e					
.25	60	30	15	10	8	6	5	4	4
.50	148	74	37	25	19	15	12	11	9
.60	186	93	47	31	23	19	16	13	12
2/3	215	107	54	36	27	21	18	15	13
.70	230	115	58	38	29	23	19	16	14
.75	256	128	64	43	32	26	21	18	16
.80	286	143	72	48	36	29	24	20	18
.85	322	161	81	54	40	32	27	23	20
.90	371	185	93	62	46	37	31	26	23
.95	447	223	112	74	56	45	37	32	28
.99	604	302	151	101	76	60	50	43	38

Power	.05	.10	.20	.30	.40	.50	.60	.70	.80
				u = 16					
				e					
.25	70	35	17	12	9	7	6	5	4
.50	168	84	42	28	21	17	14	12	10
.60	210	105	52	35	26	21	17	15	13
2/3	241	121	60	40	30	24	20	17	15
.70	258	129	65	43	32	26	22	18	16
.75	287	143	72	48	36	29	24	20	18
.80	319	160	80	53	40	32	27	23	20
.85	359	179	90	60	45	36	30	26	22
.90	411	205	103	68	51	41	34	29	26
.95	493	246	123	82	62	49	41	35	31
.99	662	331	166	110	83	66	55	47	41

Table 7.4.15

n to detect e by X^2 at a = .10, u = 20, 24

					u = 20 e				
Power	.05	.10	.20	.30	.40	.50	.60	.70	.80
.25	78	39	19	13	10	8	6	6	5
.50	185	92	46	31	23	18	15	13	12
.60	231	115	58	38	29	23	19	16	14
2/3	264	132	66	44	33	26	22	19	17
.70	283	141	71	47	35	28	24	20	18
.75	313	157	78	52	39	31	26	22	20
.80	348	174	87	58	43	35	29	25	22
.85	390	195	98	65	49	39	33	28	24
.90	446	223	111	74	56	45	37	32	28
.95	533	267	133	89	67	53	44	38	33
.99	712	356	178	119	89	71	59	51	45

					u = 24 e				
Power	.05	.10	.20	.30	.40	.50	.60	.70	.80
.25	85	42	21	14	11	8	7	6	5
.50	200	100	50	33	25	20	17	14	13
.60	249	125	62	42	31	25	21	18	16
2/3	285	143	71	44	36	29	22	20	18
.70	305	152	76	51	38	30	25	22	19
.75	337	168	84	56	42	34	28	24	21
.80	374	187	94	62	47	37	31	27	23
.85	419	209	105	70	52	42	35	30	26
.90	478	239	119	80	60	48	40	34	30
.95	570	285	142	95	71	57	47	41	36
.99	758	379	189	126	95	76	63	54	47

The tables in this section give values for the significance criterion (**a**), the degrees of freedom (**u**), the ES to be detected (**e**), and the *desired power*. The necessary total sample size **n** then may be found. As with the other sample size tables in this handbook, they will be used primarily in the planning of experiments where they provide a basis for the decision as to the sample size to use.

For typographic convenience, the 42 tables are arranged generally three to a table number, by **a** levels and successively tabled **u** values within each **a** level. The subtable for the relevant **a**, **u** combination is found and entered with **e** and desired power. The same provisions for **a**, **u**, and **e** are made as for the power tables in Section 7.3, as follows:

1. Significance Criterion, **a**. Table sets are provided for nondirectional **a** of .01, .05, and .10, each set made up of tables for the values of **u**.

2. Degrees of Freedom, **u**. For each **a** level, tables are provided in succession for the 14 values of **u** = 1 (1) 10, 12 (4) 24.

3. Effect Size, **e**. **e** is defined by formula (7.2.1) and interpreted as described in Section 7.2. As before, 9 values of **e** are given: .05, .10 (.10) .80.

For **e** values not tabled, find **n** by

$$(7.4.1) \qquad\qquad n = \frac{.05n_{.05}}{e},$$

where $n_{.05}$ is the necessary sample size for the given **a**, **u**, and desired power at **e** = .05 (read from the table), and **e** is the nontabulated ES. Round to the nearest integer. This formula may be used not only for **e** values in the range covered by the table, but also for **e** less than .05 or greater than .80.

4. Desired Power. Provision is made for desired power values of .25, .50, .60, 2/3, .70 (.05), .95, .99. See Section 2.4.1 for the basis for selection of these values, and a discussion of the proposal that .80 serve as a convention for desired power in the absence of another basis for a choice.

A caveat is necessary at this point. Some values of **n** are given in the tables which are quite small (i.e., large **e** and **a**, small **u** and power). These are not to be taken as a sanction for the use of χ^2 tests where the null-hypothetical frequencies (P_0n) become very small, since such tests are of questionable validity. These small **n** values are given for the sake of completeness and for other applications of χ^2, not illustrated here, which are not limited in this way. For useful guidance with regard to sample size requirements in χ^2, the reader is referred to Walker and Lev (1953, p. 107) and to the textbooks cited in Section 7.2.

7.4.1 CASE 0: GOODNESS OF FIT. For Case 0 tests, one finds the subtable for the significance criterion (**a**) and degrees of freedom (**u**) which obtain, locates **e** and desired power, and finds **n**, the necessary total sample size. For nontabulated **e**, use formula (7.4.1).

Illustrative Examples

7.6 Reconsider the problem posed in example 7.2, where a psychometrician is testing by means of χ^2 the conformity of a sample distribution of test scores to the normal curve for **m** = 9 step intervals, the latter constituting H_0. He wished a lenient (**a** = .10) test of H_0. Given that the population departure is **e** = .05, it was found that power was .75 for **n** = 200. On the assumption that the power is too small for a convincing "demonstration" of normality, how many cases would he need for power to be .99?

Recalling that in such applications, **u** = **m** − 3 = 6, his specification summary is

$$\mathbf{a} = .10, \quad \mathbf{u} = 6, \quad \mathbf{e} = .05, \quad \text{power} = .99.$$

He uses the last subtable of Table 7.4.12 for **a** = .10, **u** = 6, column **e** = .05, and row power = .99, and finds **n** = 493. With this sample size, he runs a **b** risk of only 1 − .99 = .01 that, if the departure from normality is **e** = .05, he will fail to detect it at **a** = .10.

If this sample size is a great strain on his resources, he might consider settling for power = .95 (hence **b** = .05), where, from the same subtable, he finds the necessary **n** to be 357.

7.7 Consider example 7.1 again, now from the point of view of sample size decision as part of experimental planning. The market researcher wishes to detect a departure in the population from equal preference among **m** = 4 package designs by means of a χ^2 test with **u** = **m** − 1 = 3, using an **a** = .05 significance criterion. The alternate hypothesis which was posited resulted in **e** = .0833. From the power tables, it was found that, using **n** = 100, power was .66. If the conventional .80 power were desired, what **n** would be required?

$$\mathbf{a} = .05, \quad \mathbf{u} = 3, \quad \mathbf{e} = .0833, \quad \text{power} = .80.$$

Since **e** = .0833 is not tabled, the use of formula (7.4.1) is required. For $\mathbf{n}_{.05}$, the sample size needed to detect **e** = .05 with power = .80 for **a** = .05 and **u** = 3, we use the third subtable of Table 7.4.6 (for **a** = .05, **u** = 3) for column **e** = .05 and row power = .80, and find $\mathbf{n}_{.05}$ = 218. Substituting in formula (7.4.1),

$$\mathbf{n} = \frac{(.05)(218)}{.0833} = 130.8.$$

Thus, 131 respondents will lead to a .80 probability of rejecting the null hypothesis of equal preference at $a = .05$, given that the population departure is indexed by $e = .0833$.

7.4.2   CASE 1: CONTINGENCY TEST. As in Case 0, one finds the necessary total sample size n in Case 1 by finding the subtable for the significance criterion (a) and degrees of freedom $[u = (k - 1)(r - 1)]$ which obtain, and seeking e and the power desired. Formula (7.4.1) is again used for nontabulated e.

Illustrative Examples

7.8   In example 7.5, a community psychiatry research team was studying the relationship between religious-ethnic group membership $(r = 5)$ and diagnosis $(k = 6)$ for child clinic referrals. To detect $e = .05$ at the $a = .01$ significance level by a χ^2 contingency test with $u = (5 - 1)(6 - 1) = 20$, it was found that for $n = 400$, power was .56. What sample size is required for conventional desired power of .80? The specification summary is

$$a = .01, \quad u = 20, \quad e = .05, \quad \text{power} = .80.$$

The first subtable for Table 7.4.5 (for $a = .01$, $u = 20$) for column $e = .05$ and row power $= .80$, is used to determine $n = 563$.

Later in example 7.5, the same problem was considered using the less stringent $a = .05$ significance criterion. To find n for power of .80, in the first subtable of Table 7.4.10 (for $a = .05$, $u = .20$) locate column $e = .05$ and row power $= .80$; the result is $n = 419$. Note that this is consistent with the finding in example 7.5 that at $a = .05$ with $n = 400$, power was found to be .78.

7.9   Reconsider example 7.3, where a political scientist was studying the relationship between sex $(r = 2)$ and political preference $(k = 3)$. Assuming the degree of relationship given by the alternate-hypothetical P_{1i} of Table 7.2.1, and the null-hypothetical or no association P_{0i} of Table 7.2.2, e was found to equal .12. For the χ^2 contingency test with $u = (2 - 1)(3 - 1) = 2$, at the $a = .01$ level with $n = 140$ cases, power was found to be .84. Assume now that power is desired to be .99, so that $b = .01 = a$, i.e., that the Type I and Type II risks are equal and very small. What sample size is needed?

$$a = .01, \quad u = 2, \quad e = .12, \quad \text{power} = .99.$$

Since $e = .12$ is not tabulated, recourse will be taken to formula (7.4.1). To find the n needed to detect $e = .05$ for $a = .01$, $u = 2$, and power $= .99$ the second subtable of Table 7.4.1 (for $a = .01$, $u = 2$ is used for column

$e = .05$ and row power $= .99$, and $n_{.05} = 548$ is found. Substituting in formula (7.4.1),

$$n = \frac{(.05)(548)}{.12} = 228.3.$$

Thus, 228 respondents are needed to yield $a = b = .01$ risks in a contingency test of this 2×3 table, given an ES of $e = .12$.

Maintaining the $a = b$ requirement, but at .05, what n would be necessary?

$$a = .05, \quad u = 2, \quad e = .12, \quad \text{power} = .95.$$

To find $n_{.05}$, the second subtable of Table 7.4.6 (for $a = .05$, $u = 2$) is used for column $e = .05$ and row power $= .95$, and 309 is found. Substituting in formula (7.4.1),

$$n = \frac{.05(309)}{.12} = 128.8.$$

The reduction in stringency from $a = b = .01$ to $a = b = .05$ results in a reduction in sample size demand from 228 to 129.

8

F Tests on Means in the
Analysis of Variance and Covariance

8.1 INTRODUCTION AND USE

This chapter deals with an entire class of problems in tests of the equality of a set of **k** population means, where **k** equals two or more. The methods of this chapter can also be used for tests of the equality of sets of mean *differences*, as in tests of interactions. The test statistic is the **F** ratio, and the model is that of the test on means of "fixed effect" variates in the analysis of variance and covariance (McNemar, 1962; Hays, 1963). In its simplest form, it is a "one-way" ("randomized groups") design with equal **n** in each sample. The power and sample size tables in this chapter are designed for greatest simplicity in these applications (Case 0). More complicated designs involving fixed effects can also be power-analyzed with the help of these tables, as will be described below. In all cases, however, the null hypothesis states that the means or mean difference of specified ("fixed") populations are equal, or, equivalently, that "effects" defined as linear functions of means are all zero. Section 8.3.4 shows how power analysis on various tests of means, which will have been described in the context of the analysis of variance, can be performed in analogous analysis of co-variance designs.

The tests here can be viewed as extensions of the tests of Chapter 2, where only two fixed population means are involved. Or, conversely, the **t** test on two means is, in fact, merely a special case of the **F** test on **k** means where **k** = 2, as is detailed in most statistics textbooks. As such, the same formal model assumptions are made: that the values in the **k** populations are normally distributed and have the same variance, σ^2. It is, however, well

266

established that moderate violations of these assumptions have generally negligible effects on the validity of null hypothesis tests and power analyses. For evidence on the issue of the "robustness" of **F** tests with regard to both Type I and Type II error in the face of assumption violation, see Scheffé (1959, Chapter 10), and for a less technical summary, Cohen (1965, pp. 114–116). Note that no assumption is made about the distribution of the **k** population means for fixed effects.

The **F** test on means for fixed effects can occur under a variety of circumstances for which the tables in this chapter may be used:

Case 0. One-way analysis of variance with **n**'s equal. This is the simplest design, where without other considerations, one compares **k** means based on samples of equal size.

Case 1. One-way analysis of variance with unequal **n**'s.

Case 2. Comparisons of means of fixed effects in factorial and other complex designs.

Case 3. Tests of interactions (i.e., of differences among mean differences).

Analysis of Covariance. Each of the above cases has its analog in the analysis of covariance.

8.2 THE EFFECT SIZE INDEX: **f**

Our need for a pure number to index the degree of departure from no effect (i.e., **k** equal population means) is here satisfied in a way related to the solution in Chapter 2, where there were only two means. Recall that the difference in means was "standardized" by dividing it by the (common) within-population standard deviation, i.e.,

$$(8.2.1) \qquad d = \frac{m_1 - m_2}{\sigma}.$$

Since both numerator and denominator are expressed in the (frequently arbitrary) original unit of measurement, their ratio, **d**, is a pure or dimensionless number.

With $k \geq 2$ means such as we deal with here, we represent the spread of the means not by their range as above (except secondarily, see below), but by a quantity formally like a standard deviation, again dividing by the common standard deviation of the populations involved. It is thus

$$(8.2.1) \qquad f = \frac{\sigma_m}{\sigma},$$

where, for equal **n** (Cases 0 and 2),

$$(8.2.2) \qquad \sigma_m = \sqrt{\frac{\sum_{i=1}^{k}(m_i - m)^2}{k}},$$

the standard deviation of the population means expressed in original scale units. The values in the parentheses are the departures of the population means (m_i) from the mean of the combined populations or the mean of the means for equal sample sizes (**m**), and are sometimes called the (fixed) "effects"; the σ's of formulas (8.2.1) and (2.2.1) are the same, the standard deviation within the populations, also expressed in original scale units, **f** is thus also a pure number, the standard deviation of the standardized means. That is to say that if all the values in the combined populations were to be converted into **z** "standard" scores (McNemar, 1962, pp 35–37) using the within-population standard deviation, **f** is the standard deviation of these **k** mean **z** scores.

f can take on values between zero, when the population means are all equal (or the effects are all zero), and an indefinitely large number as σ_m increases relative to σ.

The structure of **F** ratio tests on means, hence the index **f**, is "naturally" nondirectional (as was the index **e** of the preceding chapter). Only when there are two population means are there only two directions in which discrepancies between null and alternative hypotheses can occur. With **k** > 2 means, departures can occur in many "directions." The result of all these departures from the null are included in the upper tail rejection region, and, as normally used, **F** tests do not discriminate among these and are therefore nondirectional.

f is related to an index ϕ used in standard treatments of power,[1] nomographs for which are widely reprinted in statistical testbooks (e.g., Dixon & Massey, 1957; Guenther, 1964) and books of tables (Owen, 1962). ϕ standardizes by the standard *error* of the sample mean and is thus (in part) a function of the size of each sample, **n**, while **f** is solely a descriptor of the population. Their relationship is given by

$$(8.2.3) \qquad f = \frac{\phi}{\sqrt{n}},$$

or

$$(8.2.4) \qquad \phi = f\sqrt{n}$$

---

[1] This use of the symbol ϕ is not to be confused with its other uses in the text, as the fourfold-point product-moment correlation in Chapter 7 or as the arcsine transformation of a proportion in Chapter 6.

The above description has, for the sake of clarity, proceeded on the assumption that the sizes of the **k** samples are all the same. No change in the basic conception of **f** takes place when we use it to index the effect size for tests on means of samples of unequal size (Case 1) or as an ES measure for tests on interactions (Case 3). In these applications, the definition of **f** as the "standard deviation of standardized means" requires some further elaboration, which is left to the sections concerned with these cases.

The remainder of this section provides systems for the translation of **f** into (a) a range measure, **d**, and (b) correlation ratio and variance proportion measures, and offers operational definitions of "small," "medium," and "large" ES. Here, too, *the exposition proceeds on the assumption of equal* **n** *per sample* and is appropriate to the **F** test on means (Cases 0 and 2). In later discussion of Cases 1 and 3, qualifications will be offered, as necessary.

8.2.1 **f** AND THE STANDARDIZED RANGE OF POPULATION MEANS, **d**. Although our primary ES index is **f**, the standard deviation of the standardized **k** population means, it may facilitate the use and understanding of this index to translate it to and from **d**, the range of standardized means, i.e., the distance between the smallest and largest of the **k** means:

$$(8.2.5) \qquad \mathbf{d} = \frac{\mathbf{m}_{max} - \mathbf{m}_{min}}{\sigma},$$

where $\mathbf{m}_{max}$ = the largest of the **k** means,
$\mathbf{m}_{min}$ = the smallest of the **k** means, and
σ = the (common) standard deviation within the populations (as before).

Notice that in the case of **k** = 2 means (**n** equal), the **d** of (8.2.5.) becomes the **d** used as the ES index for the **t** test of Chapter 2. The relationship between **f** and **d** for 2 means is simply

$$(8.2.6) \qquad \mathbf{f} = \tfrac{1}{2}\mathbf{d},$$

i.e., the standard deviation of two values is simply half their difference, and therefore

$$(8.2.7) \qquad \mathbf{d} = 2\mathbf{f}.$$

As the number of means increases beyond two, the relationship between their standard deviation (**f**) and their range (**d**) depends upon exactly how the means are dispersed over their range. With **k** means, two (the largest and smallest) define **d**, but then the remaining **k** − 2 may fall variously over the **d** interval; thus, **f** is not uniquely determined without further specification of the pattern of separation of the means. We will identify three patterns and describe the relationship each one has to **f**, which is also, in general, a function of the number of means. The patterns are:

1. Minimum variability: one mean at each end of **d**, the remaining **k** − 2 means all at the midpoint.
2. Intermediate variability: the **k** means equally spaced over **d**.
3. Maximum variability: the means all at the end points of **d**.

For each of these patterns, there is a fixed relationship between **f** and **d** for any given number of means, **k**.

Pattern 1. For any given range of means, **d**, the minimum standard deviation, f_1, results when the remaining **k** − 2 means are concentrated at the mean of the means (0 when expressed in standard units), i.e., half-way between the largest and smallest. For Pattern 1,

$$(8.2.8) \qquad\qquad f_1 = d\sqrt{\frac{1}{2k}}$$

gives the value of **f** for **k** means when the range **d** is specified. For example, 7 (= **k**) means dispersed in Pattern 1 would have the (standardized) values − $\frac{1}{2}$**d**, 0, 0, 0, 0, 0, + $\frac{1}{2}$**d**. Their standard deviation would be

$$f_1 = d\sqrt{\frac{1}{2(7)}} = \sqrt{.071429} = .267d,$$

slightly more than one-quarter of the range. Thus, a set of 7 population means spanning half a within-population standard deviation would have **f** = .267(.5) = .13.

The above gives **f** as a function of **d**. The reciprocal relationship is required to determine what value of the range is implied by any given (e.g., tabled) value of **f** when Pattern 1 holds, and is

$$(8.2.9) \qquad\qquad d_1 = f\sqrt{2k}.$$

For example, for the 7 (= **k**) means dispersed in Pattern 1 above, their range would be

$$d_1 = f\sqrt{2(7)} = f\sqrt{14} = 3.74f.$$

A value of **f** = .50 for these means would thus imply a standardized range of 3.74(.50) = 1.87.

For the convenience of the user of this handbook, Table 8.2.1 gives the constants (**c** and **b**) relating **f** to **d** for this pattern and the others discussed below for **k** = 2(1) 16, 25, covering the power and sample size tables provided. Their use is illustrated later in the chapter.

Table 8.2.1

Constants for Transforming d to f_j and f to d_j for Patterns j = 1, 2, 3

k	$f_j = c_j d$			$d_j = b_j f$		
	c_1	c_2	c_3	b_1	b_2	b_3
2	.500	.500	.500	2.00	2.00	2.00
3	.408	.408	.471	2.45	2.45	2.12
4	.354	.373	.500	2.83	2.68	2.00
5	.316	.354	.490	3.16	2.83	2.04
6	.289	.342	.500	3.46	2.93	2.00
7	.267	.333	.495	3.74	3.00	2.02
8	.250	.327	.500	4.00	3.06	2.00
9	.236	.323	.497	4.24	3.10	2.01
10	.224	.319	.500	4.47	3.13	2.00
11	.213	.316	.498	4.69	3.16	2.01
12	.204	.314	.500	4.90	3.19	2.00
13	.196	.312	.499	5.10	3.21	2.01
14	.189	.310	.500	5.29	3.22	2.00
15	.183	.309	.499	5.48	3.24	2.00
16	.177	.307	.500	5.66	.325	2.00
$\vdots$	$\vdots$	$\vdots$	$\vdots$	$\vdots$	$\vdots$	$\vdots$
25	.141	.300	.500	7.07	3.01	2.00

Pattern 2. A pattern of medium variability results when the **k** means are equally spaced over the range, and therefore at intervals of **d**/(k − 1). For Pattern 2, the **f** which results from any given range **d** is

(8.2.10)
$$f_2 = \frac{d}{2} \sqrt{\frac{k+1}{3(k-1)}} .$$

For example, for **k** = 7,

$$f_2 = \frac{d}{2} \sqrt{\frac{7+1}{3(7-1)}} = \frac{d}{2} \sqrt{\frac{8}{18}} = .333d,$$

i.e., 7 equally spaced means would have the values $-\frac{1}{2}$**d**, $-\frac{1}{3}$**d**, $-\frac{1}{6}$**d**, 0, $+\frac{1}{6}$**d**, $+\frac{1}{3}$**d**, and $+\frac{1}{2}$**d**, and a standard deviation equal to one-third of their range.

Note that this value for the same **k** is larger than $f_1 = .267d$ for Pattern 1. For a range of half a within-population standard deviation, $f_2 = .333(.5) = .17$ (while comparably, $f_1 = .13$).

The reciprocal relationship for determining the range implied by a tabled (or any other) value of **f** for Pattern 2 is

(8.2.11)
$$d_2 = 2f \sqrt{\frac{3(k-1)}{k+1}}.$$

For 7 means in Pattern 2, their range would be

$$d_2 = 2f \sqrt{\frac{3(7-1)}{7+1}} = 2f \sqrt{\frac{18}{8}} = 3f.$$

Thus, a value of **f** $= .50$ for these equally spaced means would imply a standardized range of $3(.50) = 1.50$.

Table 8.2.1 gives the relevant constants (b_2 and c_2) for varying **k**, making the solution of formulas (8.2.10) and (8.2.11) generally unnecessary.

Pattern 3. It is demonstrable and intuitively evident that for any given range the dispersion which yields the maximum standard deviation has the **k** means falling at both extremes of the range. When **k** is even, $\frac{1}{2}$**k** fall at $-\frac{1}{2}$**d** and the other $\frac{1}{2}$**k** fall at $+\frac{1}{2}$**d**; when **k** is odd, $(k+1)/2$ of the means fall at either end and the $(k-1)/2$ remaining means at the other. With this pattern, for all *even* numbers of means,

(8.2.12)
$$f_3 = \tfrac{1}{2}d.$$

When **k** is odd, and there is thus one more mean at one extreme than at the other,

(8.2.13)
$$f_3 = d \frac{\sqrt{k^2 - 1}}{2k}.$$

For example, for **k** $= 7$ means in Pattern 3 (4 means at either $-\frac{1}{2}$**d** or $+\frac{1}{2}$**d**, 3 means at the other), their standard deviation is

$$f_3 = d \frac{\sqrt{7^2 - 1}}{2(7)} = d \frac{\sqrt{48}}{14} = .495d.$$

Note that f_3 is larger (for **k** $= 7$) than $f_2 = .333d$ and $f_1 = .267d$. If, as before, we posit a range of half a within-population standard deviation, $f_3 = .495(.5) = .25$.

The reciprocal relationship used to determine the range implied by a given value of **f** when **k** is even is simply

(8.2.14)
$$d_3 = 2f,$$

and when **k** is odd,

(8.2.15) $$d_3 = f \frac{2k}{\sqrt{k^2 - 1}}.$$

For the running example of **k** = 7 means, in Pattern 3 their range would be

$$d_3 = f \frac{2(7)}{\sqrt{7^2 - 1}} = f \frac{14}{\sqrt{48}} = 2.02f,$$

so that if we posit, as before, a value of **f** = .50, for these 7 extremely placed means, $d_3 = 2.02(.5) = 1.01$, i.e., slightly more than a within-population standard deviation.

As can be seen from Table 8.2.1, there is not as much variability as a function of **k** in the relationship between **f** and **d** for Pattern 3 as for the others. f_3 is either (for **k** even) exactly or (for **k** odd) approximately $\frac{1}{2}$**d**, the minimum value being $f_3 = .471$**d** at **k** = 3.

This section has described and tabled the relationship between the primary ES index for the **F** test, **f**, the standard deviation of standardized means, and **d**, the standardized range of means, for three patterns of distribution of the **k** means. This makes it possible to use **d** as an alternate index of effect size, or equivalently, to determine the **d** implied by tabled or other values of **f**, and **f** implied by specified values of **d**. (The use of **d** will be illustrated in the problems of Sections 8.3 and 8.4) The reader is reminded that these relationships hold only for equal sample sizes (Cases 0 and 2).

8.2.2 **f**, THE CORRELATION RATIO, AND PROPORTION OF VARIANCE. Expressing **f** in terms of **d** provides one useful perspective on the appraisal of effect size with multiple means. Another frame of reference in which to understand **f** is described in this section, namely, in terms of correlation between population membership and the dependent variable, and in the related terms of the proportion of the total variance (PV) of the **k** populations combined which is accounted for by population membership.

Just as the **d** of this chapter is a generalization to **k** populations of the **d** used as an ES index for **t** tests on two means of Chapter 2, so is η (eta), the correlation ratio, a similar generalization of the Pearson **r**, and η^2 a generalization of r^2, the proportion of variance (PV) accounted for by population membership.

To understand η^2, consider the set of **k** populations, all of the same variance, σ^2, but each with its own mean, m_i. The variance of the means

$\sigma_m{}^2$ is some quantity which differs from zero when the **k** means are not all equal. If we square both sides of formula (8.2.1), we note that

(8.2.16)
$$\mathbf{f}^2 = \frac{\sigma_m{}^2}{\sigma^2},$$

is the ratio of the variance of the means to the variance of the values within the populations.

Now consider that the populations are combined into a single "super-population" whose mean is **m** (the mean of the population $\mathbf{m_i}$'s when the populations are considered equally numerous; otherwise, their mean when each $\mathbf{m_i}$ is weighted by its population size). The variance of the "superpopulation," or total variance $(\sigma_t{}^2)$, is larger than the within-population variance because it is augmented by the variance of the constituent population means. It is simply the sum of these two variances:

(8.2.17)
$$\sigma_t{}^2 = \sigma^2 + \sigma_m{}^2.$$

We now define η^2 as the proportion of the total superpopulation variance made up by the variance of the population means:

(8.2.18)
$$\eta^2 = \frac{\sigma_m{}^2}{\sigma_t{}^2} = \frac{\sigma_m{}^2}{\sigma^2 + \sigma_m{}^2}.$$

The combination of this formula with formula (8.2.16) and some simple algebraic manipulation yields

(8.2.19)
$$\eta^2 = \frac{\mathbf{f}^2}{1 + \mathbf{f}^2},$$

and

(8.2.20)
$$\eta = \sqrt{\frac{\mathbf{f}^2}{1 + \mathbf{f}^2}}.$$

Thus, a simple function of $\mathbf{f}^2$ yields η^2, a measure of dispersion of the $\mathbf{m_i}$ and hence of the implication of difference in population membership to the overall variability. When the population means are all equal, $\sigma_m{}^2$ and hence $\mathbf{f}^2$ is zero, and $\eta^2 = 0$, indicating that none of the total variance is due to difference in population membership. As formula (8.2.18) makes clear, when all the cases in each population have the same value, $\sigma^2 = 0$, and all of the total variance is produced by the variance of the means, so that $\eta^2 = 1.00$. Table 8.2.2 provides η^2 and η values as a function of **f**.

Note that η^2, like all measures of ES, describes a population state of affairs. It can also be computed on samples and its population value estimated therefrom. (See examples 8.17 and 8.19.) Depending on the basis of the estimation, the estimate is variously called η^2, ϵ^2 (Peters and Van Voorhis, 1940, pp. 312–325, 353–357; Cureton, 1966, pp. 605–607), or estimated ω^2 (Hays, 1963, pp. 323–331, 381–385). In general, η^2 is presented in applied statistics textbooks only in connection with its use in the appraisal of the curvilinear regression of **Y** on **X**, where the populations are defined by equal segments along the **X** variable, and $\sigma_m{}^2$ is the variance of the **X**-segments' **Y** means. Although this is a useful application of η^2, it is a rather limited special case; unfortunately, this narrow view of η^2 has preempted the attention of behavioral scientists and relegated the more general and most useful application of η^2 to an undeserved obscurity. For the broader view, see Hays (1963) (under ω^2), Cohen (1965, pp. 104–105), and Friedman (1968).

η^2 is literally a generalization of the (point-biserial) r^2 of Chapter 2 which gives the PV for the case where there are **k** = 2 populations. It is possible to express the relationship between the dependent variable **Y** and population membership **X** as a simple (i.e., zero-order) product moment r^2, when **X** is restricted to two possibilities, i.e., membership in A (**X** = 0) or membership in B (**X** = 1) (see Chapter 2). When we generalize **X** to represent a nominal scale of **k** possible alternative population memberships, r^2 no longer suffices, and the more general η^2 is used. It is interesting to note that if **k**-population membership is rendered as a set of independent variables (say, as dichotomous "dummy" variables), the simple r^2 generalizes to *multiple* R^2, which is demonstrably identically equal to η^2 (Cohen, 1968).

We have interpreted η^2 as the PV associated with alternative membership in populations. A mathematically equivalent description of η^2 proceeds by the following contrast: Assume that we "predict" all the members of our populations as having the same **Y** value, the **m** of our superpopulation. The gross error of this "prediction" can be appraised by finding for each subject the discrepancy between his value and **m**, squaring this value, and adding such squared values over all subjects. Call this $\mathbf{E_t}$. Another "prediction" can be made by assigning to each subject the mean of *his* population, $\mathbf{m_i}$. Again, we determine the discrepancy between his actual value and this "prediction" ($\mathbf{m_i}$), square and total over all subjects from all populations. Call this $\mathbf{E_p}$. To the extent to which the **k** population means are spread, $\mathbf{E_p}$ will be smaller than $\mathbf{E_t}$.

(8.2.21)
$$\eta^2 = \frac{\mathbf{E_t} - \mathbf{E_p}}{\mathbf{E_t}} = 1 - \frac{\mathbf{E_p}}{\mathbf{E_t}},$$

i.e., the proportionate amount *by which* errors are reduced by using own population mean ($\mathbf{m_i}$) rather than superpopulation mean (**m**) as a basis for "prediction." Or, we can view these as alternative means of *characterizing* the members of our populations, and η^2 indexes the degree of increased incisiveness that results from using the m_i rather than m.

The discussion has thus far proceeded with η^2, the PV measure. As previously noted, PV measures in behavioral science applications are distressingly low. For purposes of morale, and to offer a scale which is comparable to that of the familiar product moment r, we can index ES by means of η, the correlation ratio, in addition to or instead of the lower value yielded by η^2. As can be seen from taking the square root in formula (8.2.18), η is the ratio of the *standard deviation* of population means to the *standard deviation* of the values in the superpopulation, i.e., the combined populations.

Table 8.2.2

η^2 and η as a Function of f; f as a Function of η^2 and η

f	η^2	η	η^2	f	η	f
.00	.0000	.000	.00	.000	.00	.000
.05	.0025	.050	.01	.101	.05	.050
.10	.0099	.100	.02	.143	.10	.101
.15	.0220	.148	.03	.176	.15	.152
.20	.0385	.196	.04	.204	.20	.204
.25	.0588	.243	.05	.229	.25	.258
.30	.0826	.287	.06	.253	.30	.314
.35	.1091	.330	.07	.274	.35	.374
.40	.1379	.371	.08	.295	.40	.436
.45	.1684	.410	.09	.314	.45	.504
.50	.2000	.447	.10	.333	.50	.577
.55	.2322	.482	.15	.420	.55	.659
.60	.2647	.514	.20	.500	.60	.750
.65	.2970	.545	.25	.577	.65	.855
.70	.3289	.573	.30	.655	.70	.980
.75	.3600	.600	.40	.816	.75	1.134
.80	.3902	.625	.50	1.000	.80	1.333
.85	.4194	.648	.60	1.225	.85	1.614
.90	.4475	.669	.70	1.528	.90	2.065
.95	.4744	.689	.80	2.000	.95	3.042
1.00	.5000	.707	.90	3.000	1.00	–

Since standard deviations are as respectable as variances, no special apology is required in working with η rather than η^2.

In formulas (8.2.19) and (8.2.20), we have η^2 and η as functions of **f**. This is useful for assessing the implication of a given value of **f** (in terms of which our tables are organized) to PV or correlation. The reciprocal relation, **f** as a function of η, is also useful when the investigator, thinking in PV or correlational terms, needs to determine the **f** they imply, e.g., in order to use the tables:

$$(8.2.22) \qquad\qquad \mathbf{f} = \sqrt{\frac{\eta^2}{1 - \eta^2}}$$

For the convenience of the user of this handbook, this formula is solved for various values of η and η^2 and the results presented in Table 8.2.2.

Table 8.2.2 deserves a moment's attention. As discussed in the next section (and, indeed, as noted in previous chapters, particularly Chapter 3), effect sizes in behavioral science are generally small, and, in terms of **f**, will generally be found in the .00–.40 range. With **f** small, $\mathbf{f}^2$ is smaller, and $1 + \mathbf{f}^2$, the denominator of η^2 [formula (8.2.19)] is only slightly greater than one. The result is that for small values of **f** such as are typically encountered, η is approximately equal to **f**, being only slightly smaller, and therefore η^2 is similarly only slightly smaller than $\mathbf{f}^2$. Thus, in the range of our primary interest, **f** provides in itself an approximate correlation measure, and $\mathbf{f}^2$ an approximate PV measure. For very large effect sizes, say $\mathbf{f} > .40$, **f** and η diverge too much for this rough and ready approximation, and $\mathbf{f}^2$ and η^2 even more so.

8.2.3   "SMALL," "MEDIUM," AND "LARGE" **f** VALUES. It has already been suggested that values of **f** as large as .50 are not common in behavioral science, thus providing a prelude to the work of this section. Again, as in previous chapters, we take on the task of helping the user of this handbook to achieve a workable frame of reference for the ES index or measure of the alternate-hypothetical state of affairs, in this case **f**.

The optimal procedure for setting **f** in a given investigation is that the investigator, drawing on previous findings and theory in that area and his own scientific judgment, specify the **k** means and σ he expects and compute the resulting **f** from these values by means of formulas (8.2.1) and (8.2.2). If this demand for specification is too "strong," he may specify the range of means, **d**, from formula (8.2.5), choose one of the patterns of mean dispersion of Section 8.2.1, and use Table 8.2.1 to determine the implied value of **f**. On the same footing as this procedure, which may be used instead of or in conjunction with it, is positing the expected results in terms of the proportion of total variance associated with membership in the **k** populations, i.e., η^2. Formula (8.2.22) and Table 8.2.2 then provide the translation from η^2 to **f**. (In the case of **f** for interactions, see Section 8.3.4.)

All the above procedures are characterized by their use of magnitudes selected by the investigator to represent the situation of the *specific* research he is planning. When experience with a given research area or variable is insufficient to formulate alternative hypotheses as "strong" as these procedures demand, and to serve as a set of conventions or operational definitions, we define specific values of **f** for "small," "medium," and "large" effects. The reader is referred to Sections 1.4 and 2.2.3 for review of the considerations leading to the setting of ES conventions, and the advantages and disadvantages inherent in them. Briefly, we note here that these qualitative adjectives are relative, and, being general, may not be reasonably descriptive in any specific area. Thus, what a sociologist may consider a small effect size may well be appraised as medium by a clinical psychologist.

It must be reiterated here that however problematic the setting of an ES, it is a task which simply cannot be shirked. The investigator who insists that he has absolutely no way of knowing how large an ES to posit fails to appreciate that this necessarily means that he has no rational basis for deciding whether he needs to make ten observations or ten thousand.

Before presenting the operational definitions for **f**, a word about their consistency. They are fully consistent with the definitions of Chapter 2 for $k = 2$ populations in terms of **d**, which, as noted, is simply 2**f**. They are also generally consistent with the other ES indices which can be translated into PV measures (see Sections 3.2.2 and 6.2.1).

We continue, for the present, to conceive of the populations as being sampled with equal **n**'s.

SMALL EFFECT SIZE: **f** = .10. We define a small effect as a standard deviation of **k** population means one-tenth as large as the standard deviation of the observations within the populations. For $k = 2$ populations, this definition is exactly equivalent to the comparable definition of a small difference, **d** = 2(.10) = .20 of Chapter 2 [formula (8.2.7) and, more generally, Table 8.2.1]. As **k** increases, a given **f** implies a greater range for Patterns 1 and 2. Thus, with $k = 6$ means, one at each end of the range and the remaining 4 at the middle (Pattern 1), an **f** of .10 implies a range d_1 of 3.46(.10) = .35, while equal spacing (Pattern 2) implies a range d_2 of 2.93(.10) = .29. (The constants 3.46 and 2.93 are respectively the b_1 and b_2 values at $k = 6$ in Table 8.2.1.) When **f** = .10 occurs with the extreme Pattern 3, the d_3 is at (for **k** even) or slightly above (for **k** odd) 2**f** = .20 (Table 8.2.1). Thus, depending on **k** and the pattern of the means over the range, a small effect implies **d** at least .20, and, with large **k** disposed in Pattern 1, a small effect can be expressed in a d_1 of the order of .50 or larger (for example, see Table 8.2.1 in column b_1 for $k \geq 12$).

When expressed in correlation and PV terms, the $f = .10$ definition of a small effect is fully consistent with the definitions of Chapters 2, 3, and 6 (various forms of product moment r). An $f = .10$ is equivalent to $\eta = .100$ and $\eta^2 = .0099$, about 1 % of the total superpopulation variance accounted for by group membership. As already noted (particularly in Section 2.2.3), scientifically important (or at least meaningful) effects may be of this modest order of magnitude. The investigator who is inclined to disregard ES criteria for effects this small on the grounds that he would never be seeking to establish such small effects needs to be reminded that he is likely to be thinking in terms of theoretical constructs, which are implicitly measured without error. Any source of irrelevant variance in his measures (psychometric unreliability, dirty test tubes, lack of experimental control, or whatever) will serve to reduce his effect sizes *as measured*, so that what would be a medium or even large effect if one could use "true" measures may be attenuated to a small effect in practice (Cohen, 1962, p. 151).

MEDIUM EFFECT SIZE: $f = .25$. A standard deviation of k population means one-quarter as large as the standard deviation of the observations within the populations, is the operational definition of a medium effect size. With $k = 2$ populations, this accords with the $d = 2(.25) = .50$ definition of a medium difference between two means of Chapter 2, and this is a minimum value for the range over k means. With increasing k for either minimum (Pattern 1) or intermediate (Pattern 2) variability, the range implied by $f = .25$ increases from $d = .50$. For example, with $k = 7$ population means, if $k - 2 = 5$ of them are at the middle of the range and the remaining two at the endpoints of the range (Pattern 1), a medium $d_1 = 3.74(.25) = .94$ (Table 8.2.1 gives $b_1 = 3.74$ at $k = 7$). Thus, medium effect size for 7 means disposed in Pattern 1 implies a range of means of almost one standard deviation. If the seven means are spaced equally over the range (Pattern 2), a medium $d_2 = 3.00(.25) = .75$ (Table 8.2.1 gives $b_2 = 3.00$ for $k = 7$), i.e., a span of means of three-quarters of a within-population standard deviation. As a concrete example of this, consider the IQ's of seven populations made up of certain occupational groups, e.g., house painters, chauffeurs, auto mechanics, carpenters, butchers, riveters, and linemen. Assume a within-population standard deviation for IQ of 12 ($= \sigma$) and that their IQ means are equally spaced. Now, assume a medium ES, hence $f = .25$. (Expressed in IQ units, this would mean that the standard deviation of the seven IQ means would be $f\sigma = .25(12) = 3$.) The range of these means would be $d_2 = .75$ of the within-population σ. Expressed in units of IQ, this would be $d_2\sigma = .75(12) = 9$ IQ points, say from 98 to 107. (These values are about right [Berelson & Steiner, 1964, pp. 223–224], but of course any seven equally spaced values whose range is 9 would satisfy the criterion of a medium ES as defined here.)

Viewed from the perspective of correlation and proportion of variance accounted for, we note that $f = .25$ implies a correlation ratio (η) of .243 and a PV (here η^2) of .0588, i.e., not quite 6% of the total variance of the combined populations accounted for by population membership (Table 8.2.2). Again, note that this is identical with the correlational-PV criterion of a medium difference between two means (Section 2.2), necessarily so since in this limiting case $\eta = r$ (point biserial). It is also consistent with the definition of a medium difference between two proportions, when expressed as an r (fourfold point or ϕ correlation), which equals .238 to .248 when, the proportions are in the interval .20 to .80 (Section 6.2). It is, however smaller than the criterion for a medium ES in hypotheses concerning the Pearson r (Section 3.2), where the medium r is .30 (and $r^2 = .09$).

LARGE EFFECT SIZE: $f = .40$. Our operational definition (or proposed convention) of a large spread of k means is that the standard deviation of the means be .40 of the standard deviation of the observations within the populations. This is consistent with the criterion of a large difference between two means of $d = 2(.40) = .80$ (Section 2.2.2) and is the minimum range (since $k = 2$) which can be called large by this definition. With the means disposed in Pattern 1, a large span for 6 means is $d_1 = 3.46(.40) = 1.38$, for 7 means $d_1 = 3.74(.40) = 1.50$, for 8 means $d_1 = 4.00(.40) = 1.60$, etc., i.e., about $1\frac{1}{2}$ standard deviations (b_1 constants from Table 8.2.1). For equally spaced means (Pattern 2), this implies for 6 means, a range of $d_2 = 2.93(.40) = 1.17$, for 7 means a range of $d_2 = 3.00(.40) = 1.20$, and for 8 means a range of $d_2 = 3.06(.40) = 1.22$, etc., i.e., about $1\frac{1}{5}$ standard deviations (b_2 constants from Table 8.2.1). We use a similar illustration to that given for medium effect size, where for $k = 7$ occupation groups with equally spaced population mean IQs, we found the range $d_2 = b_2 f = 3.00(.25) = .75$, or, expressed in IQ units, $.75\sigma = .75(12) = 9.0$. Consider now a new set of 7 occupations: house painter, chauffeur, upholsterer, mechanic, lathe operator, machinist, laboratory assistant. Their mean IQ's, to have a large range, would need to cover uniformly the interval $d_2 = b_2 f = 3.00(.40) = 1.20$, or expressed in IQ units, again assuming that $\sigma = 12$, $1.20\sigma = 1.20(12) = 14.4$, say from 98 to 112 (Berelson & Steiner, 1964, pp. 223–224). Again note that any set of 7 occupation groups with IQ means spanning the same range would represent a large effect as defined here, wherever that range occurs.

In terms of correlation and proportion of variance accounted for, $f = .40$ implies a correlation ratio (η) of .371 and a PV (here η^2) of .1379, somewhat more than twice the PV for a medium effect ($\eta^2 = .0588$). Note the necessary consistency with the definition in correlation–PV terms of a large difference between two means (η = point biserial r; see Section 2.2). This definition is also fully consistent with the definition of a large difference between two proportions, when expressed as an r (fourfold point or ϕ

correlation), which equals .37–.39 when the proportions fall between .20 and .80 (Section 6.2). However, it is smaller than the criterion for a large ES in hypotheses concerning the Pearson **r**, where large **r** is defined as .50, $r^2 =$ PV = .25 (Section 3.2).

8.3   POWER TABLES

The power tables for this section are given on pages 282–347; the text follows on page 348.

Table 8.3.1

Power of F test at a = .01, u = 1

							f						
n	F_c	.05	.10	.15	.20	.25	.30	.35	.40	.50	.60	.70	.80
2	98.503	01	01	01	01	02	02	03	04	04	05	06	08
3	21.198	01	01	01	02	02	02	03	04	05	07	09	11
4	13.745	01	01	01	02	02	03	04	05	07	10	14	19
5	11.259	01	01	02	02	03	03	05	06	10	15	21	29
6	10.044	01	01	02	02	03	04	06	08	13	20	29	40
7	9.330	01	01	02	03	04	05	07	10	17	26	38	50
8	8.861	01	01	02	03	04	06	09	12	21	32	46	60
9	8.531	01	02	02	03	05	07	10	14	25	39	54	68
10	8.285	01	02	02	04	06	08	12	17	29	45	61	75
11	8.096	01	02	03	04	06	09	14	19	34	51	67	81
12	7.946	01	02	03	05	07	11	16	22	38	56	73	86
13	7.823	01	02	03	05	08	12	18	25	42	61	78	89
14	7.721	01	02	03	05	08	13	20	28	46	66	82	92
15	7.636	01	02	03	06	09	15	22	30	50	70	85	94
16	7.562	01	02	04	06	10	16	24	33	54	74	88	96
17	7.499	01	02	04	07	11	17	26	36	58	78	91	97
18	7.444	01	02	04	07	12	19	28	39	62	81	92	98
19	7.396	01	02	04	08	13	20	30	41	65	83	94	98
20	7.353	01	02	04	08	14	22	32	44	68	86	95	99
21	7.314	01	02	05	08	15	24	34	47	71	88	96	99
22	7.280	01	03	05	09	16	25	37	49	73	90	97	99
23	7.248	01	03	05	09	17	27	39	52	76	91	98	*
24	7.220	01	03	05	10	18	28	41	54	78	93	98	
25	7.194	01	03	06	10	19	30	43	57	80	94	99	
26	7.171	01	03	06	11	20	31	45	59	82	95	99	
27	7.149	01	03	06	12	21	33	47	61	84	96	99	
28	7.129	01	03	06	12	22	35	49	63	86	96	99	
29	7.110	01	03	07	13	23	36	50	65	87	97	*	
30	7.093	01	03	07	13	24	38	53	67	89	97		
31	7.077	02	03	07	14	25	39	55	69	90	98		
32	7.062	02	03	07	15	26	41	56	71	91	98		
33	7.048	02	04	08	15	27	42	58	73	92	99		
34	7.035	02	04	08	16	28	44	60	75	93	99		
35	7.023	02	04	08	17	30	45	62	76	94	99		
36	7.011	02	04	08	17	31	47	63	78	94	99		
37	7.001	02	04	09	18	32	48	65	79	95	99		
38	6.990	02	04	09	19	33	50	66	80	96	99		
39	6.981	02	04	09	19	34	51	68	82	96	*		

Table 8.3.1 *(continued)*

n	F_c	.05	.10	.15	.20	.25	.30	.35	.40	.50	.60	.70	.80
								f					
40	6.971	02	04	10	20	35	53	69	83	97	*	*	*
42	6.954	02	04	10	21	37	55	72	85	97			
44	6.939	02	05	11	23	39	58	75	87	98			
46	6.925	02	05	11	24	41	60	77	89	98			
48	6.912	02	05	12	25	44	63	79	90	99			
50	6.901	02	05	13	27	46	65	81	92	99			
52	6.890	02	05	13	28	48	67	83	93	99			
54	6.880	02	06	14	30	50	70	85	94	99			
56	6.871	02	06	15	31	52	72	86	95	*			
58	6.862	02	06	16	33	54	73	88	95				
60	6.854	02	06	16	34	56	75	89	96				
64	6.840	02	07	18	37	59	79	91	97				
68	6.828	02	07	19	40	63	82	93	98				
72	6.817	02	08	21	42	66	84	95	99				
76	6.807	02	08	22	45	69	87	96	99				
80	6.798	02	09	24	48	72	89	97	99				
84	6.790	03	09	25	50	74	90	97	*				
88	6.783	03	10	27	53	77	92	98					
92	6.776	03	10	29	55	79	93	98					
96	6.770	03	11	30	57	81	94	99					
100	6.764	03	11	32	60	83	95	99					
120	6.742	03	14	40	70	90	98	*					
140	6.727	04	17	47	78	95	99						
160	6.715	04	21	54	84	97	*						
180	6.706	04	24	61	89	99							
200	6.699	05	28	67	92	99							
250	6.686	07	37	79	97	*							
300	6.677	08	45	87	99								
350	6.671	10	53	92	*								
400	6.667	11	60	95									
450	6.663	13	67	97									
500	6.661	15	73	99									
600	6.656	19	82	*									
700	6.653	24	88										
800	6.651	28	93										
900	6.649	32	95										
1000	6.648	37	97										

* Power values below this point are greater than .995.

Table 8.3.2

Power of F test at a = .01, u = 2

n	F_c	.05	.10	.15	.20	.25	.30	.35	.40	.50	.60	.70	.80
						f							
2	30.817	01	01	01	01	02	02	03	03	03	04	06	07
3	10.925	01	01	01	02	02	02	03	04	05	07	10	13
4	8.022	01	01	01	02	02	03	04	05	08	12	17	24
5	6.927	01	01	02	02	03	04	05	07	11	18	27	38
6	6.359	01	01	02	02	03	05	07	09	16	26	38	51
7	6.013	01	01	02	03	04	06	08	11	21	33	48	63
8	5.780	01	01	02	03	05	07	10	14	26	41	58	73
9	5.614	01	02	02	04	05	08	12	17	31	49	67	81
10	5.488	01	02	03	04	06	10	14	21	37	56	74	87
11	5.390	01	02	03	04	07	11	17	24	42	63	80	91
12	5.313	01	02	03	05	08	13	19	27	48	69	85	94
13	5.249	01	02	03	05	09	14	22	31	53	74	89	96
14	5.195	01	02	03	06	10	16	24	34	58	79	92	98
15	5.150	01	02	04	06	11	18	27	38	62	82	94	99
16	5.111	01	02	04	07	12	20	30	41	67	86	96	99
17	5.078	01	02	04	07	13	21	32	45	70	89	97	99
18	5.048	01	02	04	08	14	23	35	48	74	91	98	*
19	5.022	01	02	05	09	15	25	38	52	77	93	98	
20	4.999	01	02	05	09	17	27	40	55	80	94	99	
21	4.977	01	03	05	10	18	29	43	58	83	95	99	
22	4.959	01	03	05	10	19	31	46	61	85	96	*	
23	4.943	01	03	06	11	20	33	48	64	87	97		
24	4.928	01	03	06	12	22	35	51	66	89	98		
25	4.914	01	03	06	12	23	37	53	69	91	98		
26	4.901	01	03	07	13	24	39	56	71	92	99		
27	4.889	01	03	07	14	26	41	58	74	93	99		
28	4.878	01	03	07	15	27	43	60	76	94	99		
29	4.868	01	03	07	15	28	45	62	78	95	99		
30	4.859	02	03	08	16	30	47	65	80	96	*		
31	4.850	02	04	08	17	31	49	67	81	96			
32	4.842	02	04	08	18	33	51	69	83	97			
33	4.834	02	04	09	19	34	53	70	84	98			
34	4.827	02	04	09	19	35	54	72	86	98			
35	4.820	02	04	09	20	37	56	74	87	98			
36	4.814	02	04	10	21	38	58	76	88	99			
37	4.808	02	04	10	22	40	59	77	89	99			
38	4.802	02	04	10	23	41	61	79	90	99			
39	4.797	02	04	11	24	42	63	80	91	99			

Table 8.3.2 (continued)

n	F_c	.05	.10	.15	.20	.25	.30	.35	.40	.50	.60	.70	.80
40	4.791	02	05	11	25	44	64	81	92	99	*	*	*
42	4.782	02	05	12	26	46	67	84	94	*			
44	4.774	02	05	13	28	49	70	86	95				
46	4.766	02	05	14	30	51	73	88	96				
48	4.760	02	05	14	32	54	75	90	97				
50	4.753	02	06	15	33	56	77	91	97				
52	4.747	02	06	16	35	59	79	92	98				
54	4.742	02	06	17	37	61	81	93	98				
56	4.737	02	06	18	39	63	83	94	99				
58	4.732	02	07	19	40	65	85	95	99				
60	4.728	02	07	20	42	67	86	96	99				
64	4.720	02	08	22	46	71	89	97	99				
68	4.713	02	08	24	49	75	91	98	*				
72	4.707	02	09	26	52	78	93	99					
76	4.702	02	09	28	55	81	95	.99					
80	4.697	03	10	30	58	83	96	99					
84	4.693	03	10	32	61	85	97	*					
88	4.689	03	11	34	64	88	97						
92	4.685	03	12	36	67	89	98						
96	4.682	03	13	38	69	91	98						
100	4.678	03	13	40	72	92	99						
120	4.666	04	17	49	82	97	*						
140	4.657	04	21	58	89	99							
160	4.651	05	26	66	93	99							
180	4.646	05	30	73	96	*							
200	4.642	06	34	79	98								
250	4.634	07	45	89	99								
300	4.629	09	56	95	*								
350	4.626	11	65	97									
400	4.623	13	72	99									
450	4.621	16	79	*									
500	4.620	18	84										
600	4.617	24	91										
700	4.616	29	95										
800	4.614	35	98										
900	4.613	40	99										
1000	4.612	46	99										

* Power values below this point are greater than .995.

Table 8.3.3

Power of F test at a = .01, u = 3

n	F_c	.05	.10	.15	.20	.25	.30	.35	.40	.50	.60	.70	.80
2	16.694	01	01	01	01	02	02	02	03	04	05	06	07
3	7.591	01	01	01	02	02	03	03	04	06	08	12	16
4	5.953	01	01	01	02	02	03	04	06	09	15	22	31
5	5.292	01	01	02	02	03	04	06	08	14	23	34	48
6	4.938	01	01	02	03	04	05	08	11	20	32	47	63
7	4.718	01	01	02	03	04	06	10	14	26	42	59	75
8	4.568	01	02	02	03	05	08	12	17	32	51	69	84
9	4.460	01	02	02	04	06	10	15	21	39	59	78	90
10	4.378	01	02	03	04	07	11	17	25	45	67	84	94
11	4.313	01	02	03	05	08	13	20	29	52	74	89	97
12	4.262	01	02	03	05	09	15	23	34	58	79	92	98
13	4.219	01	02	03	06	10	17	27	38	63	84	95	99
14	4.183	01	02	04	07	12	19	30	42	68	88	97	99
15	4.153	01	02	04	07	13	22	33	46	73	91	98	*
16	4.126	01	02	04	08	14	24	36	50	77	93	99	
17	4.104	01	02	04	09	16	26	40	54	81	95	99	
18	4.084	01	02	05	09	17	29	43	58	84	96	99	
19	4.067	01	02	05	10	19	31	46	62	86	97	*	
20	4.051	01	03	05	11	20	33	49	65	89	98		
21	4.038	01	03	06	11	22	36	52	68	91	99		
22	4.025	01	03	06	12	23	38	55	71	92	99		
23	4.013	01	03	06	13	25	40	58	74	94	99		
24	4.003	01	03	07	14	26	43	61	77	95	99		
25	3.993	01	03	07	15	28	45	63	79	96	*		
26	3.984	01	03	07	16	30	48	66	81	97			
27	3.976	01	03	08	17	31	50	68	83	97			
28	3.969	02	03	08	18	33	52	71	85	98			
29	3.962	02	04	08	19	35	54	73	87	98			
30	3.955	02	04	09	20	36	56	75	88	99			
31	3.949	02	04	09	21	38	58	77	90	99			
32	3.944	02	04	10	22	40	60	79	91	99			
33	3.939	02	04	10	23	41	62	80	92	99			
34	3.934	02	04	10	24	43	64	82	93	99			
35	3.929	02	04	11	25	45	66	83	94	*			
36	3.925	02	04	11	26	46	68	85	94				
37	3.921	02	05	12	27	48	70	86	95				
38	3.917	02	05	12	28	49	71	87	96				
39	3.914	02	05	13	29	51	73	88	96				

Table 8.3.3 *(continued)*

n	F_c	.05	.10	.15	.20	.25	.30	.35	.40	.50	.60	.70	.80
40	3.910	02	05	13	30	53	74	89	97	*	*	*	*
42	3.904	02	05	14	32	56	77	91	98				
44	3.898	02	06	15	34	58	80	93	98				
46	3.893	02	06	16	36	61	82	94	99				
48	3.889	02	06	17	38	64	84	95	99				
50	3.884	02	06	18	41	66	86	96	99				
52	3.880	02	07	19	43	69	88	97	99				
54	3.876	02	07	21	45	71	90	97	*				
56	3.873	02	07	22	47	73	91	98					
58	3.870	02	08	23	49	75	92	98					
60	3.867	02	08	24	51	77	93	99					
64	3.862	02	09	26	55	81	95	99					
68	3.857	02	09	29	59	84	96	99					
72	3.853	03	10	31	62	87	97	*					
76	3.849	03	11	34	65	89	98						
80	3.845	03	11	36	69	91	99						
84	3.842	03	12	38	72	93	99						
88	3.839	03	13	41	74	94	99						
92	3.837	03	14	43	77	95	99						
96	3.834	03	15	45	79	96	*						
100	3.832	03	16	48	81	97							
120	3.824	04	21	59	90	99							
140	3.818	04	26	68	95	*							
160	3.813	05	31	76	97								
180	3.810	06	36	82	99								
200	3.807	07	42	87	99								
250	3.802	09	54	95	*								
300	3.798	11	66	98									
350	3.796	13	75	99									
400	3.794	16	82	*									
450	3.793	19	87										
500	3.792	22	91										
600	3.790	29	96										
700	3.789	35	98										
800	3.788	42	99										
900	3.787	49	*										
1000	3.787	55											

* Power values below this point are greater than .995.

Table 8.3.4

Power of F test at a = .01, u = 4

n	F_c	.05	.10	.15	.20	.25	.30	.35	.40	.50	.60	.70	.80
2	11.392	01	01	01	01	02	02	02	03	04	05	06	08
3	5.994	01	01	01	02	02	02	03	04	06	10	14	20
4	4.893	01	01	01	02	03	03	04	06	11	18	27	39
5	4.431	01	01	02	02	03	05	06	09	17	28	42	57
6	4.177	01	01	02	03	04	06	09	12	23	39	56	73
7	4.018	01	01	02	03	05	08	11	16	31	50	69	84
8	3.910	01	01	02	04	06	09	14	21	39	60	78	91
9	3.828	01	02	03	04	07	11	17	25	46	69	86	95
10	3.769	01	02	03	05	08	13	21	30	54	76	91	97
11	3.721	01	02	03	05	09	15	24	35	60	82	94	99
12	3.682	01	02	03	06	11	18	28	40	67	87	96	99
13	3.649	01	02	04	07	12	20	32	45	72	90	98	*
14	3.623	01	02	04	07	13	23	35	50	77	93	99	
15	3.601	01	02	04	08	15	26	39	54	81	95	99	
16	3.581	01	02	05	09	17	28	43	59	85	97	*	
17	3.564	01	02	05	10	18	31	47	63	88	98		
18	3.549	01	03	05	11	20	34	50	67	90	98		
19	3.536	01	03	06	11	22	37	54	70	92	99		
20	3.524	01	03	06	12	24	39	57	74	94	99		
21	3.514	01	03	06	13	26	42	60	77	95	*		
22	3.504	01	03	07	14	27	45	64	80	96			
23	3.495	01	03	07	15	29	48	67	82	97			
24	3.487	01	03	07	16	31	50	69	84	98			
25	3.480	01	03	08	17	33	53	72	86	98			
26	3.473	01	03	08	19	35	55	74	88	99			
27	3.467	02	04	09	20	37	58	77	90	99			
28	3.462	02	04	09	21	39	60	79	91	99			
29	3.457	02	04	10	22	41	63	81	92	99			
30	3.452	02	04	10	23	43	65	83	93	*			
31	3.448	02	04	11	24	45	67	84	94				
32	3.443	02	04	11	25	47	69	86	95				
33	3.439	02	04	12	27	49	71	87	96				
34	3.436	02	05	12	28	50	73	89	97				
35	3.432	02	05	13	29	52	75	90	97				
36	3.429	02	05	13	30	54	76	91	98				
37	3.426	02	05	14	32	56	78	92	98				
38	3.423	02	05	14	33	57	79	93	98				
39	3.420	02	05	15	34	59	81	94	99				

Table 8.3.4 *(continued)*

n	F_c	.05	.10	.15	.20	.25	.30	.35	.40	.50	.60	.70	.80
							f						
40	3.418	02	05	15	35	61	82	94	99	*	*	*	*
42	3.413	02	06	17	38	64	85	96	99				
44	3.409	02	06	18	40	67	87	97	99				
46	3.405	02	06	19	43	70	89	97	*				
48	3.401	02	07	20	45	72	91	98					
50	3.398	02	07	22	48	75	92	98					
52	3.395	02	07	23	50	77	93	99					
54	3.392	02	08	24	52	79	94	99					
56	3.389	02	08	26	55	81	95	99					
58	3.386	02	09	27	57	83	96	99					
60	3.384	02	09	28	59	85	97	*					
64	3.380	02	10	31	63	88	98						
68	3.376	03	11	34	67	90	98						
72	3.373	03	11	37	71	92	99						
76	3.371	03	12	39	74	94	99						
80	3.368	03	13	42	77	95	*						
84	3.366	03	14	45	80	96							
88	3.364	03	15	48	82	97							
92	3.361	03	16	50	84	98							
96	3.360	03	17	53	86	98							
100	3.358	03	19	55	88	99							
120	3.352	04	24	67	94	*							
140	3.347	05	30	76	98								
160	3.344	06	37	84	99								
180	3.341	06	43	89	*								
200	3.339	07	49	93									
250	3.335	10	63	98									
300	3.332	12	74	99									
350	3.330	15	82	*									
400	3.329	19	89										
450	3.328	22	93										
500	3.327	26	96										
600	3.326	34	98										
700	3.325	42	*										
800	3.324	49											
900	3.323	56											
1000	3.323	63											

* Power values below this point are greater than .995.

Table 8.3.5

Power of F test at a = .01, u = 5

n	F_c	.05	.10	.15	.20	.25	.30	.35	.40	.50	.60	.70	.80
2	8.746	01	01	01	01	02	02	02	03	04	05	07	09
3	5.064	01	01	01	02	02	03	03	04	07	11	17	24
4	4.248	01	01	02	02	03	04	05	07	12	21	32	46
5	3.895	01	01	02	02	03	05	07	10	19	33	49	66
6	3.699	01	01	02	03	04	07	10	14	28	45	64	80
7	3.576	01	01	02	03	05	08	13	19	36	57	76	90
8	3.489	01	02	02	04	07	10	16	24	45	67	85	95
9	3.426	01	02	03	05	08	13	20	30	53	76	91	98
10	3.388	01	02	03	05	09	15	24	35	61	83	95	99
11	3.339	01	02	03	06	10	18	28	41	68	88	97	*
12	3.309	01	02	04	07	12	21	32	46	74	92	98	
13	3.284	01	02	04	07	14	24	37	52	79	95	99	
14	3.263	01	02	04	08	15	27	41	57	84	97	*	
15	3.244	01	02	05	09	17	30	45	62	87	98		
16	3.229	01	02	05	10	19	33	49	66	90	99		
17	3.215	01	03	05	11	21	36	53	70	92	99		
18	3.203	01	03	06	12	23	39	57	74	94	99		
19	3.192	01	03	06	13	25	42	61	77	96	*		
20	3.182	01	03	07	14	27	45	64	81	97			
21	3.174	01	03	07	15	30	48	68	83	98			
22	3.166	01	03	07	16	32	51	71	86	98			
23	3.159	01	03	08	18	34	54	74	88	99			
24	3.153	01	03	08	19	36	57	76	90	99			
25	3.147	01	04	09	20	38	60	79	91	99			
26	3.142	02	04	09	21	40	63	81	93	*			
27	3.137	02	04	10	23	43	65	83	94				
28	3.133	02	04	10	24	45	67	85	95				
29	3.129	02	04	11	25	47	70	87	96				
30	3.125	02	04	11	27	49	72	88	97				
31	3.121	02	04	12	28	51	74	90	97				
32	3.118	02	05	12	29	53	76	91	98				
33	3.115	02	05	13	31	55	78	92	98				
34	3.112	02	05	14	32	57	80	93	98				
35	3.109	02	05	14	34	59	81	94	99				
36	3.107	02	05	15	35	61	83	95	99				
37	3.104	02	05	16	36	63	84	95	99				
38	3.102	02	06	16	38	64	86	96	99				
39	3.100	02	06	17	39	66	87	97	99				

Table 8.3.5 *(continued)*

n	F_c	.05	.10	.15	.20	.25	.30	.35	.40	.50	.60	.70	.80
40	3.097	02	06	18	41	68	88	97	*	*	*	*	*
42	3.093	02	06	19	43	71	90	98					
44	3.090	02	07	20	46	74	92	98					
46	3.087	02	07	22	49	77	93	99					
48	3.084	02	07	23	52	79	94	99					
50	3.081	02	08	25	54	81	96	99					
52	3.079	02	08	26	57	84	96	*					
54	3.076	02	09	28	59	85	97						
56	3.074	02	09	30	61	87	98						
58	3.072	02	10	31	64	89	98						
60	3.070	02	10	33	66	90	99						
64	3.067	03	11	36	70	92	99						
68	3.064	03	12	39	74	94	99						
72	3.061	03	13	42	77	96	*						
76	3.059	03	14	45	80	97							
80	3.057	03	15	48	83	98							
84	3.055	03	16	51	86	98							
88	3.053	03	18	54	88	99							
92	3.052	03	19	57	90	99							
96	3.050	04	20	60	91	99							
100	3.049	04	21	62	93	*							
120	3.044	04	28	74	97								
140	3.040	05	35	83	99								
160	3.037	06	42	89	*								
180	3.035	07	49	93									
200	3.033	08	55	96									
250	3.030	11	70	99									
300	3.028	14	80	*									
350	3.026	18	88										
400	3.025	22	93										
450	3.024	26	96										
500	3.023	30	98										
600	3.022	39	99										
700	3.022	47	*										
800	3.021	56											
900	3.021	63											
1000	3.020	70											

* Power values below this point are greater than .995.

Table 8.3.6

Power of F test at a = .01, u = 6

n	F_c	.05	.10	.15	.20	.25	.30	.35	.40	.50	.60	.70	.80
								f					
2	7.191	01	01	01	01	02	02	02	03	04	06	07	10
3	4.456	01	01	01	02	02	03	03	05	08	13	19	28
4	3.812	01	01	02	02	03	04	06	08	14	24	37	53
5	3.528	01	01	02	03	04	06	08	12	22	38	56	73
6	3.369	01	01	02	03	05	07	11	16	32	51	71	86
7	3.266	01	02	02	04	06	09	15	22	41	64	83	94
8	3.196	01	02	03	04	07	12	19	28	51	74	90	97
9	3.143	01	02	03	05	09	14	23	34	60	82	95	99
10	3.103	01	02	03	06	10	17	27	40	68	88	97	*
11	3.072	01	02	03	06	12	20	32	46	74	92	99	
12	3.047	01	02	04	07	13	23	37	52	80	95	99	
13	3.026	01	02	04	08	15	27	41	58	85	97	*	
14	3.008	01	02	05	09	17	30	46	63	89	98		
15	2.992	01	02	05	10	20	34	51	68	92	99		
16	2.979	01	02	05	11	22	37	55	72	94	99		
17	2.968	01	03	06	12	24	41	59	76	95	*		
18	2.957	01	03	06	13	26	44	63	80	97			
19	2.949	01	03	07	15	29	48	67	83	98			
20	2.941	01	03	07	16	31	51	71	86	98			
21	2.934	01	03	08	17	34	54	74	88	99			
22	2.928	01	03	08	19	36	57	77	90	99			
23	2.922	01	03	09	20	38	60	80	92	99			
24	2.917	02	04	09	21	41	63	82	93	*			
25	2.912	02	04	10	23	43	66	84	95				
26	2.908	02	04	10	24	46	69	86	96				
27	2.904	02	04	11	26	48	71	88	96				
28	2.900	02	04	11	27	50	74	90	97				
29	2.896	02	04	12	29	53	76	91	98				
30	2.893	02	05	13	30	55	78	92	98				
31	2.890	02	05	13	32	57	80	93	99				
32	2.887	02	05	14	33	59	82	94	99				
33	2.884	02	05	15	35	61	83	95	99				
34	2.882	02	05	15	36	63	85	96	99				
35	2.880	02	05	16	38	65	86	97	99				
36	2.877	02	06	17	40	67	88	97	*				
37	2.875	02	06	18	41	69	89	98					
38	2.873	02	06	18	43	71	90	98					
39	2.871	02	06	19	44	72	91	98					

Table 8.3.6 (continued)

n	F_c	.05	.10	.15	.20	.25	.30	.35	.40	.50	.60	.70	.80
40	2.870	02	06	20	46	74	92	99	*	*	*	*	*
42	2.866	02	07	22	49	77	94	99					
44	2.863	02	07	23	52	80	95	99					
46	2.861	02	08	25	55	82	96	*					
48	2.858	02	08	27	57	85	97						
50	2.856	02	09	28	60	87	98						
52	2.854	02	09	30	63	88	98						
54	2.852	02	10	32	65	90	99						
56	2.850	02	10	33	68	91	99						
58	2.848	02	11	35	70	93	99						
60	2.847	02	11	37	72	94	99						
64	2.844	03	12	40	76	95	*						
68	2.841	03	13	44	80	97							
72	2.839	03	14	47	83	98							
76	2.837	03	16	51	86	98							
80	2.835	03	17	54	88	99							
84	2.834	03	18	57	90	99							
88	2.832	03	20	60	92	99							
92	2.831	04	21	63	93	*							
96	2.830	04	23	66	95								
100	2.829	05	24	69	96								
120	2.825	05	32	80	99								
140	2.821	06	39	88	*								
160	2.819	07	47	93									
180	2.817	08	54	96									
200	2.815	09	61	98									
250	2.813	12	76	*									
300	2.811	16	86										
350	2.810	20	92										
400	2.809	24	96										
450	2.808	29	98										
500	2.807	34	99										
600	2.806	44	*										
700	2.806	53											
800	2.805	62											
900	2.805	69											
1000	2.805	76											

* Power values below this point are greater than .995.

Table 8.3.7

Power of F test at a = .01, u = 8

n	F_c	.05	.10	.15	.20	.25	.30	.35	.40	.50	.60	.70	.80
							f						
2	5.467	01	01	01	01	02	02	02	03	05	06	09	12
3	3.705	01	01	01	02	02	03	04	06	10	16	25	37
4	3.256	01	01	02	02	03	05	07	09	18	31	47	65
5	3.053	01	01	02	03	04	06	10	14	28	47	67	84
6	2.936	01	01	02	03	05	09	14	20	40	63	82	93
7	2.861	01	02	02	04	07	11	18	27	51	75	91	98
8	2.808	01	02	03	05	08	14	23	34	61	84	96	99
9	2.770	01	02	03	06	10	18	28	42	71	90	98	*
10	2.740	01	02	03	07	12	21	34	49	78	94	99	
11	2.716	01	02	04	08	14	25	40	56	84	97	*	
12	2.697	01	02	04	09	17	29	45	62	89	98		
13	2.681	01	02	05	10	19	33	51	68	92	99		
14	2.667	01	02	05	11	22	37	56	74	95	*		
15	2.656	01	03	06	12	24	42	61	78	96			
16	2.646	01	03	06	13	27	46	66	82	98			
17	2.638	01	03	07	15	30	50	70	86	98			
18	2.630	01	03	07	16	33	54	74	88	99			
19	2.624	01	03	08	18	35	57	77	91	99			
20	2.618	01	03	08	20	38	61	81	93	*			
21	2.612	01	03	09	21	41	64	83	94				
22	2.608	01	04	10	23	44	68	86	96				
23	2.603	02	04	10	25	47	71	88	97				
24	2.599	02	04	11	26	50	74	90	97				
25	2.596	02	04	12	28	52	76	92	98				
26	2.592	02	04	12	30	55	79	93	98				
27	2.589	02	05	13	32	58	81	94	99				
28	2.586	02	05	14	34	60	83	95	99				
29	2.583	02	05	15	35	63	85	96	99				
30	2.581	02	05	15	37	65	87	97	*				
31	2.579	02	05	16	39	67	88	97					
32	2.576	02	06	17	41	70	90	98					
33	2.574	02	06	18	43	72	91	98					
34	2.573	02	06	19	45	74	92	99					
35	2.571	02	06	20	46	75	93	99					
36	2.569	02	06	21	48	77	94	99					
37	2.567	02	07	22	50	79	95	99					
38	2.566	02	07	23	52	80	95	99					
39	2.564	02	07	24	54	82	96	*					

Table 8.3.7 (continued)

n	F_c					f							
		.05	.10	.15	.20	.25	.30	.35	.40	.50	.60	.70	.80
40	2.563	02	07	25	55	83	97	*	*	*	*	*	*
42	2.561	02	08	27	58	86	97						
44	2.558	02	08	29	62	88	98						
46	2.556	02	09	31	65	90	99						
48	2.554	02	10	33	68	92	99						
50	2.553	02	10	35	70	93	99						
52	2.551	02	11	37	73	94	99						
54	2.550	02	11	39	75	95	*						
56	2.548	03	12	41	78	96							
58	2.547	03	13	43	80	97							
60	2.546	03	13	45	82	97							
64	2.543	03	15	49	85	98							
68	2.541	03	16	53	88	99							
72	2.540	03	18	57	90	99							
76	2.538	03	20	61	92	*							
80	2.537	03	21	64	94								
84	2.536	04	23	67	95								
88	2.535	04	24	70	96								
92	2.534	04	26	73	97								
96	2.533	04	28	76	98								
100	2.532	04	30	78	98								
120	2.529	05	39	88	*								
140	2.526	06	48	94									
160	2.524	07	57	97									
180	2.523	09	65	99									
200	2.521	10	72	99									
250	2.519	14	85	*									
300	2.518	19	92										
350	2.517	25	97										
400	2.516	30	99										
450	2.516	36	99										
500	2.515	42	*										
600	2.515	53											
700	2.514	63											
800	2.514	72											
900	2.514	79											
1000	2.513	85											

* Power values below this point are greater than .995.

Table 8.3.8

Power of F test at a = .01, u = 10

n	F_c	.05	.10	.15	.20	.25	.30	.35	.40	.50	.60	.70	.80
2	4.539	01	01	01	01	02	02	03	03	05	07	10	15
3	3.258	01	01	02	02	02	03	04	06	11	20	31	46
4	2.914	01	01	02	02	03	05	08	11	22	38	57	74
5	2.752	01	01	02	03	05	07	11	17	34	56	77	91
6	2.662	01	01	02	04	06	10	16	25	47	72	89	97
7	2.603	01	02	03	05	08	13	22	33	60	83	95	99
8	2.561	01	03	03	06	10	17	28	41	70	91	98	*
9	2.530	01	03	03	07	12	21	34	49	79	95	99	
10	2.506	01	03	04	08	14	25	40	57	86	97	*	
11	2.487	01	03	04	09	17	30	47	65	97	99		
12	2.471	01	03	05	10	20	35	53	71	94	99		
13	2.458	01	03	05	11	23	40	59	77	96	*		
14	2.448	01	03	06	13	26	44	65	82	98			
15	2.439	01	03	06	14	29	49	70	86	99			
16	2.431	01	03	07	16	32	53	74	89	99			
17	2.424	01	03	08	18	35	58	78	91	*			
18	2.418	01	03	08	19	39	62	82	94				
19	2.413	01	03	09	21	42	66	85	95				
20	2.408	01	04	10	23	45	69	88	96				
21	2.403	02	04	10	25	49	73	90	97				
22	2.399	02	04	11	27	52	76	92	98				
23	2.396	02	04	12	29	55	79	93	99				
24	2.393	02	04	13	31	58	81	95	99				
25	2.390	02	05	13	33	61	84	96	99				
26	2.387	02	05	14	35	63	86	97	*				
27	2.384	02	05	15	38	66	88	97					
28	2.382	02	05	16	40	69	90	98					
29	2.380	02	05	17	42	71	91	98					
30	2.378	02	06	18	44	73	92	99					
31	2.376	02	06	19	46	76	93	99					
32	2.374	02	06	20	48	78	94	99					
33	2.372	02	06	21	50	80	95	99					
34	2.371	02	07	22	52	81	96	*					
35	2.369	02	07	24	54	83	97						
36	2.368	02	07	25	56	85	97						
37	2.367	02	08	26	58	86	98						
38	2.365	02	08	27	60	87	98						
39	2.364	02	08	28	62	89	98						

Table 8.3.8 *(continued)*

n	F_c	.05	.10	.15	.20	.25	.30	.35	.40	.50	.60	.70	.80
40	2.363	02	08	29	63	90	99	*	*	*	*	*	*
42	2.361	02	09	32	67	92	99						
44	2.359	02	10	34	70	93	99						
46	2.358	02	10	36	73	95	*						
48	2.356	02	11	39	76	96							
50	2.355	02	12	41	78	97							
52	2.353	03	12	43	81	97							
54	2.352	03	13	46	83	98							
56	2.351	03	14	48	85	98							
58	2.350	03	15	50	87	99							
60	2.349	03	16	53	88	99							
64	2.347	03	17	57	91	99							
68	2.346	03	19	61	93	*							
72	2.344	03	21	65	95								
76	2.343	04	23	69	96								
80	2.342	04	25	72	97								
84	2.341	04	27	75	98								
88	2.340	04	29	78	99								
92	2.339	04	31	81	99								
96	2.338	05	33	83	99								
100	2.338	05	35	86	99								
120	2.335	06	46	93	*								
140	2.333	07	56	97									
160	2.331	08	65	99									
180	2.330	10	73	*									
200	2.329	12	79										
250	2.327	17	91										
300	2.326	23	96										
350	2.326	29	99										
400	2.325	36	*										
450	2.325	42											
500	2.324	51											
600	2.324	61											
700	2.323	71											
800	2.323	80											
900	2.323	86											
1000	2.323	91											

* Power values below this point are greater than .995.

Table 8.3.9

Power of F test at a = .01, u = 12

n	F_c	.05	.10	.15	.20	.25	.30	.35	.40	.50	.60	.70	.80
2	3.960	01	01	01	01	02	02	03	04	05	08	12	18
3	2.958	01	01	01	02	03	04	05	07	13	23	37	54
4	2.679	01	01	02	03	04	06	09	13	26	44	65	82
5	2.548	01	01	02	03	05	08	13	20	40	64	84	95
6	2.472	01	02	02	04	07	12	19	29	54	79	94	99
7	2.422	01	02	03	05	09	15	25	38	67	89	98	*
8	2.387	01	02	03	06	11	20	32	48	78	95	99	
9	2.361	01	02	04	07	14	25	39	57	85	98	*	
10	2.340	01	02	04	08	17	30	47	65	91	99		
11	2.325	01	02	05	10	20	35	54	72	94	*		
12	2.312	01	02	05	11	23	40	60	78	97			
13	2.301	01	03	06	13	26	45	66	83	98			
14	2.292	01	03	06	15	30	51	72	87	99			
15	2.285	01	03	07	16	33	56	77	91	99			
16	2.278	01	03	08	18	37	60	81	93	*			
17	2.272	01	03	08	20	41	65	84	95				
18	2.267	01	03	09	23	45	69	87	97				
19	2.262	01	04	10	25	48	73	90	98				
20	2.258	02	04	11	27	52	76	92	98				
21	2.255	02	04	12	29	55	80	94	99				
22	2.251	02	04	13	32	59	83	95	99				
23	2.248	02	05	14	34	62	85	96	99				
24	2.246	02	05	15	36	65	87	97	*				
25	2.243	02	05	16	39	68	89	98					
26	2.241	02	05	17	41	71	91	98					
27	2.239	02	05	18	43	73	92	99					
28	2.237	02	06	19	46	76	94	99					
29	2.235	02	06	20	48	78	95	99					
30	2.233	02	06	21	50	80	96	*					
31	2.231	02	07	22	53	82	96						
32	2.230	02	07	24	55	84	97						
33	2.228	02	07	25	57	86	98						
34	2.227	02	07	26	59	87	98						
35	2.226	02	08	27	61	88	98						
36	2.225	02	08	29	63	90	99						
37	2.224	02	08	30	65	91	99						
38	2.223	02	09	31	67	92	99						
39	2.222	02	09	32	69	93	99						

Table 8.3.9 *(continued)*

n	F_c	.05	.10	.15	.20	.25	.30	.35	.40	.50	.60	.70	.80
40	2.221	02	09	34	71	94	99	*	*	*	*	*	*
42	2.219	02	10	36	74	95	*						
44	2.217	02	11	39	77	96							
46	2.216	02	12	42	80	97							
48	2.215	02	12	44	82	98							
50	2.213	03	13	47	85	98							
52	2.212	03	14	50	87	99							
54	2.211	03	15	52	88	99							
56	2.210	03	16	55	90	99							
58	2.209	03	17	57	91	*							
60	2.209	03	18	59	93								
64	2.207	03	20	64	95								
68	2.206	03	22	68	96								
72	2.204	04	24	72	97								
76	2.203	04	26	76	98								
80	2.202	04	29	79	99								
84	2.202	04	31	82	99								
88	2.201	04	33	84	99								
92	2.200	05	36	87	*								
96	2.199	05	38	89									
100	2.199	05	40	91									
120	2.197	07	52	96									
140	2.195	08	63	99									
160	2.194	10	72	*									
180	2.193	12	79										
200	2.192	14	85										
250	2.191	20	94										
300	2.190	26	98										
350	2.189	34	99										
400	2.188	41	*										
450	2.188	48											
500	2.188	55											
600	2.187	68											
700	2.187	78											
800	2.187	86											
900	2.186	91											
1000	2.186	94											

* Power values below this point are greater than .995.

Table 8.3.10

Power of F test at a = .01, u = 15

n	F_c	.05	.10	.15	.20	.25	.30	.35	.40	.50	.60	.70	.80
2	3.409	01	01	01	01	02	02	03	04	06	10	15	23
3	2.656	01	01	02	02	03	04	06	08	16	29	46	64
4	2.437	01	01	02	03	04	07	10	15	31	53	75	90
5	2.332	01	01	02	04	06	10	16	25	48	74	91	98
6	2.272	01	02	03	05	08	14	23	35	64	87	97	*
7	2.232	01	02	03	06	10	19	31	46	77	94	99	
8	2.203	01	02	03	07	13	24	39	56	86	98	*	
9	2.182	01	02	04	08	16	30	47	66	92	99		
10	2.166	01	02	05	10	20	36	55	74	95	*		
11	2.153	01	02	05	11	24	42	63	81	98			
12	2.143	01	03	06	13	28	48	69	86	99			
13	2.134	01	03	07	15	32	54	75	90	99			
14	2.127	01	03	07	17	36	59	80	93	*			
15	2.120	01	03	08	20	40	65	85	95				
16	2.115	01	03	09	22	44	69	88	97				
17	2.110	01	04	10	25	49	74	91	98				
18	2.106	01	04	11	27	53	78	93	99				
19	2.102	02	04	12	30	57	81	95	99				
20	2.099	02	04	13	32	60	84	96	99				
21	2.096	02	04	14	35	64	87	97	*				
22	2.093	02	05	15	38	68	89	98					
23	2.091	02	05	16	41	71	91	99					
24	2.088	02	05	17	43	74	93	99					
25	2.086	02	06	19	46	77	94	99					
26	2.084	02	06	20	49	79	95	*					
27	2.083	02	06	21	51	81	96						
28	2.081	02	07	23	54	84	97						
29	2.079	02	07	24	56	86	98						
30	2.078	02	07	25	59	87	98						
31	2.077	02	08	27	61	89	99						
32	2.076	02	08	28	63	90	99						
33	2.074	02	08	30	66	92	99						
34	2.073	02	09	31	68	93	99						
35	2.072	02	09	33	70	94	99						
36	2.071	02	09	34	72	95	*						
37	2.070	02	10	36	74	95							
38	2.070	02	10	37	76	96							
39	2.069	02	11	39	77	97							

Table 8.3.10 (continued)

n	F_c	.05	.10	.15	.20	.25	.30	.35	.40	.50	.60	.70	.80
40	2.068	02	11	40	79	97	*	*	*	*	*	*	*
42	2.066	02	12	43	82	98							
44	2.065	02	13	46	85	99							
46	2.064	03	14	49	87	99							
48	2.063	03	15	52	89	99							
50	2.062	03	16	55	91	99							
52	2.061	03	17	58	92	*							
54	2.060	03	18	61	94								
56	2.059	03	19	63	95								
58	2.059	03	20	66	96								
60	2.058	03	22	68	96								
64	2.057	03	24	73	98								
68	2.056	04	26	77	98								
72	2.055	04	29	80	99								
76	2.054	04	32	84	99								
80	2.053	04	34	86	*								
84	2.052	05	37	89									
88	2.052	05	40	91									
92	2.051	05	43	92									
96	2.051	06	45	94									
100	2.050	06	48	95									
120	2.048	07	61	98									
140	2.047	09	71	*									
160	2.046	11	80										
180	2.045	14	87										
200	2.044	16	91										
250	2.043	24	97										
300	2.042	32	99										
350	2.042	40	*										
400	2.041	48											
450	2.041	57											
500	2.041	64											
600	2.040	76											
700	2.040	86											
800	2.040	92											
900	2.040	95											
1000	2.040	98											

* Power values below this point are greater than .995.

Table 8.3.11

Power of F test at a = .01, u = 24

							f						
n	F_c	.05	.10	.15	.20	.25	.30	.35	.40	.50	.60	.70	.80
2	2.620	01	01	01	02	02	03	04	05	09	15	25	38
3	2.184	01	01	02	02	04	05	08	12	26	46	68	85
4	2.049	01	01	02	03	06	09	15	24	48	75	92	98
5	1.983	01	02	03	05	08	15	24	38	69	91	99	*
6	1.944	01	02	03	06	11	21	35	52	84	97	*	
7	1.918	01	02	04	08	15	29	46	66	92	99		
8	1.900	01	02	04	10	20	37	57	76	97	*		
9	1.886	01	02	05	12	25	45	67	85	99			
10	1.876	01	03	06	14	30	53	75	90	*			
11	1.867	02	03	07	17	36	60	82	94				
12	1.860	02	03	08	20	41	67	87	96				
13	1.854	02	03	09	23	47	73	91	98				
14	1.850	02	04	10	26	53	79	94	99				
15	1.846	02	04	11	30	58	83	96	99				
16	1.842	02	04	13	33	63	87	97	*				
17	1.839	02	04	14	37	68	90	98					
18	1.836	02	05	16	41	72	93	99					
19	1.833	02	05	17	44	76	95	99					
20	1.831	02	05	19	48	80	96	*					
21	1.829	02	06	20	51	83	97						
22	1.827	02	06	22	55	86	98						
23	1.826	02	07	24	58	88	99						
24	1.824	02	07	26	62	90	99						
25	1.823	02	07	28	65	92	99						
26	1.821	02	08	30	68	93	99						
27	1.820	02	08	32	71	95	*						
28	1.819	02	09	34	73	96							
29	1.818	02	09	36	76	96							
30	1.817	02	10	38	78	97							
31	1.816	02	10	40	80	98							
32	1.815	02	11	42	82	98							
33	1.815	02	12	44	84	99							
34	1.814	02	12	46	86	99							
35	1.813	02	13	48	87	99							
36	1.813	02	13	50	89	99							
37	1.812	03	14	52	90	99							
38	1.811	03	15	54	91	*							
39	1.811	03	15	56	92								

Table 8.3.11 *(continued)*

n	F_c	.05	.10	.15	.20	.25	.30	.35	.40	.50	.60	.70	.80
40	1.810	03	16	58	93	*	*	*	*	*	*	*	*
42	1.809	03	17	62	95								
44	1.809	03	19	65	96								
46	1.808	03	20	68	97								
48	1.807	03	22	72	98								
50	1.806	03	24	74	98								
52	1.806	03	25	77	99								
54	1.805	04	27	80	99								
56	1.805	04	29	82	99								
58	1.804	04	30	84	*								
60	1.804	04	32	86									
64	1.803	04	36	89									
68	1.802	05	39	92									
72	1.802	05	43	94									
76	1.801	05	47	95									
80	1.800	06	50	97									
84	1.800	06	54	98									
88	1.800	06	57	98									
92	1.799	07	60	99									
96	1.799	07	64	99									
100	1.799	08	67	99									
120	1.797	10	79	*									
140	1.796	13	88										
160	1.796	16	94										
180	1.795	20	97										
200	1.795	24	98										
250	1.794	35	*										
300	1.793	46											
350	1.793	57											
400	1.793	67											
450	1.793	75											
500	1.792	82											
600	1.792	92											
700	1.792	96											
800	1.792	99											
900	1.792	99											
1000	1.792	*											

* Power values below this point are greater than .995.

Table 8.3.12

Power of F test at a = .05, u = 1

n	F_c	.05	.10	.15	.20	.25	.30	.35	.40	.50	.60	.70	.80
								f					
2	18.513	05	05	06	06	07	07	08	09	10	12	14	16
3	7.709	05	05	06	07	08	09	10	12	16	20	26	32
4	5.987	05	06	06	07	09	11	13	16	23	30	39	48
5	5.318	05	06	07	08	11	13	16	20	29	39	50	61
6	4.965	05	06	07	09	12	15	20	24	35	47	60	71
7	4.747	05	06	08	10	14	18	23	28	41	55	68	79
8	4.600	05	06	08	11	15	20	26	32	47	62	75	85
9	4.494	05	07	09	12	17	22	29	36	52	68	80	89
10	4.414	05	07	09	13	18	25	32	40	57	73	85	93
11	4.351	05	07	10	14	20	27	35	44	62	77	88	95
12	4.301	05	07	10	15	22	29	38	47	66	81	91	97
13	4.260	05	07	11	16	23	32	41	51	70	84	93	98
14	4.225	05	08	11	17	25	34	44	54	73	87	95	98
15	4.196	06	08	12	18	26	36	47	57	76	89	96	99
16	4.171	06	08	12	19	28	38	49	60	79	91	97	99
17	4.149	06	08	13	20	30	40	52	63	82	93	98	*
18	4.130	06	08	14	21	31	42	54	66	84	94	98	
19	4.113	06	09	14	22	33	44	57	68	86	95	99	
20	4.098	06	09	15	23	34	46	59	70	88	96	99	
21	4.085	06	09	15	24	36	48	61	73	89	97	99	
22	4.073	06	09	16	26	37	50	63	75	91	97	*	
23	4.062	06	10	16	27	39	52	65	77	92	98		
24	4.052	06	10	17	28	40	54	67	78	93	98		
25	4.043	06	10	18	29	42	56	69	80	94	99		
26	4.034	06	10	18	30	43	58	71	82	95	99		
27	4.026	06	10	19	31	45	59	72	83	95	99		
28	4.020	06	11	19	32	46	61	74	84	96	99		
29	4.013	06	11	20	33	47	62	76	86	97	99		
30	4.007	06	11	21	34	49	64	77	87	97	*		
31	4.001	06	11	21	35	50	65	78	88	97			
32	3.996	06	12	22	36	51	67	80	89	98			
33	3.991	06	12	22	37	53	68	81	90	98			
34	3.986	07	12	23	38	54	69	82	91	98			
35	3.982	07	12	24	39	55	71	83	92	99			
36	3.978	07	13	24	40	56	72	84	92	99			
37	3.974	07	13	25	40	58	73	85	93	99			
38	3.970	07	13	25	41	59	74	86	94	99			
39	3.967	07	13	26	42	60	75	87	94	99			

Table 8.3.12 *(continued)*

n	F_c	.05	.10	.15	.20	.25	.30	.35	.40	.50	.60	.70	.80
								f					
40	3.963	07	14	27	43	61	77	88	95	99	*	*	*
42	3.957	07	14	28	45	63	79	89	96	*			
44	3.952	07	15	29	47	65	80	91	96				
46	3.947	07	15	30	49	67	82	92	97				
48	3.942	07	16	31	50	69	84	93	97				
50	3.938	07	16	32	52	71	85	94	98				
52	3.934	08	17	33	53	73	87	95	98				
54	3.931	08	17	34	55	74	88	95	99				
56	3.928	08	18	36	57	76	89	96	99				
58	3.924	08	18	37	58	77	90	97	99				
60	3.922	08	19	38	60	79	91	97	99				
64	3.916	08	20	40	62	81	93	98	*				
68	3.912	08	21	42	65	83	94	98					
72	3.908	09	22	44	68	85	95	99					
76	3.904	09	23	46	70	87	96	99					
80	3.901	09	24	48	72	89	97	99					
84	3.898	09	25	50	74	90	97	*					
88	3.895	09	26	52	76	92	98						
92	3.893	10	27	54	78	93	98						
96	3.891	10	28	55	80	94	99						
100	3.889	10	29	57	81	94	99						
120	3.881	11	34	65	88	97	*						
140	3.875	13	39	72	92	99							
160	3.871	14	44	77	95	99							
180	3.868	15	48	82	97	*							
200	3.865	16	52	86	98								
250	3.860	20	62	92	99								
300	3.857	23	70	96	*								
350	3.855	26	76	98									
400	3.853	30	82	99									
450	3.852	33	86	*									
500	3.851	36	89										
600	3.849	42	94										
700	3.848	47	97										
800	3.847	53	98										
900	3.847	58	99										
1000	3.846	62	99										

* Power values below this point are greater than .995.

Table 8.3.13

Power of F test at a = .05, u = 2

n	F_c	.05	.10	.15	.20	.25	.30	.35	.40	.50	.60	.70	.80
2	9.552	05	05	06	06	07	07	08	08	10	12	15	18
3	5.143	05	05	06	07	08	09	10	12	17	22	29	37
4	4.256	05	06	06	08	09	11	14	17	24	33	44	54
5	3.885	05	06	07	09	11	14	17	22	32	44	56	69
6	3.682	05	06	07	10	13	16	21	26	39	53	67	79
7	3.555	05	06	08	11	14	19	25	31	46	62	76	87
8	3.467	05	06	08	12	16	22	28	36	53	69	83	92
9	3.403	05	07	09	13	18	24	32	40	59	75	88	95
10	3.354	05	07	10	14	20	27	35	45	64	81	91	97
11	3.316	05	07	10	15	21	30	39	49	69	85	94	98
12	3.285	06	07	11	16	23	32	42	53	74	88	96	99
13	3.260	06	08	11	17	25	35	46	57	77	91	97	99
14	3.238	06	08	12	18	27	38	49	61	81	93	98	*
15	3.220	06	08	13	20	29	40	52	64	84	95	99	
16	3.205	06	08	13	21	31	43	55	67	86	96	99	
17	3.191	06	09	14	22	33	45	58	70	89	97	99	
18	3.179	06	09	14	23	34	48	61	73	90	98	*	
19	3.168	06	09	15	24	36	50	64	76	92	99		
20	3.159	06	09	16	26	38	52	66	78	93	99		
21	3.150	06	09	16	27	40	54	69	80	95	99		
22	3.143	06	10	17	28	42	57	71	82	96	99		
23	3.136	06	10	18	29	43	59	73	84	96	*		
24	3.130	06	10	18	30	45	61	75	86	97			
25	3.124	06	10	19	32	47	63	77	87	98			
26	3.119	06	11	20	33	48	65	79	89	98			
27	3.114	06	11	20	34	50	66	80	90	98			
28	3.110	06	11	21	35	52	68	82	91	99			
29	3.105	06	12	22	36	53	70	83	92	99			
30	3.102	06	12	22	37	55	71	85	93	99			
31	3.098	07	12	23	39	56	73	86	94	99			
32	3.095	07	12	24	40	58	75	87	94	99			
33	3.091	07	13	24	41	59	76	88	95	*			
34	3.088	07	13	25	42	61	77	89	96				
35	3.086	07	13	26	43	62	79	90	96				
36	3.083	07	13	26	44	63	80	91	97				
37	3.081	07	14	27	45	65	81	92	97				
38	3.078	07	14	28	46	66	82	92	97				
39	3.076	07	14	28	47	67	83	93	98				

Table 8.3.13 (continued)

n	F_c	.05	.10	.15	.20	.25	.30	.35	.40	.50	.60	.70	.80
40	3.074	07	15	29	48	68	84	94	98	*	*	*	*
42	3.070	07	15	30	51	71	86	95	98				
44	3.066	07	16	32	53	73	88	96	99				
46	3.063	07	16	33	55	75	89	96	99				
48	3.060	08	17	34	57	77	90	97	99				
50	3.058	08	18	36	58	79	92	98	99				
52	3.055	08	18	37	60	80	93	98	*				
54	3.053	08	19	38	62	82	94	98					
56	3.051	08	19	40	64	83	94	99					
58	3.049	08	20	41	65	85	95	99					
60	3.047	08	21	42	67	86	96	99					
64	3.044	08	22	45	70	88	97	99					
68	3.041	09	23	47	73	90	98	*					
72	3.039	09	24	49	75	92	98						
76	3.036	09	25	52	78	93	99						
80	3.034	09	27	54	80	94	99						
84	3.032	10	28	56	82	95	99						
88	3.031	10	29	58	84	96	99						
92	3.029	10	30	60	85	97	*						
96	3.028	10	31	62	87	97							
100	3.026	11	32	64	88	98							
120	3.021	12	38	73	94	99							
140	3.018	14	44	79	97	*							
160	3.015	15	49	85	98								
180	3.013	16	54	89	99								
200	3.011	18	59	92	*								
250	3.008	22	69	97									
300	3.006	25	78	99									
350	3.004	29	84	*									
400	3.003	33	89										
450	3.002	36	92										
500	3.002	40	95										
600	3.001	47	98										
700	3.000	53	99										
800	3.000	59	*										
900	2.999	65											
1000	2.999	70											

* Power values below this point are greater than .995.

Table 8.3.14

Power of F test at a = .05, u = 3

n	F_c	.05	.10	.15	.20	.25	.30	.35	.40	.50	.60	.70	.80
								f					
2	6.591	05	05	06	06	07	07	08	09	11	13	17	20
3	4.066	05	05	06	07	08	09	11	13	18	25	33	42
4	3.490	05	06	07	08	10	12	15	18	27	38	50	62
5	3.239	05	06	07	09	12	15	19	24	36	50	64	76
6	3.098	05	06	08	10	13	18	23	29	44	60	75	86
7	3.009	05	06	08	11	15	21	27	35	52	69	83	92
8	2.947	05	07	09	12	17	24	31	40	59	77	89	96
9	2.901	05	07	09	14	19	27	36	46	66	82	93	98
10	2.867	05	07	10	15	21	30	40	51	71	87	96	99
11	2.839	06	07	11	16	24	33	44	55	76	91	97	99
12	2.817	06	08	11	17	26	36	48	60	81	93	98	*
13	2.798	06	08	12	19	28	39	52	64	84	95	99	
14	2.783	06	08	13	20	30	42	55	68	87	97	99	
15	2.770	06	08	13	21	32	45	59	71	90	98	*	
16	2.758	06	09	14	23	34	48	62	75	92	98		
17	2.748	06	09	15	24	37	51	65	78	94	99		
18	2.740	06	09	16	26	39	53	68	80	95	99		
19	2.732	06	09	16	27	41	56	71	83	96	99		
20	2.725	06	10	17	28	43	59	73	85	97	*		
21	2.719	06	10	18	30	45	61	76	87	98			
22	2.714	06	10	18	31	47	63	78	88	98			
23	2.709	06	10	19	32	49	66	80	90	99			
24	2.704	06	11	20	34	51	68	82	91	99			
25	2.700	06	11	21	35	53	70	84	93	99			
26	2.696	06	11	22	37	54	72	85	94	99			
27	2.692	07	12	22	38	56	74	87	94	99			
28	2.689	07	12	23	39	58	75	88	95	*			
29	2.686	07	12	24	41	60	77	89	96				
30	2.683	07	13	25	42	61	79	90	96				
31	2.680	07	13	25	43	63	80	91	97				
32	2.678	07	13	26	45	65	81	92	97				
33	2.675	07	14	27	46	66	83	93	98				
34	2.673	07	14	28	47	68	54	94	98				
35	2.671	07	14	29	48	69	85	94	98				
36	2.669	07	14	29	50	70	86	95	99				
37	2.668	07	15	30	51	72	87	96	99				
38	2.666	07	15	31	52	73	88	96	99				
39	2.664	07	15	32	53	74	89	97	99				

Table 8.3.14 (continued)

n	F_c	.05	.10	.15	.20	.25	.30	.35	.40	.50	.60	.70	.80
40	2.663	07	16	32	54	76	90	97	99	*	*	*	*
42	2.660	07	16	34	57	78	91	98	*				
44	2.657	08	17	35	59	80	93	98					
46	2.655	08	18	37	61	82	94	99					
48	2.653	08	18	39	63	84	95	99					
50	2.651	08	19	40	65	85	96	99					
52	2.649	08	20	42	67	87	96	99					
54	2.648	08	20	43	69	88	97	99					
56	2.646	08	21	45	71	89	97	*					
58	2.645	08	22	46	72	90	98						
60	2.643	09	22	47	74	91	98						
64	2.641	09	24	50	77	93	99						
68	2.639	09	25	53	80	95	99						
72	2.637	09	27	56	82	96	99						
76	2.635	10	28	58	84	97	*						
80	2.633	10	29	61	86	97							
84	2.632	10	31	63	88	98							
88	2.631	10	32	65	90	98							
92	2.630	11	34	67	91	99							
96	2.629	11	35	69	92	99							
100	2.628	11	36	71	93	99							
120	2.624	13	43	80	97	*							
140	2.621	14	49	86	99								
160	2.619	16	55	91	99								
180	2.618	18	61	94	*								
200	2.616	19	66	96									
250	2.614	24	77	99									
300	2.612	28	84	*									
350	2.611	32	90										
400	2.611	37	93										
450	2.610	41	96										
500	2.609	45	98										
600	2.609	53	99										
700	2.608	60	*										
800	2.608	66											
900	2.607	72											
1000	2.607	77											

* Power values below this point are greater than .995.

Table 8.3.15

Power of F test at a = .05, u = 4

n	F_c	.05	.10	.15	.20	.25	.30	.35	.40	.50	.60	.70	.80
													f
2	5.192	05	05	06	07	08	08	09	10	13	15	19	24
3	3.478	05	05	06	07	09	10	12	14	20	28	38	48
4	3.056	05	06	07	08	10	13	16	20	30	42	56	69
5	2.866	05	06	07	09	12	16	21	26	40	55	70	83
6	2.759	05	06	08	10	14	19	25	32	49	66	81	91
7	2.690	05	06	09	12	16	22	30	39	58	76	88	96
8	2.642	05	07	09	13	19	26	35	45	65	83	93	98
9	2.606	05	07	10	14	21	29	40	51	72	88	96	99
10	2.579	06	07	10	16	23	33	44	56	78	92	98	*
11	2.558	06	08	11	17	26	37	49	61	82	94	99	
12	2.540	06	08	12	19	28	40	53	66	86	96	99	
13	2.525	06	08	13	20	31	43	57	70	89	98	*	
14	2.513	06	08	13	22	33	47	61	74	92	98		
15	2.503	06	09	14	23	36	50	65	78	94	99		
16	2.494	06	09	15	25	38	53	68	81	95	99		
17	2.486	06	09	16	26	40	56	71	83	96	*		
18	2.479	06	09	17	28	43	59	74	86	97			
19	2.473	06	10	17	30	45	62	77	88	98			
20	2.468	06	10	18	31	47	65	79	90	99			
21	2.463	06	10	19	33	50	67	82	91	99			
22	2.458	06	11	20	34	52	69	84	93	99			
23	2.454	06	11	21	36	54	72	85	94	99			
24	2.451	06	11	22	37	56	74	87	95	*			
25	2.447	06	12	23	39	58	76	89	96				
26	2.444	07	12	23	40	60	78	90	96				
27	2.441	07	12	24	42	62	80	91	97				
28	2.439	07	13	25	43	64	81	92	98				
29	2.436	07	13	26	45	66	83	93	98				
30	2.434	07	13	27	46	67	84	94	98				
31	2.432	07	14	28	48	69	86	95	99				
32	2.430	07	14	29	49	71	87	96	99				
33	2.428	07	14	30	51	72	88	96	99				
34	2.427	07	15	30	52	74	89	97	99				
35	2.425	07	15	31	54	75	90	97	99				
36	2.424	07	15	32	55	76	91	97	*				
37	2.422	07	16	33	56	78	92	98					
38	2.421	07	16	34	57	79	92	98					
39	2.419	07	16	35	59	80	93	98					

Table 8.3.15 *(continued)*

n	F_c	.05	.10	.15	.20	.25	.30	.35	.40	.50	.60	.70	.80
40	2.418	07	17	36	60	81	94	99	*	*	*	*	*
42	2.416	08	18	37	62	83	95	99					
44	2.414	08	18	39	65	85	96	99					
46	2.412	08	19	41	67	87	97	99					
48	2.410	08	20	43	69	89	97	*					
50	2.409	08	21	44	71	90	98						
52	2.407	08	21	46	73	91	98						
54	2.406	08	22	48	75	92	99						
56	2.405	09	23	49	77	93	99						
58	2.404	09	24	51	78	94	99						
60	2.403	09	24	52	80	95	99						
64	2.401	09	26	55	83	96	*						
68	2.399	09	28	58	85	97							
72	2.397	10	29	61	87	98							
76	2.396	10	31	64	89	98							
80	2.395	10	32	66	91	99							
84	2.394	11	34	69	92	99							
88	2.393	11	35	71	94	99							
92	2.392	11	37	73	95	*							
96	2.391	11	39	75	96								
100	2.390	12	40	77	96								
120	2.387	13	47	85	99								
140	2.385	15	54	91	99								
160	2.383	17	61	94	*								
180	2.382	18	67	97									
200	2.381	20	72	98									
250	2.379	25	82	*									
300	2.378	29	89										
350	2.377	34	94										
400	2.376	39	96										
450	2.376	44	98										
500	2.376	49	99										
600	2.375	57	*										
700	2.374	65											
800	2.374	72											
900	2.374	78											
1000	2.374	82											

* Power values below this point are greater than .995.

Table 8.3.16

Power of F test at a = .05, u = 5

n	F_c	.05	.10	.15	.20	.25	.30	.35	.40	.50	.60	.70	.80
							f						
2	4.387	05	05	06	07	08	08	09	10	13	17	21	26
3	3.106	05	06	06	07	09	11	13	15	22	31	42	53
4	2.773	05	06	07	08	11	14	17	22	33	47	61	75
5	2.621	05	06	07	10	13	17	22	29	44	61	76	88
6	2.534	05	06	08	11	15	21	27	35	54	72	86	94
7	2.478	05	07	09	12	18	24	33	42	63	81	92	98
8	2.438	05	07	09	14	20	28	38	49	71	87	96	99
9	2.409	05	07	10	15	23	32	43	55	77	92	98	*
10	2.391	06	07	11	17	25	36	48	61	83	95	99	
11	2.368	06	08	12	19	28	40	53	66	87	97	99	
12	2.354	06	08	13	20	31	44	58	71	90	98	*	
13	2.342	06	08	13	22	33	47	62	75	93	99		
14	2.332	06	09	14	24	36	51	66	79	95	99		
15	2.324	06	09	15	25	39	55	70	82	96	*		
16	2.316	06	09	16	27	42	58	73	85	97			
17	2.310	06	10	17	29	44	61	76	88	98			
18	2.304	06	10	18	30	47	64	79	90	99			
19	2.299	06	10	19	32	49	67	82	92	99			
20	2.294	06	11	20	34	52	70	84	93	99			
21	2.290	06	11	21	36	54	72	86	94	*			
22	2.286	06	11	22	37	57	75	88	95				
23	2.283	06	11	22	39	59	77	90	96				
24	2.280	06	12	23	41	61	79	91	97				
25	2.277	07	12	24	43	63	81	92	98				
26	2.275	07	13	25	44	65	83	93	98				
27	2.272	07	13	26	46	67	84	94	98				
28	2.270	07	13	27	47	69	86	95	99				
29	2.268	07	14	28	49	71	87	96	99				
30	2.266	07	14	29	51	73	88	96	99				
31	2.265	07	14	30	52	74	90	97	99				
32	2.263	07	15	31	54	76	91	97	*				
33	2.262	07	15	32	55	77	92	98					
34	2.260	07	16	33	57	79	93	98					
35	2.259	07	16	34	58	80	93	98					
36	2.257	07	16	35	60	81	94	99					
37	2.256	07	17	36	61	83	95	99					
38	2.255	07	17	37	62	84	95	99					
39	2.254	08	18	38	64	85	96	99					

Table 8.3.16 *(continued)*

n	F_c	.05	.10	.15	.20	.25	.30	.35	.40	.50	.60	.70	.80
40	2.253	08	18	39	65	86	96	99	*	*	*	*	*
42	2.251	08	19	41	68	88	97	*					
44	2.249	08	20	43	70	89	98						
46	2.248	08	21	45	72	91	98						
48	2.246	08	21	47	74	92	99						
50	2.245	08	22	48	76	93	99						
52	2.244	09	23	50	78	94	99						
54	2.243	09	24	52	80	95	99						
56	2.242	09	25	54	82	96	*						
58	2.241	09	26	55	83	96							
60	2.240	09	26	57	85	97							
64	2.238	09	28	60	87	98							
68	2.237	10	30	63	89	99							
72	2.235	10	32	66	91	99							
76	2.234	10	33	69	93	99							
80	2.233	11	35	72	94	99							
84	2.232	11	37	74	95	*							
88	2.232	11	39	76	96								
92	2.231	12	40	78	97								
96	2.230	12	42	80	97								
100	2.229	12	44	82	98								
120	2.227	14	52	89	99								
140	2.225	16	59	94	*								
160	2.224	18	66	97									
180	2.223	20	72	98									
200	2.222	23	77	99									
250	2.220	28	87	*									
300	2.219	33	93										
350	2.218	39	96										
400	2.218	44	98										
450	2.217	49	99										
500	2.217	54	*										
600	2.217	63											
700	2.216	71											
800	2.216	77											
900	2.216	83											
1000	2.216	87											

* Power values below this point are greater than .995.

Table 8.3.17

Power of F test at a = .05, u = 6

							f						
n	F_c	.05	.10	.15	.20	.25	.30	.35	.40	.50	.60	.70	.80
2	3.866	05	05	06	07	08	08	09	11	14	18	23	29
3	2.848	05	06	06	08	09	11	13	16	24	34	46	51
4	2.573	05	06	07	09	11	14	18	23	36	51	66	80
5	2.445	05	06	08	10	13	18	24	31	48	66	81	91
6	2.372	05	06	08	11	16	22	30	38	58	77	90	96
7	2.324	05	07	09	13	19	26	35	46	68	85	95	99
8	2.291	05	07	10	15	21	30	41	53	76	91	98	*
9	2.266	06	07	11	16	24	35	47	60	82	94	99	
10	2.246	06	08	11	18	27	39	52	66	87	97	*	
11	2.231	06	08	12	20	30	43	57	71	90	98		
12	2.219	06	08	13	22	33	47	62	76	93	99		
13	2.209	06	09	14	23	36	51	67	80	95	99		
14	2.200	06	09	15	25	39	55	71	83	97	*		
15	2.193	06	09	16	27	42	59	74	86	98			
16	2.186	06	10	17	29	45	62	78	89	98			
17	2.181	06	10	18	31	48	66	81	91	99			
18	2.176	06	10	19	33	51	69	83	93	99			
19	2.171	06	11	20	35	53	72	86	94	*			
20	2.168	06	11	21	37	56	74	88	95				
21	2.164	06	11	22	39	58	77	90	96				
22	2.161	06	12	23	40	61	79	91	97				
23	2.158	07	12	24	42	63	81	93	98				
24	2.156	07	12	25	44	65	83	94	98				
25	2.153	07	13	26	46	68	85	95	99				
26	2.151	07	13	27	48	70	87	96	99				
27	2.149	07	14	28	50	72	88	96	99				
28	2.147	07	14	29	51	74	89	97	99				
29	2.145	07	14	30	53	75	91	97	*				
30	2.144	07	15	31	55	77	92	98					
31	2.142	07	15	33	56	79	93	98					
32	2.141	07	16	34	58	80	93	99					
33	2.140	07	16	35	60	82	94	99					
34	2.138	07	17	36	61	83	95	99					
35	2.137	07	17	37	63	84	96	99					
36	2.136	07	17	38	64	85	96	99					
37	2.135	08	18	39	66	87	97	99					
38	2.134	08	18	40	67	88	97	*					
39	2.133	08	19	41	68	89	97						

Table 8.3.17 *(continued)*

							f						
n	F_c	.05	.10	.15	.20	.25	.30	.35	.40	.50	.60	.70	.80
40	2.132	08	19	42	70	89	98	*	*	*	*	*	*
42	2.131	08	20	44	72	91	98						
44	2.129	08	21	46	75	92	99						
46	2.128	08	22	48	77	94	99						
48	2.126	08	23	50	79	95	99						
50	2.125	09	24	52	81	96	99						
52	2.124	09	25	54	82	96	*						
54	2.123	09	26	56	84	97							
56	2.122	09	27	58	86	97							
58	2.122	09	27	60	87	98							
60	2.121	09	28	61	88	98							
64	2.119	10	30	65	91	99							
68	2.118	10	32	68	92	99							
72	2.117	10	34	71	94	99							
76	2.116	11	36	74	95	*							
80	2.115	11	38	76	96								
84	2.114	12	40	78	97								
88	2.114	12	42	81	98								
92	2.113	12	44	83	98								
96	2.112	13	45	84	99								
100	2.112	13	47	86	99								
120	2.110	15	56	92	*								
140	2.108	17	64	96									
160	2.107	19	71	98									
180	2.106	21	76	99									
200	2.105	23	81	*									
250	2.104	29	90										
300	2.103	35	95										
350	2.102	40	98										
400	2.102	46	99										
450	2.102	52	*										
500	2.101	57											
600	2.101	67											
700	2.100	75											
800	2.100	82											
900	2.100	87											
1000	2.100	91											

* Power values below this point are greater than .995.

Table 8.3.18

Power of F test at a = .05, u = 8

n	F_c	.05	.10	.15	.20	.25	.30	.35	.40	.50	.60	.70	.80
										f			
2	3.230	05	05	06	07	08	09	10	11	15	20	26	34
3	2.510	05	06	06	08	10	12	15	18	28	40	53	67
4	2.305	05	06	07	09	12	16	21	27	42	59	75	87
5	2.208	05	06	08	11	15	20	27	35	55	74	88	96
6	2.152	05	07	09	12	18	25	34	44	66	84	95	99
7	2.115	05	07	10	14	21	30	41	53	76	91	98	*
8	2.089	06	07	10	16	24	35	47	60	83	95	99	
9	2.070	06	08	11	18	27	40	54	67	88	98	*	
10	2.055	06	08	12	20	31	45	60	73	92	99		
11	2.043	06	08	13	22	34	49	65	79	95	99		
12	2.033	06	09	14	24	38	54	70	83	97	*		
13	2.025	06	09	15	26	41	58	74	87	98			
14	2.018	06	09	17	29	45	62	78	90	99			
15	2.013	06	10	18	31	48	66	82	92	99			
16	2.008	06	10	19	33	51	70	85	94	*			
17	2.004	06	10	20	35	54	73	87	95				
18	2.000	06	11	21	37	57	76	90	97				
19	1.996	06	11	22	40	60	79	91	97				
20	1.993	06	12	23	42	63	82	93	98				
21	1.990	07	12	25	44	66	84	94	99				
22	1.988	07	13	26	46	68	86	95	99				
23	1.986	07	13	27	48	71	88	96	99				
24	1.984	07	13	28	50	73	89	97	99				
25	1.982	07	14	29	52	75	91	98	*				
26	1.980	07	14	31	54	77	92	98					
27	1.978	07	15	32	56	79	93	99					
28	1.977	07	15	33	58	81	94	99					
29	1.976	07	16	34	60	83	95	99					
30	1.974	07	16	36	62	84	96	99					
31	1.973	07	17	37	64	86	96	99					
32	1.972	07	17	38	65	87	97	*					
33	1.971	08	18	39	67	88	97						
34	1.970	08	18	41	69	89	98						
35	1.969	08	19	42	70	90	98						
36	1.968	08	19	43	72	91	98						
37	1.967	08	20	44	73	92	99						
38	1.967	08	20	46	75	93	99						
39	1.966	08	21	47	76	94	99						

Table 8.3.18 (continued)

						f							
n	F_c	.05	.10	.15	.20	.25	.30	.35	.40	.50	.60	.70	.80
40	1.965	08	21	48	77	94	99	*	*	*	*	*	*
42	1.964	08	22	50	80	95	99						
44	1.963	08	23	53	82	96	*						
46	1.962	09	25	55	84	97							
48	1.961	09	26	57	86	98							
50	1.960	09	27	59	87	98							
52	1.959	09	28	61	89	99							
54	1.958	09	29	63	90	99							
56	1.957	09	30	65	91	99							
58	1.957	10	31	67	92	99							
60	1.956	10	32	69	93	99							
64	1.955	10	34	72	95	*							
68	1.954	11	37	75	96								
72	1.953	11	39	78	97								
76	1.952	12	41	81	98								
80	1.952	12	43	83	98								
84	1.951	12	45	85	99								
88	1.950	13	48	87	99								
92	1.950	13	50	89	99								
96	1.949	14	52	90	*								
100	1.949	14	54	92									
120	1.947	17	63	96									
140	1.946	19	71	98									
160	1.945	22	78	99									
180	1.944	24	83	*									
200	1.944	27	88										
250	1.943	34	95										
300	1.942	41	98										
350	1.941	48	99										
400	1.941	54	*										
450	1.941	60											
500	1.940	66											
600	1.940	75											
700	1.940	82											
800	1.940	88											
900	1.940	92											
1000	1.939	95											

* Power values below this point are greater than .995.

Table 8.3.19

Power of F test at a = .05, u = 10

n	F_c	.05	.10	.15	.20	.25	.30	.35	.40	.50	.60	.70	.80
											f		
2	2.854	05	05	06	07	08	09	10	12	16	23	30	39
3	2.258	05	06	07	09	11	13	17	21	32	46	62	76
4	2.133	05	06	07	10	13	17	23	30	47	65	81	92
5	2.053	05	06	08	11	16	22	30	40	61	80	92	98
6	2.008	05	07	09	13	19	28	38	50	73	90	97	*
7	1.978	05	07	10	15	23	33	45	59	82	95	99	
8	1.956	06	07	11	17	27	39	53	67	88	98	*	
9	1.940	06	08	12	20	31	44	60	74	93	99		
10	1.928	06	08	13	22	34	50	66	80	96	*		
11	1.913	06	09	14	24	38	55	71	84	97			
12	1.910	06	09	15	27	42	60	76	88	98			
13	1.903	06	09	17	29	46	65	81	91	99			
14	1.898	06	10	18	32	50	69	84	94	*			
15	1.893	06	10	19	34	53	73	87	95				
16	1.889	06	11	20	37	57	76	90	97				
17	1.885	06	11	22	39	60	79	92	98				
18	1.882	06	12	23	42	64	82	94	98				
19	1.879	06	12	24	44	67	85	95	99				
20	1.877	07	12	26	47	69	87	96	99				
21	1.874	07	13	27	49	72	89	97	99				
22	1.872	07	13	29	51	75	91	98	*				
23	1.870	07	14	30	54	77	92	98					
24	1.869	07	14	31	56	79	93	99					
25	1.867	07	15	33	58	81	94	99					
26	1.866	07	15	34	60	83	95	99					
27	1.864	07	16	36	62	85	96	99					
28	1.863	07	17	37	64	86	97	*					
29	1.862	07	17	38	66	88	97						
30	1.861	07	18	40	68	89	98						
31	1.860	08	18	41	70	90	98						
32	1.859	08	19	43	72	91	99						
33	1.858	08	19	44	73	92	99						
34	1.857	08	20	45	75	93	99						
35	1.856	08	21	47	76	94	99						
36	1.856	08	21	48	78	95	99						
37	1.855	08	22	49	79	95	99						
38	1.854	08	22	51	81	96	*						
39	1.854	08	23	52	82	96							

Table 8.3.19 *(continued)*

							f						
n	F_c	.05	.10	.15	.20	.25	.30	.35	.40	.50	.60	.70	.80
40	1.853	08	23	53	83	97	*	*	*	*	*	*	*
42	1.852	09	25	56	85	98							
44	1.851	09	26	58	87	98							
46	1.850	09	27	61	89	99							
48	1.849	09	28	63	90	99							
50	1.848	09	30	65	92	99							
52	1.848	10	31	67	93	99							
54	1.847	10	32	69	94	*							
56	1.846	10	33	71	95								
58	1.846	10	35	73	96								
60	1.845	10	36	75	96								
64	1.845	11	38	78	97								
68	1.844	11	41	81	98								
72	1.843	12	43	84	99								
76	1.842	12	46	86	99								
80	1.842	13	48	88	99								
84	1.841	13	51	90	*								
88	1.841	14	53	92									
92	1.840	14	55	93									
96	1.840	15	57	94									
100	1.839	15	60	95									
120	1.838	18	69	98									
140	1.837	21	77	99									
160	1.836	24	84	*									
180	1.836	27	88										
200	1.835	30	92										
250	1.834	38	97										
300	1.834	46	99										
350	1.833	53	*										
400	1.833	60											
450	1.833	66											
500	1.832	72											
600	1.832	81											
700	1.832	88											
800	1.832	92											
900	1.832	95											
1000	1.832	97											

* Power values below this point are greater than .995.

Table 8.3.20

Power of F test at a = .05, u = 12

n	F_c	.05	.10	.15	.20	.25	.30	.35	.40	.50	.60	.70	.80
										f			
2	2.604	05	05	06	07	08	09	11	13	18	25	34	44
3	2.148	05	06	07	08	10	13	17	22	34	50	66	80
4	2.010	05	06	08	10	14	18	25	33	52	71	86	95
5	1.944	05	06	09	12	17	24	33	44	67	85	95	99
6	1.905	05	07	10	14	21	30	42	54	78	93	99	*
7	1.879	06	07	11	16	25	36	50	64	87	97	*	
8	1.860	06	08	12	19	29	43	58	72	92	99		
9	1.847	06	08	13	21	33	49	65	79	95	*		
10	1.836	06	08	14	24	38	55	71	85	98			
11	1.827	06	09	15	26	42	60	77	89	99			
12	1.821	06	09	17	29	46	65	81	92	99			
13	1.815	06	10	18	32	51	70	85	94	*			
14	1.810	06	10	19	35	55	74	88	96				
15	1.806	06	11	21	37	58	78	91	97				
16	1.802	06	11	22	40	62	81	93	98				
17	1.799	06	12	24	43	66	84	95	99				
18	1.796	07	12	25	46	69	87	96	99				
19	1.794	07	13	27	48	72	89	97	99				
20	1.792	07	13	28	51	75	91	98	*				
21	1.790	07	14	30	54	77	92	98					
22	1.788	07	14	31	56	80	94	99					
23	1.786	07	15	33	59	82	95	99					
24	1.785	07	15	34	61	84	96	99					
25	1.784	07	16	36	63	86	97	*					
26	1.782	07	17	37	65	88	97						
27	1.781	07	17	39	68	89	98						
28	1.780	07	18	41	70	90	98						
29	1.779	08	18	42	72	92	99						
30	1.778	08	19	44	73	93	99						
31	1.777	08	20	45	75	94	99						
32	1.776	08	20	47	77	94	99						
33	1.776	08	21	48	78	95	99						
34	1.775	08	22	50	80	96	*						
35	1.774	08	22	51	81	96							
36	1.774	08	23	53	83	97							
37	1.773	08	24	54	84	97							
38	1.773	08	24	55	85	98							
39	1.772	09	25	57	86	98							

Table 8.3.20 (continued)

n	F_c	.05	.10	.15	.20	.25	.30	.35	.40	.50	.60	.70	.80
40	1.771	09	26	58	87	98	*	*	*	*	*	*	*
42	1.771	09	27	61	89	99							
44	1.770	09	28	63	91	99							
46	1.769	09	30	66	92	99							
48	1.768	10	31	68	94	*							
50	1.768	10	32	71	95								
52	1.767	10	34	73	96								
54	1.766	10	35	75	96								
56	1.766	11	36	77	97								
58	1.766	11	38	78	97								
60	1.765	11	39	80	98								
64	1.764	11	42	83	99								
68	1.763	12	45	86	99								
72	1.763	12	47	88	99								
76	1.762	13	50	90	*								
80	1.762	14	53	92									
84	1.761	14	55	93									
88	1.761	15	58	95									
92	1.760	15	60	96									
96	1.760	16	62	96									
100	1.760	16	65	97									
120	1.759	19	74	99									
140	1.758	23	82	*									
160	1.757	26	88										
180	1.756	29	92										
200	1.756	33	95										
250	1.755	41	98										
300	1.755	50	*										
350	1.754	58											
400	1.754	65											
450	1.754	71											
500	1.754	77											
600	1.753	86											
700	1.753	91											
800	1.753	95											
900	1.753	97											
1000	1.753	98											

* Power values below this point are greater than .995.

Table 8.3.21

Power of F test at a = .05, u = 15

n	F_c	.05	.10	.15	.20	.25	.30	.35	.40	.50	.60	.70	.80
2	2.352	05	05	06	07	08	10	12	14	20	28	39	51
3	1.992	05	06	07	09	11	15	19	25	39	57	74	87
4	1.880	05	06	08	11	15	20	28	37	58	78	92	98
5	1.826	05	07	09	13	19	27	38	50	74	91	98	*
6	1.794	05	07	10	15	23	34	47	61	85	96	*	
7	1.772	06	07	11	18	28	41	56	71	92	99		
8	1.757	06	08	12	21	33	48	65	79	96	*		
9	1.745	06	08	14	24	38	55	72	85	98			
10	1.736	06	09	15	27	43	61	78	90	99			
11	1.729	06	09	17	30	47	67	83	93	*			
12	1.724	06	10	18	33	52	72	87	96				
13	1.719	06	10	20	36	57	77	90	97				
14	1.715	06	11	21	39	61	81	93	98				
15	1.711	06	11	23	42	65	84	95	99				
16	1.708	06	12	25	45	69	87	96	99				
17	1.706	07	12	26	48	72	90	97	*				
18	1.704	07	13	28	51	76	92	98					
19	1.702	07	14	30	54	78	93	99					
20	1.700	07	14	31	57	81	95	99					
21	1.698	07	15	33	60	84	96	99					
22	1.696	07	16	35	63	86	97	*					
23	1.695	07	16	37	65	88	97						
24	1.694	07	17	39	68	89	98						
25	1.693	07	17	40	70	91	98						
26	1.692	07	18	42	72	92	99						
27	1.691	08	19	44	74	93	99						
28	1.690	08	20	46	76	94	99						
29	1.689	08	20	47	78	95	*						
30	1.688	08	21	49	80	96							
31	1.687	08	22	51	82	97							
32	1.687	08	22	52	83	97							
33	1.686	08	23	54	84	98							
34	1.686	08	24	56	86	98							
35	1.685	09	25	57	87	98							
36	1.684	09	25	59	88	99							
37	1.684	09	26	60	89	99							
38	1.683	09	27	62	90	99							
39	1.683	09	28	63	91	99							

Table 8.3.21 (continued)

n	F_c	.05	.10	.15	.20	.25	.30	.35	.40	.50	.60	.70	.80
40	1.683	09	28	65	92	99	*	*	*	*	*	*	*
42	1.682	09	30	68	93	*							
44	1.681	10	32	70	95								
46	1.680	10	33	73	96								
48	1.680	10	35	75	97								
50	1.679	10	36	77	97								
52	1.679	11	38	79	98								
54	1.678	11	39	81	98								
56	1.678	11	41	83	99								
58	1.677	11	43	84	99								
60	1.677	12	44	86	99								
64	1.676	12	47	89	99								
68	1.676	13	50	91	*								
72	1.675	13	53	93									
76	1.675	14	56	94									
80	1.674	15	59	95									
84	1.674	15	62	96									
88	1.674	16	64	97									
92	1.673	17	67	98									
96	1.673	17	69	98									
100	1.673	18	71	99									
120	1.672	21	81	*									
140	1.671	25	88										
160	1.670	29	92										
180	1.670	33	96										
200	1.670	37	97										
250	1.669	47	99										
300	1.669	56	*										
350	1.668	64											
400	1.668	72											
450	1.668	78											
500	1.668	83											
600	1.667	91											
700	1.667	95											
800	1.667	97											
900	1.667	99											
1000	1.667	99											

* Power values below this point are greater than .995.

Table 8.3.22

Power of F test at a = .05, u = 24

							f						
n	F_c	.05	.10	.15	.20	.25	.30	.35	.40	.50	.60	.70	.80
2	1.964	05	06	06	08	09	11	14	17	26	39	53	69
3	1.737	05	06	07	10	13	18	24	32	52	73	88	96
4	1.663	05	07	09	12	18	26	37	49	74	91	98	*
5	1.627	05	07	10	15	24	35	49	64	88	98	*	
6	1.605	06	08	12	19	30	45	61	76	95	*		
7	1.590	06	08	13	22	36	54	71	85	98			
8	1.580	06	09	15	26	43	62	79	91	99			
9	1.572	06	09	17	30	49	69	86	95	*			
10	1.566	06	10	19	34	55	76	90	97				
11	1.561	06	11	21	38	61	81	94	99				
12	1.557	06	11	23	42	66	86	96	99				
13	1.554	06	12	25	47	71	89	98	*				
14	1.551	07	13	27	51	76	92	98					
15	1.549	07	13	29	54	80	94	99					
16	1.546	07	14	32	58	83	96	99					
17	1.545	07	15	34	62	86	97	*					
18	1.543	07	16	36	65	89	98						
19	1.542	07	16	38	69	91	99						
20	1.540	07	17	41	72	92	99						
21	1.539	07	18	43	75	94	99						
22	1.538	08	19	45	77	95	*						
23	1.537	08	20	48	80	96							
24	1.536	08	21	50	82	97							
25	1.536	08	22	52	84	98							
26	1.535	08	23	54	86	98							
27	1.534	08	24	57	87	99							
28	1.533	08	25	59	89	99							
29	1.533	09	25	61	90	99							
30	1.532	09	26	63	92	99							
31	1.532	09	27	65	93	*							
32	1.531	09	28	66	94								
33	1.531	09	29	68	94								
34	1.531	09	30	70	95								
35	1.530	09	31	72	96								
36	1.530	10	32	73	96								
37	1.529	10	34	75	97								
38	1.529	10	35	76	97								
39	1.529	10	36	78	98								

Table 8.3.22 *(continued)*

														f
n	F_c	.05	.10	.15	.20	.25	.30	.35	.40	.50	.60	.70	.80	
40	1.529	10	37	79	98	*	*	*	*	*	*	*	*	
42	1.528	11	39	82	99									
44	1.528	11	41	84	99									
46	1.527	11	43	86	99									
48	1.527	12	45	88	*									
50	1.526	12	47	90										
52	1.526	12	49	91										
54	1.526	13	51	92										
56	1.525	13	53	93										
58	1.525	13	55	94										
60	1.525	14	57	95										
64	1.524	14	60	97										
68	1.524	15	64	98										
72	1.523	16	67	98										
76	1.523	17	70	99										
80	1.523	18	73	99										
84	1.523	18	76	99										
88	1.522	19	79	*										
92	1.522	20	81											
96	1.522	21	83											
100	1.522	22	85											
120	1.521	26	92											
140	1.520	31	96											
160	1.520	36	98											
180	1.520	41	99											
200	1.519	47	*											
250	1.519	59												
300	1.519	70												
350	1.519	78												
400	1.518	85												
450	1.518	90												
500	1.518	94												
600	1.518	98												
700	1.518	99												
800	1.518	*												
900	1.518													
1000	1.518													

* Power values below this point are greater than .995.

Table 8.3.23

Power of F test at a = .10, u = 1

n	F_c	.05	.10	.15	.20	.25	.30	.35	.40	.50	.60	.70	.80
2	8.526	10	11	12	13	13	14	15	17	20	23	27	30
3	4.545	10	11	12	13	15	17	19	22	28	35	42	50
4	3.776	10	11	13	14	17	20	23	27	36	45	55	64
5	3.458	10	11	13	16	19	23	27	32	43	55	66	76
6	3.285	10	12	14	17	21	26	31	37	50	63	74	83
7	3.177	10	12	15	19	23	29	35	42	56	69	80	89
8	3.102	10	12	15	20	25	32	39	47	62	75	85	92
9	3.048	10	13	16	21	28	35	43	51	66	80	89	95
10	3.007	10	13	17	23	30	37	46	55	71	83	92	97
11	2.975	11	13	18	24	32	40	49	58	75	87	94	98
12	2.949	11	14	19	25	34	43	52	62	78	89	96	99
13	2.927	11	14	19	27	36	45	55	65	81	91	97	99
14	2.909	11	14	20	28	37	48	58	68	83	93	98	99
15	2.894	11	15	21	29	39	50	60	70	86	95	98	*
16	2.881	11	15	22	31	41	52	63	73	88	96	99	
17	2.869	11	15	23	32	43	54	65	75	89	97	99	
18	2.859	11	16	23	33	45	56	68	77	91	97	99	
19	2.850	11	16	24	34	46	58	70	79	92	98	*	
20	2.843	11	16	25	36	48	60	72	81	93	98		
21	2.836	11	17	26	37	50	62	73	83	94	99		
22	2.829	11	17	26	38	51	64	75	84	95	99		
23	2.823	11	18	27	39	53	66	77	86	96	99		
24	2.818	12	18	28	40	54	67	78	87	96	99		
25	2.813	12	18	29	42	56	69	80	88	97	99		
26	2.809	12	19	29	43	57	70	81	89	97	*		
27	2.805	12	19	30	44	58	72	83	90	98			
28	2.801	12	19	31	45	60	73	84	91	98			
29	2.797	12	20	32	46	61	74	85	92	98			
30	2.794	12	20	32	47	62	76	86	93	99			
31	2.791	12	20	33	48	63	77	87	93	99			
32	2.788	12	21	34	49	65	78	88	94	99			
33	2.786	12	21	34	50	66	79	89	95	99			
34	2.783	12	21	35	51	67	80	90	95	99			
35	2.781	13	22	36	52	68	81	90	96	99			
36	2.779	13	22	36	53	69	82	91	96	*			
37	2.777	13	22	37	54	70	83	92	96				
38	2.775	13	23	38	55	71	84	92	97				
39	2.773	13	23	38	56	72	85	93	97				

Table 8.3.23 *(continued)*

n	F_c	.05	.10	.15	.20	.25	.30	.35	.40	.50	.60	.70	.80
40	2.771	13	24	39	57	73	85	93	97	*	*	*	*
42	2.768	13	24	40	59	75	87	94	98				
44	2.765	13	25	42	60	77	88	95	98				
46	2.762	14	26	43	62	78	90	96	99				
48	2.760	14	26	44	63	80	91	96	99				
50	2.758	14	27	45	65	81	92	97	99				
52	2.756	14	28	47	66	82	92	97	99				
54	2.754	14	28	48	68	84	93	98	99				
56	2.752	14	29	49	69	85	94	98	*				
58	2.750	15	30	50	71	86	95	98					
60	2.749	15	30	51	72	87	95	99					
64	2.746	15	31	53	74	89	96	99					
68	2.743	16	33	56	76	90	97	99					
72	2.741	16	34	58	78	92	98	99					
76	2.739	16	35	59	80	93	98	*					
80	2.738	17	36	61	82	94	99						
84	2.736	17	38	63	84	95	99						
88	2.735	17	39	65	85	96	99						
92	2.733	18	40	67	86	96	99						
96	2.732	18	41	68	88	97	99						
100	2.731	18	42	70	89	97	*						
120	2.727	20	48	76	93	99							
140	2.724	22	53	82	96	99							
160	2.721	24	57	86	98	*							
180	2.719	25	62	89	99								
200	2.718	27	65	92	99								
250	2.716	31	74	96	*								
300	2.714	35	80	98									
350	2.713	39	85	99									
400	2.712	42	89	*									
450	2.711	46	92										
500	2.711	49	94										
600	2.710	55	97										
700	2.709	61	98										
800	2.709	66	99										
900	2.708	70	*										
1000	2.708	74											

* Power values below this point are greater than .995.

Table 8.3.24

Power of F test at a = .10, u = 2

							f						
n	F_c	.05	.10	.15	.20	.25	.30	.35	.40	.50	.60	.70	.80
2	5.462	10	11	12	13	13	14	15	17	20	23	27	32
3	3.463	10	11	12	14	15	17	20	22	29	36	45	53
4	3.006	10	11	13	15	17	20	24	28	38	48	59	70
5	2.807	10	12	13	16	20	24	29	34	46	59	71	81
6	2.695	10	12	14	18	22	27	33	40	54	68	80	89
7	2.624	10	12	15	19	24	30	37	45	61	75	86	93
8	2.575	11	13	16	21	27	34	41	50	67	81	90	96
9	2.538	11	13	17	22	29	37	45	55	72	85	94	98
10	2.511	11	13	18	24	31	40	49	59	76	89	96	99
11	2.489	11	14	18	25	33	43	53	63	80	92	97	99
12	2.471	11	14	19	27	36	46	56	67	84	94	98	*
13	2.456	11	14	20	28	38	49	60	70	86	95	99	
14	2.444	11	15	21	30	40	51	63	73	89	97	99	
15	2.434	11	15	22	31	42	54	66	76	91	97	*	
16	2.425	11	16	23	32	44	56	68	79	92	98		
17	2.417	11	16	24	34	46	59	71	81	94	99		
18	2.410	11	16	24	35	48	61	73	83	95	99		
19	2.404	11	17	25	37	50	63	75	85	96	99		
20	2.398	12	17	26	38	52	65	77	87	97	*		
21	2.393	12	17	27	39	53	67	79	88	97			
22	2.389	12	18	28	41	55	69	81	90	98			
23	2.385	12	18	29	42	57	71	83	91	98			
24	2.381	12	19	29	43	59	73	84	92	99			
25	2.378	12	19	30	45	60	74	86	93	99			
26	2.375	12	19	31	46	62	76	87	94	99			
27	2.372	12	20	32	47	63	78	88	95	99			
28	2.369	12	20	33	48	65	79	89	95	99			
29	2.367	12	20	33	50	66	80	90	96	*			
30	2.365	12	21	34	51	68	82	91	96				
31	2.363	13	21	35	52	69	83	92	97				
32	2.361	13	22	36	53	70	84	93	97				
33	2.359	13	22	37	54	71	85	93	98				
34	2.357	13	22	37	55	73	86	94	98				
35	2.355	13	23	38	56	74	87	95	98				
36	2.354	13	23	39	57	75	88	95	98				
37	2.352	13	24	40	59	76	89	96	99				
38	2.351	13	24	40	60	77	89	96	99				
39	2.350	13	24	41	61	78	90	96	99				

Table 8.3.24 *(continued)*

n	F_c	f										
		.05	.10	.15	.20	.25	.30	.35	.40	.50	.60	.70	.80
40	2.348	13	25	42	62	79	91	97	99	*	*	*	*
42	2.346	14	25	43	64	81	92	97	99				
44	2.344	14	26	45	65	82	93	98	*				
46	2.342	14	27	46	67	84	94	98					
48	2.341	14	28	48	69	85	95	99					
50	2.339	14	28	49	71	87	96	99					
52	2.338	15	29	50	72	88	96	99					
54	2.336	15	30	52	74	89	97	99					
56	2.335	15	31	53	75	90	97	99					
58	2.334	15	31	54	76	91	98	*					
60	2.333	15	32	55	78	92	98						
64	2.331	16	33	58	80	93	98						
68	2.329	16	35	60	82	95	99						
72	2.328	17	36	62	84	96	99						
76	2.326	17	38	65	86	96	99						
80	2.325	17	39	67	88	97	*						
84	2.324	18	40	69	89	98							
88	2.323	18	42	70	90	98							
92	2.322	18	43	72	92	99							
96	2.321	19	44	74	93	99							
100	2.321	19	45	75	93	99							
120	2.318	21	52	82	97	*							
140	2.315	23	57	87	98								
160	2.314	25	62	91	99								
180	2.313	27	67	94	*								
200	2.312	29	71	96									
250	2.310	33	80	98									
300	2.309	37	86	99									
350	2.308	42	90	*									
400	2.307	46	94										
450	2.307	49	96										
500	2.306	53	97										
600	2.306	60	99										
700	2.305	66	*										
800	2.305	71											
900	2.305	76											
1000	2.304	80											

* Power values below this point are greater than .995.

Table 8.3.25

Power of F test at a = .10, u = 3

n	F_c	.05	.10	.15	.20	.25	.30	.35	.40	.50	.60	.70	.80
2	4.191	10	11	12	12	13	15	16	17	20	25	29	35
3	2.924	10	11	12	14	15	18	20	23	31	39	49	59
4	2.606	10	11	13	15	18	21	25	30	41	53	65	76
5	2.462	10	12	14	17	20	25	30	37	50	64	77	87
6	2.381	10	12	15	18	23	29	35	43	59	73	85	93
7	2.327	11	12	15	20	26	32	40	49	66	81	91	96
8	2.291	11	13	16	22	28	36	45	54	72	86	94	98
9	2.264	11	13	17	23	31	40	49	59	78	90	97	99
10	2.243	11	14	18	25	33	43	54	64	82	93	98	*
11	2.226	11	14	19	27	36	46	58	68	86	95	99	
12	2.213	11	14	20	28	38	50	61	72	89	97	99	
13	2.202	11	15	21	30	41	53	65	76	91	98	*	
14	2.192	11	15	22	31	43	56	68	79	93	98		
15	2.184	11	16	23	33	45	59	71	82	95	99		
16	2.177	11	16	24	35	48	61	74	84	96	99		
17	2.171	11	16	25	36	50	64	77	86	97	*		
18	2.166	11	17	26	38	52	66	79	88	98			
19	2.162	12	17	27	39	54	69	81	90	98			
20	2.157	12	18	28	41	56	71	83	91	99			
21	2.154	12	18	29	43	58	73	85	93	99			
22	2.150	12	18	29	44	60	75	86	94	99			
23	2.147	12	19	30	46	62	77	88	95	99			
24	2.144	12	19	31	47	64	79	89	95	*			
25	2.142	12	20	32	48	66	80	90	96				
26	2.139	12	20	33	50	67	82	91	97				
27	2.137	12	21	34	51	69	83	91	97				
28	2.135	12	21	35	53	70	84	93	98				
29	2.133	13	21	36	54	72	86	94	98				
30	2.132	13	22	37	55	73	87	95	98				
31	2.130	13	22	38	57	75	88	95	99				
32	2.129	13	23	39	58	76	89	96	99				
33	2.127	13	23	39	59	77	90	96	99				
34	2.126	13	23	40	60	78	91	97	99				
35	2.124	13	24	41	61	79	91	97	99				
36	2.123	13	24	42	63	81	92	98	99				
37	2.122	13	25	43	64	82	93	98	*				
38	2.121	14	25	44	65	83	93	98					
39	2.120	14	26	45	66	84	94	98					

Table 8.3.25 (continued)

n	F_c	.05	.10	.15	.20	.25	.30	.35	.40	.50	.60	.70	.80
40	2.119	14	26	45	67	84	94	99	*	*	*	*	*
42	2.118	14	27	47	69	86	95	99					
44	2.116	14	28	49	71	88	96	99					
46	2.115	14	28	50	73	89	97	99					
48	2.113	15	29	52	75	90	97	*					
50	2.112	15	30	53	76	91	98						
52	2.111	15	31	55	78	92	98						
54	2.110	15	32	56	79	93	99						
56	2.109	15	33	58	81	94	99						
58	2.108	16	33	59	82	95	99						
60	2.107	16	34	60	83	95	99						
64	2.106	16	36	63	85	96	99						
68	2.104	17	37	66	88	97	*						
72	2.103	17	39	68	89	98							
76	2.102	17	41	70	91	98							
80	2.101	18	42	72	92	99							
84	2.101	18	44	74	93	99							
88	2.100	19	45	76	94	99							
92	2.099	19	46	78	95	99							
96	2.098	20	48	80	96	*							
100	2.098	20	49	81	96								
120	2.096	22	56	87	99								
140	2.094	24	62	92	99								
160	2.093	26	68	95	*								
180	2.092	28	72	97									
200	2.091	30	77	98									
250	2.089	35	85	99									
300	2.088	40	91	*									
350	2.088	45	94										
400	2.087	50	97										
450	2.087	54	98										
500	2.087	58	99										
600	2.086	65	*										
700	2.086	71											
800	2.086	77											
900	2.085	81											
1000	2.085	85											

* Power values below this point are greater than .995.

Table 8.3.26

Power of F test at a = .10, u = 4

n	F_c	.05	.10	.15	.20	.25	.30	.35	.40	.50	.60	.70	.80
2	3.520	10	11	11	12	13	15	16	18	21	26	32	38
3	2.605	10	11	12	14	16	18	21	25	33	43	53	64
4	2.361	10	11	13	15	18	22	27	32	44	57	70	81
5	2.249	10	12	14	17	21	26	32	39	54	69	82	91
6	2.184	10	12	15	19	24	31	38	46	63	79	89	96
7	2.142	11	13	16	21	27	35	43	53	71	85	94	98
8	2.113	11	13	17	23	30	39	48	59	77	90	97	99
9	2.091	11	13	18	24	33	43	53	64	82	94	98	*
10	2.074	11	14	19	26	36	47	58	69	87	96	99	
11	2.061	11	14	20	28	38	50	62	73	90	97	*	
12	2.050	11	15	21	30	41	54	66	77	92	98		
13	2.041	11	15	22	32	44	57	70	81	94	99		
14	2.034	11	16	23	34	46	60	73	84	96	99		
15	2.027	11	16	24	35	49	63	76	86	97	*		
16	2.022	11	16	25	37	51	66	79	88	98			
17	2.017	11	17	26	39	54	69	81	90	98			
18	2.012	12	17	27	41	56	71	84	92	99			
19	2.009	12	18	28	42	58	74	86	93	99			
20	2.005	12	18	29	44	61	76	87	94	99			
21	2.002	12	19	30	46	63	78	89	95	*			
22	1.999	12	19	31	47	65	80	90	96				
23	1.997	12	20	32	49	67	82	92	97				
24	1.994	12	20	33	51	69	83	93	97				
25	1.992	12	21	34	52	70	85	94	98				
26	1.990	12	21	35	54	72	86	95	98				
27	1.989	13	21	36	55	74	87	95	99				
28	1.987	13	22	37	57	75	89	96	99				
29	1.986	13	22	38	58	77	90	97	99				
30	1.984	13	23	39	60	78	91	97	99				
31	1.983	13	23	40	61	79	92	97	99				
32	1.982	13	24	41	62	81	92	98	*				
33	1.980	13	24	42	64	82	93	98					
34	1.979	13	25	43	65	83	94	98					
35	1.978	13	25	44	66	84	94	99					
36	1.977	14	26	45	67	85	95	99					
37	1.977	14	26	46	69	86	96	99					
38	1.976	14	26	47	70	87	96	99					
39	1.975	14	27	48	71	88	96	99					

Table 8.3.26 *(continued)*

								f					
n	F_c	.05	.10	.15	.20	.25	.30	.35	.40	.50	.60	.70	.80
40	1.974	14	27	49	72	89	97	99	*	*	*	*	*
42	1.973	14	28	51	74	90	97	*					
44	1.971	14	29	52	76	91	98						
46	1.970	15	30	54	78	93	98						
48	1.969	15	31	56	79	94	99						
50	1.968	15	32	57	81	94	99						
52	1.967	15	33	59	83	95	99						
54	1.966	16	34	61	84	96	99						
56	1.966	16	35	62	85	96	*						
58	1.965	16	36	64	86	97							
60	1.964	16	37	65	88	97							
64	1.963	17	38	68	90	98							
68	1.962	17	40	70	91	99							
72	1.961	18	42	73	93	99							
76	1.960	18	44	75	94	99							
80	1.959	19	45	77	95	*							
84	1.959	19	47	79	96								
88	1.958	19	48	81	97								
92	1.957	20	50	83	97								
96	1.957	20	52	84	98								
100	1.956	21	53	86	98								
120	1.954	23	60	91	99								
140	1.953	25	67	95	*								
160	1.952	28	73	97									
180	1.951	30	77	98									
200	1.951	32	82	99									
250	1.950	38	89	*									
300	1.949	43	94										
350	1.948	49	97										
400	1.948	53	98										
450	1.947	58	99										
500	1.947	62	*										
600	1.947	70											
700	1.947	76											
800	1.946	82											
900	1.946	86											
1000	1.946	89											

* Power values below this point are greater than .995.

Table 8.3.27

Power of F test at a = .10, u = 5

n	F_c	.05	.10	.15	.20	.25	.30	.35	.40	.50	.60	.70	.80
2	3.108	10	11	11	12	13	15	16	18	22	28	34	41
3	2.394	10	11	12	14	16	19	22	26	35	46	58	69
4	2.196	10	11	13	16	19	23	28	34	47	62	75	85
5	2.103	10	12	14	18	22	28	34	42	58	74	86	94
6	2.049	10	12	15	20	25	32	40	49	68	83	93	97
7	2.014	11	13	16	22	28	37	46	56	75	89	96	99
8	1.990	11	13	17	23	32	41	52	63	81	93	98	*
9	1.971	11	14	18	26	35	46	57	68	86	96	99	
10	1.957	11	14	19	28	38	50	62	73	90	97	*	
11	1.946	11	14	21	30	41	54	66	78	93	99		
12	1.937	11	15	22	32	44	57	70	81	95	99		
13	1.929	11	15	23	34	47	61	74	84	96	*		
14	1.923	11	16	24	36	50	64	77	87	97			
15	1.917	11	16	25	38	52	67	80	90	98			
16	1.912	11	17	26	40	55	70	83	92	99			
17	1.908	12	17	27	41	58	73	85	93	99			
18	1.905	12	18	29	43	60	76	87	95	99			
19	1.902	12	18	30	45	62	78	89	96	*			
20	1.899	12	19	31	47	65	80	91	96				
21	1.896	12	19	32	49	67	82	92	97				
22	1.894	12	20	33	51	69	84	93	98				
23	1.891	12	20	34	52	71	86	94	98				
24	1.890	12	21	35	54	73	87	95	99				
25	1.888	12	21	36	56	75	88	96	99				
26	1.886	13	22	38	57	76	90	97	99				
27	1.885	13	22	39	59	78	91	97	99				
28	1.883	13	23	40	61	79	92	98	99				
29	1.882	13	23	41	62	81	93	98	*				
30	1.881	13	24	42	64	82	94	98					
31	1.880	13	24	43	65	83	94	99					
32	1.879	13	25	44	66	85	95	99					
33	1.878	13	25	45	68	86	96	99					
34	1.877	14	26	46	69	87	96	99					
35	1.876	14	26	47	70	88	97	99					
36	1.875	14	27	48	72	89	97	99					
37	1.874	14	27	49	73	90	97	*					
38	1.874	14	28	50	74	90	98						
39	1.873	14	28	51	75	91	98						

Table 8.3.27 *(continued)*

n	F_c	.05	.10	.15	.20	.25	.30	.35	.40	.50	.60	.70	.80
40	1.872	14	29	52	76	92	98	*	*	*	*	*	*
42	1.871	14	30	54	78	93	99						
44	1.870	15	31	56	80	94	99						
46	1.869	15	32	58	82	95	99						
48	1.868	15	33	60	83	96	99						
50	1.867	15	34	61	85	96	*						
52	1.866	16	35	63	86	97							
54	1.866	16	36	65	88	98							
56	1.865	16	37	66	89	98							
58	1.864	16	38	68	90	98							
60	1.864	17	39	69	91	99							
64	1.863	17	41	72	93	99							
68	1.862	18	43	75	94	99							
72	1.861	18	45	77	95	*							
76	1.860	19	46	79	96								
80	1.860	19	48	81	97								
84	1.859	20	50	83	98								
88	1.858	20	52	85	98								
92	1.858	21	54	86	98								
96	1.858	21	55	88	99								
100	1.857	22	57	89	99								
120	1.855	24	64	94	*								
140	1.854	27	71	97									
160	1.853	29	77	98									
180	1.853	32	81	99									
200	1.852	34	85	*									
250	1.851	40	92										
300	1.851	46	96										
350	1.850	52	98										
400	1.850	57	99										
450	1.849	62	*										
500	1.849	66											
600	1.849	74											
700	1.849	80											
800	1.849	84											
900	1.848	89											
1000	1.848	92											

* Power values below this point are greater than .995.

Table 8.3.28

Power of F test at a = .10, u = 6

n	F_c	.05	.10	.15	.20	.25	.30	.35	.40	.50	.60	.70	.80
2	2.827	10	11	11	12	13	14	17	19	23	29	36	44
3	2.243	10	11	12	14	16	19	23	27	37	49	61	73
4	2.075	10	11	13	16	20	24	30	36	50	66	79	89
5	1.996	10	12	14	18	23	29	36	45	62	78	89	96
6	1.950	11	12	15	20	26	34	43	53	71	86	95	99
7	1.919	11	13	17	22	30	39	49	60	79	92	98	*
8	1.898	11	13	18	24	33	44	55	66	85	95	99	
9	1.882	11	14	19	27	37	48	61	72	89	97	*	
10	1.870	11	14	20	29	40	53	66	74	93	99		
11	1.860	11	15	21	31	43	57	70	81	95	99		
12	1.852	11	15	23	33	46	61	74	85	97	*		
13	1.846	11	16	24	35	50	64	78	88	98			
14	1.840	11	16	25	38	53	68	81	90	98			
15	1.835	11	17	26	40	56	71	84	92	99			
16	1.831	12	17	27	42	58	74	86	94	99			
17	1.827	12	18	29	44	61	77	88	95	*			
18	1.824	12	18	30	46	64	79	90	96				
19	1.821	12	19	31	48	66	82	92	97				
20	1.819	12	19	32	50	68	84	93	98				
21	1.817	12	20	34	52	71	85	94	98				
22	1.815	12	20	35	54	73	87	95	99				
23	1.813	12	21	36	56	75	89	96	99				
24	1.811	13	21	37	57	77	90	97	99				
25	1.810	13	22	38	59	78	91	97	99				
26	1.808	13	23	40	61	80	92	98	*				
27	1.807	13	23	41	63	82	93	98					
28	1.806	13	24	42	64	83	94	99					
29	1.805	13	24	43	66	84	95	99					
30	1.803	13	25	44	67	86	96	99					
31	1.802	13	25	46	69	87	96	99					
32	1.802	14	26	47	70	88	97	99					
33	1.801	14	26	48	71	89	97	*					
34	1.800	14	27	49	73	90	97						
35	1.799	14	27	50	74	91	98						
36	1.798	14	28	51	75	91	98						
37	1.798	14	29	52	76	92	98						
38	1.797	14	29	53	78	93	99						
39	1.797	14	30	54	79	94	99						

Table 8.3.28 *(continued)*

n	F_c	.05	.10	.15	.20	.25	.30	.35	.40	.50	.60	.70	.80
										f			
40	1.796	15	30	55	80	94	99	*	*	*	*	*	*
42	1.795	15	31	57	82	95	99						
44	1.794	15	32	59	84	96	99						
46	1.793	15	33	61	85	97	*						
48	1.792	16	35	63	87	97							
50	1.791	16	36	65	88	98							
52	1.791	16	37	67	89	98							
54	1.790	16	38	68	91	99							
56	1.790	17	39	70	92	99							
58	1.789	17	40	71	92	99							
60	1.789	17	41	73	93	99							
64	1.788	18	43	76	95	*							
68	1.787	18	45	78	96								
72	1.786	19	47	81	97								
76	1.785	19	49	83	98								
80	1.785	20	51	85	98								
84	1.784	20	53	86	99								
88	1.784	21	55	88	99								
92	1.783	21	57	89	99								
96	1.783	22	58	91	99								
100	1.783	22	60	92	*								
120	1.781	25	68	96									
140	1.780	28	75	98									
160	1.779	31	80	99									
180	1.779	33	85	*									
200	1.778	36	89										
250	1.778	43	94										
300	1.777	49	97										
350	1.777	55	99										
400	1.776	60	*										
450	1.776	66											
500	1.776	70											
600	1.776	78											
700	1.775	84											
800	1.775	89											
900	1.775	92											
1000	1.775	94											

* Power values below this point are greater than .995.

Table 8.3.29

Power of F test at a = .10, u = 8

n	F_c	.05	.10	.15	.20	.25	.30	.35	.40	.50	.60	.70	.80
2	2.469	10	11	11	12	14	15	17	20	25	33	41	50
3	2.038	10	11	13	15	17	21	25	30	41	55	68	80
4	1.909	10	12	14	17	21	26	32	40	56	72	85	93
5	1.847	10	12	15	19	25	32	40	49	68	84	94	98
6	1.811	11	13	16	21	29	37	48	58	78	91	98	*
7	1.787	11	13	17	24	33	43	55	66	85	95	99	
8	1.770	11	14	19	26	36	48	61	73	90	98	*	
9	1.757	11	14	20	29	40	53	67	79	94	99		
10	1.747	11	15	21	31	44	58	72	83	96	99		
11	1.740	11	15	23	34	48	63	76	87	98	*		
12	1.733	11	16	24	36	51	67	80	90	99			
13	1.728	11	16	26	39	55	71	84	93	99			
14	1.723	11	17	27	41	58	74	87	94	99			
15	1.720	12	18	28	44	61	77	89	96	*			
16	1.716	12	18	30	46	64	80	91	97				
17	1.713	12	19	31	48	67	83	93	98				
18	1.711	12	19	33	51	70	85	94	98				
19	1.709	12	20	34	53	72	87	95	99				
20	1.707	12	20	35	55	75	89	96	99				
21	1.705	12	21	37	57	77	91	97	99				
22	1.703	13	22	38	59	79	92	98	*				
23	1.702	13	22	40	61	81	93	98					
24	1.700	13	23	41	63	83	94	99					
25	1.699	13	24	42	65	84	95	99					
26	1.698	13	24	44	67	86	96	99					
27	1.697	13	25	45	69	87	96	99					
28	1.696	13	25	46	70	88	97	*					
29	1.695	13	26	48	72	90	97						
30	1.694	14	27	49	74	91	98						
31	1.693	14	27	50	75	92	98						
32	1.692	14	28	52	76	92	99						
33	1.692	14	29	53	78	93	99						
34	1.691	14	29	54	79	94	99						
35	1.691	14	30	55	80	95	99						
36	1.690	14	30	56	81	95	99						
37	1.689	15	31	58	83	96	99						
38	1.689	15	32	59	84	96	*						
39	1.688	15	32	60	85	97							

Table 8.3.29 (continued)

n	F_c	.05	.10	.15	.20	.25	.30	.35	.40	.50	.60	.70	.80
40	1.688	15	33	61	86	97	*	*	*	*	*	*	*
42	1.687	15	34	63	87	98							
44	1.686	16	35	65	89	98							
46	1.686	16	37	67	90	99							
48	1.685	16	38	69	92	99							
50	1.684	16	39	71	93	99							
52	1.684	17	40	73	94	99							
54	1.683	17	42	75	94	99							
56	1.683	17	43	76	95	*							
58	1.682	18	44	78	96								
60	1.682	18	45	79	96								
64	1.681	18	48	82	97								
68	1.681	19	50	84	98								
72	1.680	20	52	86	99								
76	1.679	20	54	88	99								
80	1.679	21	56	90	99								
84	1.679	21	58	91	99								
88	1.678	22	60	93	*								
92	1.678	23	62	94									
96	1.677	23	64	95									
100	1.677	24	66	95									
120	1.676	27	74	98									
140	1.675	30	81	99									
160	1.675	33	86	*									
180	1.674	36	90										
200	1.674	39	93										
250	1.673	47	97										
300	1.673	54	99										
350	1.672	61	*										
400	1.672	66											
450	1.672	72											
500	1.672	76											
600	1.671	84											
700	1.671	89											
800	1.671	93											
900	1.671	96											
1000	1.671	97											

* Power values below this point are greater than .995.

Table 8.3.30

Power of F test at a = .10, u = 10

n	F_c	.05	.10	.15	.20	.25	.30	.35	.40	.50	.60	.70	.80
							f						
2	2.248	10	11	12	13	14	16	18	21	27	36	45	51
3	1.904	10	11	13	15	18	22	26	32	45	60	74	85
4	1.799	10	12	14	17	22	28	35	43	61	78	90	96
5	1.747	11	12	15	20	26	34	44	54	74	89	96	99
6	1.717	11	13	17	23	31	41	52	63	83	95	99	*
7	1.697	11	13	18	25	35	47	59	71	90	98	*	
8	1.683	11	14	20	28	39	53	66	78	94	99		
9	1.672	11	15	21	31	44	58	72	84	96	*		
10	1.664	11	15	23	34	48	63	77	88	98			
11	1.657	11	16	24	37	52	68	82	91	99			
12	1.652	11	16	26	39	56	72	85	93	99			
13	1.648	11	17	27	42	59	76	88	95	*			
14	1.644	12	18	29	45	63	79	91	97				
15	1.641	12	18	30	47	66	82	93	98				
16	1.638	12	19	32	50	69	85	94	98				
17	1.635	12	20	33	53	72	87	96	99				
18	1.633	12	20	35	55	75	89	97	99				
19	1.631	12	21	37	57	78	91	98	*				
20	1.630	12	22	38	60	80	93	98					
21	1.628	13	22	40	62	82	94	99					
22	1.627	13	23	41	64	84	95	99					
23	1.625	13	24	43	66	86	96	99					
24	1.624	13	24	44	68	87	97	99					
25	1.623	13	25	46	70	89	97	*					
26	1.622	13	26	47	72	90	98						
27	1.621	14	26	49	74	91	98						
28	1.620	14	27	50	76	92	98						
29	1.620	14	28	52	77	93	99						
30	1.619	14	28	53	79	94	99						
31	1.618	14	29	55	80	95	99						
32	1.618	14	30	56	81	95	99						
33	1.617	14	31	57	83	96	99						
34	1.616	15	31	59	84	96	*						
35	1.616	15	32	60	85	97							
36	1.615	15	33	61	86	97							
37	1.615	15	33	62	87	98							
38	1.615	15	34	64	88	98							
39	1.614	15	35	65	89	98							

Table 8.3.30 *(continued)*

n	F_c	.05	.10	.15	.20	.25	.30	.35	.40	.50	.60	.70	.80
40	1.614	15	35	66	90	98	*	*	*	*	*	*	*
42	1.613	16	37	68	91	99							
44	1.612	16	38	70	93	99							
46	1.612	16	40	72	94	99							
48	1.611	17	41	74	95	*							
50	1.611	17	42	76	95								
52	1.610	17	44	78	96								
54	1.610	18	45	80	97								
56	1.609	18	46	81	97								
58	1.609	18	48	83	98								
60	1.609	19	49	84	98								
64	1.608	19	52	86	99								
68	1.607	20	54	89	99								
72	1.607	21	56	90	99								
76	1.607	21	59	92	*								
80	1.606	22	61	93									
84	1.606	23	63	94									
88	1.605	23	66	95									
92	1.605	24	68	96									
96	1.605	25	70	97									
100	1.605	25	71	97									
120	1.604	29	79	99									
140	1.603	32	86	*									
160	1.603	36	90										
180	1.602	39	93										
200	1.602	43	96										
250	1.601	51	99										
300	1.601	59	*										
350	1.600	66											
400	1.600	72											
450	1.600	77											
500	1.600	81											
600	1.600	88											
700	1.600	93											
800	1.599	96											
900	1.599	98											
1000	1.599	99											

* Power values below this point are greater than .995.

Table 8.3.31

Power of F test at a = .10, u = 12

n	F_c	.05	.10	.15	.20	.25	.30	.35	.40	.50	.60	.70	.80
2	2.097	10	11	11	13	15	17	19	22	29	39	49	61
3	1.809	10	11	13	15	19	23	28	34	49	65	79	89
4	1.719	10	12	14	18	23	30	38	47	66	82	93	98
5	1.675	11	12	16	21	28	37	47	58	78	92	98	*
6	1.649	11	13	17	24	33	44	56	68	87	97	99	
7	1.631	11	14	19	27	37	50	64	76	93	99	*	
8	1.619	11	14	20	30	42	56	70	82	96	*		
9	1.610	11	15	22	33	47	62	76	87	98			
10	1.603	11	16	24	36	51	68	81	91	99			
11	1.597	11	16	25	39	56	72	86	94	99			
12	1.592	11	17	27	42	60	77	89	96	*			
13	1.588	12	18	29	45	64	80	92	97				
14	1.585	12	18	31	48	67	84	94	98				
15	1.582	12	19	32	51	71	86	95	99				
16	1.580	12	20	34	54	74	89	96	99				
17	1.578	12	20	36	56	77	91	97	*				
18	1.576	12	21	37	59	79	92	98					
19	1.574	13	22	39	62	82	94	99					
20	1.573	13	23	41	64	84	95	99					
21	1.571	13	23	43	66	86	96	99					
22	1.570	13	24	44	69	88	97	*					
23	1.569	13	25	46	71	89	97						
24	1.568	13	26	48	73	91	98						
25	1.567	13	26	49	75	92	98						
26	1.566	14	27	51	77	93	99						
27	1.565	14	28	52	78	94	99						
28	1.565	14	29	54	80	95	99						
29	1.564	14	29	55	81	95	99						
30	1.563	14	30	57	83	96	*						
31	1.563	14	31	58	84	97							
32	1.562	15	32	60	85	97							
33	1.562	15	32	61	87	98							
34	1.561	15	33	63	88	98							
35	1.561	15	34	64	89	98							
36	1.560	15	35	65	90	99							
37	1.560	15	35	67	90	99							
38	1.560	16	36	68	91	99							
39	1.559	16	37	69	92	99							

Table 8.3.31 *(continued)*

									f					
n	F_c	.05	.10	.15	.20	.25	.30	.35	.40	.50	.60	.70	.80
40	1.559	16	38	70	93	99	*	*	*	*	*	*	*
42	1.558	16	39	73	94	99							
44	1.558	17	41	75	95	*							
46	1.557	17	42	77	96								
48	1.557	17	44	79	97								
50	1.556	18	45	81	97								
52	1.556	18	47	82	98								
54	1.555	18	48	84	98								
56	1.555	19	50	85	99								
58	1.555	19	51	86	99								
60	1.554	19	53	88	99								
64	1.554	20	55	90	99								
68	1.553	21	58	92	*								
72	1.553	22	60	93									
76	1.553	22	63	95									
80	1.552	23	65	96									
84	1.552	24	68	96									
88	1.552	24	70	97									
92	1.551	25	72	98									
96	1.551	26	74	98									
100	1.551	27	76	99									
120	1.550	31	84	*									
140	1.549	34	89										
160	1.549	38	93										
180	1.549	42	96										
200	1.548	46	97										
250	1.548	55	99										
300	1.548	63	*										
350	1.547	70											
400	1.547	76											
450	1.547	81											
500	1.547	85											
600	1.547	91											
700	1.547	95											
800	1.546	97											
900	1.546	99											
1000	1.546	99											

* Power values below this point are greater than .995.

Table 8.3.32

Power of F test at a = .10, u = 15

n	F_c	.05	.10	.15	.20	.25	.30	.35	.40	.50	.60	.70	.80
2	1.940	10	11	12	13	15	17	20	24	32	43	55	67
3	1.707	10	11	13	16	20	24	30	38	54	71	85	93
4	1.633	10	12	15	19	25	32	41	51	72	87	96	99
5	1.596	11	13	16	22	30	40	52	63	84	95	99	*
6	1.574	11	13	18	25	35	48	61	74	91	98	*	
7	1.560	11	14	20	29	41	55	69	81	96	99		
8	1.549	11	15	22	32	46	62	76	87	98	*		
9	1.541	11	15	23	36	51	68	82	92	99			
10	1.535	11	16	25	39	56	73	86	95	*			
11	1.531	12	17	27	43	61	78	90	97				
12	1.527	12	18	29	46	65	82	93	98				
13	1.523	12	18	31	49	69	85	95	99				
14	1.521	12	19	33	52	73	88	96	99				
15	1.518	12	20	35	56	76	91	97	*				
16	1.516	12	21	37	59	79	93	98					
17	1.514	12	22	39	62	82	94	99					
18	1.513	13	22	41	64	85	96	99					
19	1.511	13	23	43	67	87	97	99					
20	1.510	13	24	45	70	89	97	*					
21	1.509	13	25	46	72	90	98						
22	1.508	13	26	48	74	92	98						
23	1.507	13	26	50	76	93	99						
24	1.506	14	27	52	78	94	99						
25	1.505	14	28	54	80	95	99						
26	1.504	14	29	56	82	96	*						
27	1.504	14	30	57	83	97							
28	1.503	14	31	59	85	97							
29	1.503	15	32	61	86	98							
30	1.502	15	32	62	88	98							
31	1.502	15	33	64	89	98							
32	1.501	15	34	65	90	99							
33	1.501	15	35	67	91	99							
34	1.500	15	36	68	92	99							
35	1.500	16	37	70	93	99							
36	1.500	16	38	71	93	99							
37	1.499	16	39	72	94	*							
38	1.499	16	39	74	95								
39	1.499	16	40	75	95								

Table 8.3.32 (continued)

n	F_c	.05	.10	.15	.20	.25	.30	.35	.40	.50	.60	.70	.80
						f							
40	1.498	17	41	76	96	*	*	*	*	*	*	*	*
42	1.498	17	43	78	97								
44	1.497	17	45	80	97								
46	1.497	18	46	82	98								
48	1.496	18	48	84	98								
50	1.496	18	49	86	99								
52	1.496	19	51	87	99								
54	1.495	19	53	88	99								
56	1.495	20	54	90	99								
58	1.495	20	56	91	*								
60	1.494	20	57	92									
64	1.494	21	60	94									
68	1.494	22	63	95									
72	1.493	23	66	96									
76	1.493	24	68	97									
80	1.493	24	71	98									
84	1.492	25	73	98									
88	1.492	26	75	99									
92	1.492	27	77	99									
96	1.492	28	79	99									
100	1.491	29	81	99									
120	1.491	33	88	*									
140	1.490	37	93										
160	1.490	42	96										
180	1.490	46	98										
200	1.489	50	99										
250	1.489	60	*										
300	1.489	68											
350	1.488	75											
400	1.488	81											
450	1.488	86											
500	1.488	90											
600	1.488	95											
700	1.488	97											
800	1.488	99											
900	1.488	99											
1000	1.488	*											

* Power values below this point are greater than .995.

Table 8.3.33

Power of F test at a = .10, u = 24

n	F_c												f
		.05	.10	.15	.20	.25	.30	.35	.40	.50	.60	.70	.80
2	1.689	10	11	12	14	16	19	23	28	40	54	69	81
3	1.536	10	12	14	17	22	29	37	46	66	84	94	99
4	1.485	11	12	16	21	29	39	51	63	84	96	99	*
5	1.460	11	13	18	26	36	49	63	76	93	99	*	
6	1.445	11	14	20	30	43	58	73	85	98	*		
7	1.434	11	15	22	34	50	67	82	92	99			
8	1.427	11	16	25	39	56	74	88	95	*			
9	1.422	11	17	27	43	62	80	92	98				
10	1.417	12	18	29	48	68	85	95	99				
11	1.414	12	19	32	52	73	89	97	99				
12	1.411	12	20	35	56	78	92	98	*				
13	1.409	12	21	37	60	81	94	99					
14	1.407	12	22	40	64	85	96	99					
15	1.405	13	23	42	67	88	97	*					
16	1.404	13	24	45	71	90	98						
17	1.402	13	25	47	74	92	99						
18	1.401	13	26	50	77	94	99						
19	1.400	13	27	52	79	95	99						
20	1.399	14	28	54	82	96	*						
21	1.399	14	29	57	84	97							
22	1.398	14	30	59	86	98							
23	1.397	14	31	61	88	98							
24	1.397	15	32	63	89	99							
25	1.396	15	33	65	91	99							
26	1.395	15	35	67	92	99							
27	1.395	15	36	69	93	99							
28	1.395	15	37	71	94	*							
29	1.394	16	38	73	95								
30	1.394	16	39	74	95								
31	1.393	16	40	76	96								
32	1.393	16	41	77	97								
33	1.393	17	42	79	97								
34	1.393	17	43	80	98								
35	1.392	17	45	82	98								
36	1.392	17	46	83	98								
37	1.392	17	47	84	99								
38	1.392	18	48	85	99								
39	1.391	18	49	86	99								

Table 8.3.33 (continued)

n	F_c	.05	.10	.15	.20	.25	.30	.35	.40	.50	.60	.70	.80
									f				
40	1.391	18	50	87	99	*	*	*	*	*	*	*	*
42	1.391	19	52	89	99								
44	1.391	19	54	91	*								
46	1.390	20	56	92									
48	1.390	20	58	93									
50	1.389	21	60	94									
52	1.389	21	62	95									
54	1.389	22	64	96									
56	1.389	22	66	97									
58	1.389	23	67	97									
60	1.388	23	69	98									
64	1.388	24	72	98									
68	1.388	25	75	99									
72	1.388	26	78	99									
76	1.387	27	80	*									
80	1.387	29	83										
84	1.387	30	85										
88	1.387	31	87										
92	1.387	32	88										
96	1.386	33	90										
100	1.386	34	91										
120	1.386	40	96										
140	1.385	45	98										
160	1.385	51	99										
180	1.385	56	*										
200	1.385	61											
250	1.384	72											
300	1.384	80											
350	1.384	87											
400	1.384	91											
450	1.384	94											
500	1.384	97											
600	1.384	99											
700	1.384	*											
800	1.384												
900	1.384												
1000	1.384												

* Power values below this point are greater than .995.

The 33 tables in this section yield power values for the **F** test when, in addition to the significance criterion (**a**) and ES (**f**), the degrees of freedom for the numerator of the **F** ratio (**u**) and sample size (**n**) are specified. They are most directly used to appraise the power of **F** tests in a completed research *post hoc*, but can, of course, be similarly used for a research *plan*, the details of which (e.g., significance criterion, sample size) can be varied to study consequences to power.

The tables give values for **a**, **u**, **f**, and **n**:

1. Significance Criterion, **a**. Since **F** is naturally nondirectional (see above, Section 8.1), 11 tables (for varying **u**) are provided at each of the **a** levels, .01, .05, and .10.

2. Degrees of Freedom of the Numerator of the **F** *Ratio*, **u**. At each significance criterion, a table is provided for each of the following 11 values of **u**: 1 (1) 6 (2) 12, 15, 24. For cases 0, 1, and 2, all of which involve a comparison of **k** = **u** + 1 means, the number of means which can be compared using the tables is thus **k** = 2 (1) 7 (2) 13, 16, and 25. For tests on interactions (Case 3), **u** is the interaction **df**, and equals (**k** − 1)(**r** − 1), or (**k** − 1)(**r** − 1) (**p** − 1), etc., where **k**, **r**, **p** are the number of levels of interacting main effects. Thus, **u** = 12 for the interaction of a 4 × 5 or a 3 × 7 or a 2 × 13 factorial design or the three-way interaction of a 2 × 4 × 5, a 2 × 3 × 7, or a 3 × 3 × 4 factorial design.

For missing values of **u** (7, 9, 11, etc.), linear interpolation between tables will yield quite adequate approximations.

3. Effect Size, **f**. Provision is made for 12 values of **f**: .05 (.05) .40 (.10) .80. For Cases 0 and 2, **f** is simply defined as the standard deviation of standardized means [formula (8.2.1)]. Its definition is generalized for unequal **n** (Case 1) and for interactions (Case 3), and the relevant formulas are given in the sections dealing with those cases. For all applications, conventional levels have been proposed (Section 8.2.3), as follows:

small: **f** = .10,

medium: **f** = .25,

large: **f** = .40.

4. Sample Size, **n**. This is, for Cases 0 and 2, the **n** for *each* of the **k** sample means being compared. For the other cases, **n** is a function of the sizes of the samples or "cells" involved; see Sections 8.3.2, 8.3.4. The power tables provide for **n** = 2 (1) 40 (2) 60 (4) 100 (20) 200 (50) 500 (100) 1000. Here, too, linear interpolation is quite adequate.

The values in the body of the tables are power times 100, i.e., the percent of tests carried out under the specified conditions which will result in rejection of the null hypothesis. They are rounded to the nearest unit and are generally accurate to within one unit as tabled.

8.3.1   CASE 0: **k** MEANS WITH EQUAL **n**. The simplest case is the one-way analysis of variance of **k** samples, *each* with the same number of observations, **n** (Case 0). The **F** test is based on $u = k - 1$ numerator **df**, and $k(n - 1)$ denominator **df**. The power tables were designed for Case 0 conditions, and this section describes and illustrates their use under these conditions. Later sections describe their application with unequal **n**'s (Case 1), in factorial and other designs (Case 2), and for tests of interactions (Case 3).

In Case 0, the investigator posits an alternate hypothesis or ES in terms of **f**, the standard deviation of standardized means, by one or more of the following procedures:

1. By hypothesizing the **k** varying population means expressed in the raw unit of measurement, finding the standard deviation of these means, and dividing this by the estimated within-population standard deviation. This is a literal application of formula (8.2.1). (See example 8.8 in Section 8.3.4.)

2. By hypothesizing the range of the **k** means (**d**) and their pattern, and using the formulas of Section 8.2.1. or the c_j values of Table 8.2.1 to convert **d** to **f**.

3. By hypothesizing the ES as a proportion of the total variance for which population membership accounts (η^2) or as a correlation ratio (η), and using the formulas of Section 8.2.2 [particularly formula (8.2.22)] or Table 8.2.2 to convert η or η^2 to **f**.

4. With experience, or perhaps by using the proposed operational definitions of small, medium, and large **f** values as a framework, he can work directly with **f**, i.e., simply directly specify his alternate hypothesis or ES by selecting an appropriate value of **f**.

Since the specification of a value of **f** which correctly reflects the investigator's ES expectations is crucial, cross-checking among the above routes is recommended. Thus, for example, having reached an **f** by specifying an η^2, it would be worthwhile to determine what range of means (**d**) for a given anticipated pattern that value of **f** implies, and to ascertain whether this **d** is consistent with expectation.

Once **f** is selected, the rest is simple in Case 0 applications. Find the table for the **a** and **u** $(= k - 1)$ of the problem and locate **n**, the common sample size, and **f**. This determines their power ($\times 100$). For nontabulated **f** or **u**, linear interpolation is reasonably accurate.

Illustrative Examples

8.1   An educational psychologist performs an experiment in which **k** = 4 different teaching methods are to be contrasted. A total of **N** = 80 pupils are randomly assigned to samples of **n** = 20 pupils per methods group and are tested on an achievement criterion test following instruction. The resulting data are tested by an overall **F** test of a one-way analysis of variance design, using an **a** = .05 significance criterion.

In setting the ES which he expects in the population (i.e., the alternate hypothesis), he believes that the 4 means should span a range **d** of three-quarters of a within-population standard deviation. This judgment is based on his past experience and knowledge of the characteristics of the teaching methods. On this basis, he further expects that the four means will be about equally spaced along this range, thus in Pattern 2 (Section 8.2.1). From Table 8.2.1, he reads that for **k** = 4 in Pattern 2, **f** = .373**d**, so that, given an antici-pated **d** = .75, **f** = .373(.75) = .280. Having reached this value, he cross-checks by noting [from formula (8.2.19)] that this implies an $\eta^2 = \mathbf{f}^2/(1 + \mathbf{f}^2) =$ .280^2/(1 + .280^2) = .0727, i.e., about $7\frac{1}{4}\%$ of the measure's total variance is accounted for by group membership, or in correlation ratio terms, $\eta = \sqrt{.0727} = .270$. He observes further that **f** = .280 is just slightly above the operational definition of a medium ES (**f** = .25). He accepts the results of this cross-checking as consonant with his expectations. The necessary specifications for determining the power of the **F** test are complete. Note that in a one-way analysis of variance on **k** "levels," the numerator **df** are **u** = **k** − 1 = 3. Thus,

$$\mathbf{a} = .05, \quad \mathbf{u} = 3, \quad \mathbf{f} = .28, \quad \mathbf{n} = 20.$$

In Table 8.3.14 for **a** = .05 and **u** = 3, at row **n** = 20, he finds power for column **f** = .25 to be .43 and for **f** = .30 to be .59. Linear interpolation yields (approximate) power of

$$.43 + \frac{(.28 - .25)}{(.30 - .25)}(.59 - .43) = .43 + .10 = .53.$$

Thus, if the standard deviation of the 4 standardized population means, **f**, is .28 of a within-population standard deviation, with **n** = 20 cases per sample, his **F** test has had only a .53 probability of rejecting the null hypoth-esis at the .05 level. Note that the operative condition is the value of **f** of .28, whether the range and pattern of population means was as predicted or whether another range and pattern, which would yield the same **f**, applied.

An experiment whose power is as low as .53 for detecting its anticipated ES is relatively inconclusive when it fails to reject the null hypothesis. Given a population **f** = .28, rather than **f** = 0 as posited by the null hypothesis, it is a "toss-up" whether his results will be significant at the **a** and **n** conditions which obtain. Note that even if the **a** criterion were liberalized to .10, linear interpolation in Table 8.3.25 (for **a** = .10, **u** = 3) between **f** = .25 and .30 gives approximate power at **n** = 20 of only .56 + .09 = .65.

This problem has been presented as if the experiment were already completed (or at least committed), with a *post hoc* determination of power under the given conditions. See problem 8.9 below for a consideration of this problem as one of experimental *planning*, where, under stated conditions, the purpose is the determination of sample size to attain a specified power.

8.2 A large scale research on mental hospital treatment programs of chronic schizophrenics is undertaken by a psychiatric research team. A pool of **N** = 600 suitable patients is randomly divided into 3 (=**k**) equal samples, each assigned to a different building, and in each building a different microsocial system of roles, functions, responsibilities, and rewards of staff and patients is instituted following training. After a suitable interval, patients are assessed by the research team by means of behavior rating scales. The social-scientific "cost" of mistakenly rejecting the null hypothesis leads the team to decide on **a** = .01. The team is split, however, on the question of how large an effect the difference in the three systems will have, some expecting that 5% of behavior rating variance will be accounted for by system membership, the others expecting 10%. Hence $\eta^2 = .05$ or .10. In their discussion, they agree in their expectation that the population means are at equal intervals, hence in Pattern 2 (but note that for **k** = 3, Pattern 2 and Pattern 1 are the same). From Table 8.2.2, they note that at $\eta^2 = .05$, **f** = .229, and at $\eta^2 = .10$, **f** = .333. They determine, using the constants of Table 8.2.1, that the span of means for Pattern 2 for **f** = .229 is $d_2 = 2.45(.229) = .56$, and for **f** = .333, $d_2 = 2.45(.333) = .82$. Thus the proponents of $\eta^2 = .05$ expect a spread of the three means of a little more than half a within-population standard deviation, while the $\eta^2 = .10$ faction expect a spread of almost five-sixths of a σ. This translation brings them no closer to agreement. What is the power of the eventual **F** test under each of these two alternative hypotheses?

$$a = .01, \qquad u = k - 1 = 2, \qquad f = \begin{cases} .23 \\ .33 \end{cases}, \qquad n = 200.$$

In Table 8.3.2 (for **a** = .01, **u** = 2) at row **n** = 200, they find that at **f** = .20, power is .98, and at **f** = .25, power is greater than .995. This means they need have no dispute—if the **f** = .23 ($\eta^2 = .05$) faction is right, power is about .99; if the **f** = .33 ($\eta^2 = .10$) faction is right, power is greater than .995. If either is correct, they are virtually certain to reject the null hypothesis at **a** = .01 with the **F** test.

In a circumstance like this, where there is "power to spare" (and assuming that the $\eta^2 = .05$ "pessimists" are not substantially overestimating the ES), there may be an opportunity to capitalize on these riches by enlarging on the experimental issues. For example, assume that there was a fourth microsocial system that had been a candidate for inclusion in the experiment and that adequate physical and staff resources are available for its inclusion. It might then be worth exploring the statistical power consequences of dividing the available 600 chronic patients into **k** = 4 equal groups. Assuming no change in the conditions, and for the same **f** values, interpolation in Table 8.3.3 (for **a** = .01, **k** − 1 = **u** = 3) shows that at **n** = 140 (150 is not tabulated), power at **f** = .23 is about .97 and at **f** = .33, power again exceeds .995. Thus, this experiment could be enlarged at no substantial loss in power, assuming **f** is not materially lower than .23. But note that if **f** is really .15, the original **k** = 3, **n** = 200 experiment has still creditable power of .79 (Table 8.3.2), but the power of the revised **k** = 4, **n** = 150 experiment is only about .63 (interpolating between **n** = 140 and 160 in Table 8.3.3).

8.3.2   CASE 1: **k** MEANS WITH UNEQUAL **n**. When the sample sizes (**n$_i$**) drawn up from the **k** populations whose means (**m$_i$**) are being compared are not all the same, no fundamental conceptual change occurs, but further attention to the definition of **f** is required and procedures for power analysis require accommodation from those of Case 0.

f was defined as the standard deviation of standardized means, σ_m/σ [formula (8.2.1)], where σ_m was given for equal **n** in formula (8.2.2) as

$$\sigma_m = \sqrt{\frac{\sum_{i=1}^{k}(m_i - m)^2}{k}} \ .$$

When **n**'s are not equal, it is no longer true that the reference point from which the "effects" are calculated, **m**, is a simple mean of the **k** population means, i.e., **m** $=\sum m_i/k$, but rather a *weighted* mean of these means, the weight of each **m$_i$** being **p$_i$**, the proportion of the total **N** $=\sum n_i$ which its sample **n$_i$** comprises. Thus, for Case 1

(8.3.1) $m = \dfrac{\sum n_i m_i}{N} = \sum p_i m_i \ .$

The **m** for equal **n** is a special case of this formula, where all the **p$_i$** = **n/N** = **n/kn** = **1/k**.

Similarly, in computing the standard deviations of the means, σ_m, the separate effects of the **k** populations, $m_i - m$, must be weighted by their proportionate sample sizes:

$$(8.3.2) \qquad \sigma_m = \sqrt{\frac{\sum_{i=1}^{k} n_i(m_i - m)^2}{N}} = \sqrt{\sum_{i=1}^{k} p_i(m_i - m)^2} \; .$$

Here, too, the formula given for σ_m for equal **n** in the previous section (8.2.2) is a special case of formula (8.3.2), where all $p_i = 1/k$.

Thus, with the understanding that for unequal **n** each population mean "counts" to the extent of the relative proportion of its sample size, no change in the definition of **f** is required; it is the standard deviation of the (weighted) standardized means.

The implication of this weighting requires comment. If the populations whose means are extreme, i.e., have large $(m_i - m)^2$, also have large **n**'s relative to the others, **f** will be larger than with equal **n**; conversely, if extreme populations have small **n**'s, **f** will be smaller, This suggests that in circumstances where the researcher has reason to believe that certain of the **k** populations will provide particularly discrepant means, dividing the total **N** unequally with larger sample **n**'s drawn from these populations will increase **f** (over equal **n**), and thereby increase power.

This statistical fact, however, cannot necessarily be taken as a mandate to so design experiments. Its utilization depends on whether the purpose of the research is solely to (*a*) test with a view to reject the null hypothesis of equal population means, or whether it (*b*) seeks to reflect a "natural" population state of affairs. When there is no "natural" population, as when the populations are of different experimental manipulations of randomly assigned subjects, as in a true experiment, we are perforce in situation (*a*). When a natural population exists, our purpose may be either (*a*) or (*b*).

An illustration should clarify the distinction. In an experiment where the effect on a dependent variable of three different experimental conditions is under scrutiny, each condition is a systematic artificial creation of the experimenter. The populations are hypothetical collections of results of a given condition being applied to all subjects. Consider, by way of contrast, a survey research designed to inquire into differences among Protestants, Catholics, and Jews in scores on a scale of attitude toward the United Nations (AUN). Here there are also three populations, but population membership is not an artificial creation of the manipulative efforts of the investigator. These are natural populations, and their properties as *populations* include their relative sizes in their combined superpopulation. There is now a choice with regard to how sampling is to proceed. The investigator can draw a random sample of **N** cases of the total population and administer the AUN scale to all **N** cases, then sort them into religious groups. The proportions in each religious group will then not be equal, but reflect (within sampling error) the relative sizes of the religious affiliation populations. Alternatively, having decided to study a total of **N** cases, he can draw *equal* samples from each religion.

Now, assume that the Jews yield a small **p**, and that their AUN population mean is quite extreme. In the former sampling plan, the **f**, based on the small weight given the Jews, would be smaller than the **f** obtained with equal sample sizes, where the mean of the Jews would be weighted equally with the others. The larger **f** would have associated with it a larger η^2 (as well as greater power). But if η^2 is to be interpreted as giving the proportion of AUN variance associated with religion in the general population, i.e., *in the natural population,* where there are relatively few Jews, it is the first sampling plan and the smaller η^2 which is appropriate. The η^2 from equal sampling would have to be interpreted as the proportion of AUN variance associated with (artificially) equiprobable religious group membership. The equal-sampling η^2 is not objectionable if the investigator wishes to consider membership in a given religious group as an abstract effect quite apart from the relative frequency with which that effect (i.e., that religious group) occurs in the population, but it clearly cannot be referred to the natural population with its varying group frequencies.

On the other hand, assume that the purpose of the investigator is solely to determine *whether* religious population means differ on AUN, i.e., to determine the status of the overall null hypothesis. Thus, no issue as to the interpretation of η^2 need arise. On this assumption, if his alternate hypothesis gives him confidence that the population mean of the Jews will be discrepant, he may advantageously oversample Jews by having their **n** equal (or even draw a *larger* sample of Jews than of the other groups) in order to make **f** larger (if his alternate hypothesis is valid), and thus increase his power.

As has already been implied, the weighting of the population means does not change the meaning of η^2 nor disturb its relationship to **f**. Thus, formulas (8.2.16)–(8.2.22) and Table 8.2.2 all obtain for Case 1. This is *not* the case for the translation between **f** and **d** measures of range in the various patterns detailed in Section 8.2.1 [formulas (8.2.5)–(8.2.15) and Table 8.2.1]. The assumption throughout that material is one of equal sample sizes, and it is clear that any given **d** value for some pattern of **k** means will lead to differing **f**'s depending upon how the varying $\mathbf{p_i}$ are assigned to the $\mathbf{m_i}$. The proposed conventions in regard to small, medium, and large **f** values continue to be applicable for Case 1 (except, of course, for their explication in terms of **d** values).

Finally, in Case 1, where there is no common **n** value to use in the power tables, one enters with their arithmetic mean:

$$(8.3.3) \qquad n = \frac{\sum_{i=1}^{k} n_i}{k} = \frac{N}{k}.$$

Aside from the use of the mean sample size, the procedure for the use of Table 8.3 is identical with that of Case 0.

Illustrative Examples

8.3 A university political science class has designed a poll to inquire into student opinion about the relative responsibilities and rights of local, state, and federal governments. An index score on centralism (CI) is derived and its relationship to various respondent characteristics is studied. One such characteristic is academic area, i.e., science, humanities, social science, etc., of which there are **k** = 6 in all. Data are available on a random sample of 300 respondents drawn from the university student roster. In considering the ES they anticipate, they note that, since they intend to generalize to the natural population of the college and are sampling accordingly, they will have unequal sample sizes and their conception of **f** must take into account the differential weighting of effects in the σ_m of formula (8.3.2). So computed, they posit **f** at .15. They note ruefully that they expect the greatest effects [departures from the grand weighted mean of formula (8.3.1)] to come from the smallest academic area samples, and that if they had sampled the academic areas equally, they could anticipate an **f** of .20. However, sampling academic areas equally would result in inequalities on the "breaks" of the data which are to be studied, e.g., sex, political party affiliation, ethnic background. In any case, their interest lies in the correlates of CI in the "natural" university population.

What is the power at **a** = .05 under the conditions which obtain, namely

$$\mathbf{a} = .05, \qquad \mathbf{u} = \mathbf{k} - 1 = 5, \qquad \mathbf{f} = .15, \qquad \mathbf{n} = \mathbf{N}/\mathbf{k} = 50.$$

Note that **n** is entered at the average sample size, 300/6 = 50. Table 8.3.16 (for **a** = .05, **u** = 5) for row **n** = 50, column **f** = .15, indicates that power = .48. Clearly, the *a priori* probability of the **F** test's rejecting the null hypothesis given under these conditions is not very high.

Assume that it is undesirable to increase **a** to .10 (which would increase power to .61—see Table 8.3.27) or to draw a larger sample; is there some other possible strategem to improve the prognosis for this significance test? The following might be acceptable: The division of the cases into as many as six academic areas might be reconsidered, given the partially arbitrary nature of such a partitioning. The class might discover that a somewhat less fine discrimination into three more broadly defined academic areas such as science, humanities–arts, and engineering might be acceptable. Assume that under these conditions **f** [still based on the σ_m of formula (8.3.1)] is again computed to be about .15. The revised plan has the conditions

$$\mathbf{a} = .05, \quad \mathbf{u} = 3 - 1 = 2, \quad \mathbf{f} = .15, \quad \mathbf{n} = 300/3 = 100.$$

In Table 8.3.13 for **a** = .05 and **u** = 2, **n** = 100, and **f** = .15, power = .64, a distinct improvement over the .48 value of the previous plan. If this process can, without doing violence to the issue, be carried a step further to a partitioning into two areas, and *if* the same **f** can be assumed, Table 8.3.12 (for **a** = .05, **u** = 1) gives power at **n** = 300/2 = 150 for **f** = .15 of about .74 (by linear interpolation). It must again be stressed that all this reasoning takes place without recourse to the data which are to be analyzed, i.e., we are in the area of planning the data analysis.

Thus, when there is some freedom available in the partitioning of a sample into groups, power considerations may advantageously enter into the decision. With **f** (and total **N**) constant, fewer groups and hence smaller **u** with larger **n** will result in increased power. Although **f** will not in general remain constant over changes in partitioning, this too may become a useful lever in planning analyses, since some partitions of the total sample will lead to larger anticipated **f** values, and hence greater power, than others. Therefore, when alternative partitions are possible, the investigator should seek the one whose combined effect on **u** and expected **f** is such as to maximize power.

8.4 As part of an inquiry into the differential effectiveness of psychiatric hospitals in a national system, an analysis is to be performed on the issue as to whether the psychiatric nurses in the various hospitals differ from hospital to hospital with regard to scores on an attitude scale of Social Restrictiveness (Cohen & Struening, 1963; 1964). There are **k** = 12 psychiatric hospitals of wide geographic distribution which have supplied quasi-random samples of their nursing personnel of varying sizes, depending upon administrative considerations and the size of their nursing staffs. The total **N** = 326, so that the average **n** per hospital is 326/12 = 27.2. The investigators anticipate that the ES of hospital on attitude is of medium size, i.e., that **f** = .25. They note that the **f** in question includes the differential weighting of the σ_m of formula (8.2.3), but since they have no reason to expect any relationship between the size of a hospital mean's discrepancy from the grand mean (i.e., the hospital's "effect") and the size of its sample, there is no need to modify the conception of a medium ES being operationalized by **f** = .25.

What is the power of the **F** test on means at **a** = .05? The conditions of the test, in summary, are

$$\mathbf{a} = .05, \quad \mathbf{u} = \mathbf{k} - 1 = 11, \quad \mathbf{f} = .25, \quad \mathbf{n} = 27.$$

There are no tables for **u** = 11, so that interpolation between Tables 8.3.19 (for **a** = .05, **u** = 10) and 8.3.20 (for **a** = .05, **u** = 12) is necessary. Table 8.3.19 for row **n** = 27 and column **f** = .25 yields power of .85. Table 8.3.20 for the same **n** and **f** gives power of .89. Linear interpolation between these values yields a power estimate of .87. Thus, given that the (weighted) standard deviation of the standardized means of the populations of nurses in these 12 hospitals is .25, the probability that **F** will meet the **a** = .05 criterion is .87, a value that would probably be deemed quite satisfactory.

8.3.3 CASE 2: FIXED MAIN EFFECTS IN FACTORIAL AND COMPLEX DESIGNS. an any experimental design of whatever structural complexity, a "fixed main effect" can be subjected to approximate power analysis with the aid of the tables of this chapter. In factorial, randomized blocks, split-plot, Latin square (etc.) designs, the **F** test on a fixed main effect involving **k** levels is a test of the equality of the **k** population means, whatever other fixed or random main or interaction effects may be included in the design (Winer, 1962; McNemar, 1962; Hays, 1963; Edwards, 1960). We will illustrate the principles involved in this extension by examining power analysis of a main effect in a fixed factorial design. Except for a minor complication due to denominator **df**, and some qualification in the interpretation of η^2, this test proceeds as in Cases 0 and 1 above.

Consider, for example, an **I** × **J** factorial design, where there are **i** = 3 levels of **I**, **j** = 4 levels of **J**, and each of the **ij** = 12 cells contains $\mathbf{n_c}$ = 10 observations. The structure of the analysis in the usual model which includes interaction is:

Effect	df
I	$\mathbf{u_I} = \mathbf{i} - 1 = 2$
J	$\mathbf{u_J} = \mathbf{j} - 1 = 3$
I × **J**	$\mathbf{u_{I \times J}} = (\mathbf{i} - 1)(\mathbf{j} - 1) = 6$
Within cell (error)	$\mathbf{ij}(\mathbf{n_c} - 1) = 12(9) = 108$
Total	$\mathbf{ijn_c} - 1 = 119$

Now, consider the null hypothesis for the **J** effect, i.e., that the 4 population means of $\mathbf{J_1}$ through $\mathbf{J_4}$ are equal. The 4 sample means for **J** are each computed on $\mathbf{n_j} = \mathbf{in_c} = 3(10) = 30$ observations. (Similarly, each of the 3 means for **I** is computed on $n_I = jn_c = 4(10) = 40$ observations.) The minor complication arises at the point where one wants to determine the power of the test on **J** by applying the appropriate $u_J = 3$ table at $n = n_J = 30$. This procedure is equivalent to ignoring the fact that the **I** main effect and **I** × **J** interaction exist in the design, i.e., a Case 0 test of 4 means, each of $n = 30$. But the latter test has for its **F**-ratio *denominator* (within cell, or error) **df**, $4(30 - 1) = 116$. More generally, the denominator **df** presumed in the calculation of the table entries is, for **k** means each of **n** cases, $k(n - 1) = (u + 1)(n - 1)$. Thus, in this case, the table's value is based on 3 and 116 **df**, while the **F** test to be performed is for 3 and 108**df**. Note that it is only the denominator **df** which are affected, and always in the direction of the factorial design main effect test having fewer **df** for its denominator than the table presumes. The result is that power read from the table in Case 2 applications is an overestimate.

Fortunately, two considerations operate to make the degree of over-estimation small in most factorial design applications in behavioral science. First, for any given **n** per mean and **u**, increasing denominator **df** bring rapidly diminishing returns in increased power beyond moderate **df**, say 40 or 50. Second, simple algebraic analysis of factorial designs of any size discloses that the increased denominator **df** spuriously "claimed" by the use of the tables is the number of cells less the number of levels of the effect studied; in the above illustration, $ij - j = 8\mathbf{df}$ (i.e., $116 - 108 = 8$). Thus, aside from the absolute size of the proper denominator **df**, if the spuriously claimed increment in **df** is absolutely small, the overestimate of power will similarly be small. Thus, in a 2 × 2 design, the denominator **df** presumed by the table is 2 larger than it should be in testing either effect; even with $n_c = 6$, the increased claim of 22**df** over the proper 20**df** will not result in a material overestimate. (Note that the entry value of $n = 12$ per mean is correctly stated.) In all, then, in either factorial designs with moderate or large error **df**, or factorial designs with few cells relative to **N**, the power read from the tables will only slightly (say $< .03$) overestimate power.[2]

What happens to the interpretation of **f** when the basis of classification **K** into **k** levels is present together with others, as it is in factorial design?

---

[2] If the reader is nervous about any overestimate of power and wishes a conservative underestimate, he can proceed as follows: For any main effect at **k** levels, compute

$$n' = \frac{\text{correct denominator } \mathbf{df}}{\mathbf{k}} + 1;$$

and use the proper power table (for $k - 1 = u$ numerator **df**) with the value for **n'** for **n**. This assures a correct statement of the denominator **df**, but underestimates the stability of the means and hence underestimates power to an extent typically greater than the extent of overestimation of the standard method in the text. This method, however, assures a guaranteed lower bound on the power estimate.

However complicated the factorial design, i.e., no matter how many other factors (**I**, **J**, etc.) and interactions (**K** × **I**, **K** × **J**, **K** × **I** × **J**, etc.) may be involved, the definition of **f** for the **k** means of **K** remains the same—the standard deviation of the **k** standardized means, where the standardization is by the common within (cell) population standard deviation [formulas (8.2.1) and (8.2.2)]. Thus, there is no need to adjust one's conception of **f** for a set of **k** means when one moves from the one-way analysis of variance (Cases 0 and 1) to the case where additional bases of partitioning of the data exist. Furthermore, the translation between **f** and the **d** measures considered in 7.2.1 is also not affected. It is, however, necessary to consider the interpretation of η^2 in Case 2.

In Section 8.2.2, η^2 was defined as the proportion of the total variance made up by the variance of the means [formula 8.2.18)]. The total variance, in turn, was simply the sum of the within-population variance and the variance of the means [formula (8.2.17)]. The framework of that exposition was the analysis of variance into two components, between-population means and within-population means. In factorial design, the total variance is made up not only of the within (cell) population variance and the variance of the means of the levels of the factor under study, but also the variances of the means of the other factor(s) and also of the interactions. Therefore, the variance base of η^2 of formula (8.2.18), namely $\sigma^2 + \sigma_m{}^2$, is no longer the total variance, and the formulas involving η and η^2 [(8.2.19), (8.2.20), (8.2.22)] and Table 8.2.2 require the reinterpretation of η as a *partial* correlation ratio, and η^2 as a proportion, not of the total variance, but of the total from which there has been excluded (partialed out) the variance due to the other factor(s) and interactions.

This can be made concrete by reference to the **I** × **J** (3 × 4) factorial illustration. Consider the four population means of the levels of **J** and assume their f_J is .30. Assume further that f_I is .50 and $f_{I \times J}$ is .20. When η^2 for **J** is computed from formula (8.2.19) (or looked up in Table 8.2.2):

$$\eta^2 = \frac{f^2}{1 + f^2} = \frac{.30^2}{1 + .30^2} = .0826,$$

the results for **J** clearly are not in the slightest affected by the size of the **I** or **I** × **J** effects. The η^2 for **J** in this design might be written in the conventional notation of partial correlation, with **Y** as the dependent variable under study, as $\eta^2_{YJ \cdot I, I \times J}$, i.e., the proportion of the **Y** variance associated with **J** population membership, when variance due to **I** and to **I** × **J** is excluded from consideration. Thus, given $f_J = .30$, the variance of the **J** means accounts for .0826 of the quantity made up of itself plus the within-cell population variance.

In higher order factorial designs, the η^2 computed from an **f** for a given source **J** might be represented as $\eta^2_{\mathbf{YJ}\cdot \text{all other}}$, the "all other" meaning all the other sources of total variance, main effects, and interactions. Each source's "size" may be assessed by such a partial PV. Because of their construction, however, they do not cumulate to a meaningful total.

The proposed operational definitions of small, medium, and large ES in terms of **f** have their usual meaning. When assessing power in testing the effects of the above **I** × **J** factorial, f_I and f_J (and also $f_{I \times J}$—see Section 8.3.4) can each be set quite independently of the others (because of their partial nature), by using the operational definitions or by whatever other means suit the investigator. They can, for example, be set by stating the alternative-hypothetical *cell* means and σ, and computing the resulting **f** values for all effects (illustrated in example 8.8 of the next section).

The scope of the present treatment precludes a detailed discussion of the power analysis of fixed effects in complex designs other than the factorial. Such analyses can be accomplished using the tables of this chapter if the following principles are kept in mind:

1. The basic ES index, **f**, represents the standard deviation of *standardized* means, the standardization being accomplished by division by the appropriate σ. We have seen that for fixed factorial designs, σ is the square root of the within *cell* population variance. In other designs, and more generally, σ is the square root of the variance being estimated by the denominator ("error") mean square of the **F** test which is to be performed. For example, in repeated measurements designs using multiple groups of subjects ("split plot" designs), there are at least two error terms, (*a*) a "subjects within groups" or between-subjects error, and (*b*) an interaction term involving subjects, or within-subject error. In the definition of **f** for any source (i.e., set of means), the standardization or scaling of the σ_m will come from either (*a*) or (*b*), depending on whether the source is a between or a within source, just as will their **F** ratio denominators (Winer, 1962).

2. Since the power values were computed on the presumption that the denominator **df** for any row of any power table equals $(u + 1)(n - 1)$, as it does in Cases 0 and 1, the investigator should check how this value relates to the actual denominator **df** of the proper **F** test for his design, to determine the relationship between the **df** of the tabled value and the true value. We noted above that main effect tests from factorial designs are overestimated by the procedure, although usually only slightly so. (In the next section, we will see that interaction tests by this procedure underestimate power.) As an example of large discrepancies in **df** between correct and table-assumed denominator **df**, consider the treatment effect of an unreplicated 5 × 5 Latin Square (Edwards, 1960, Chapter 15). Five treatment means, each of 5 observations, are to be compared. The power tables for $k - 1 = u = 4$

numerator **df** at **n** = 5 have values which are based on denominator **df** of $(u + 1)(n − 1) = (5)(4) = 20$. But the Latin square residual (error) mean square, which forms the denominator of the **F** ratio, is based on $(n − 1)(n − 2) = 12\mathbf{df}$. The tabled power value may then be a substantial overestimate. A Graeco-Latin Square of the same size would have actually only 8 error **df**, so the overestimate would generally be very great.

Illustrative Examples

8.5 An experimental psychologist has designed an experiment to investigate the effect of genetic strain (**I**) at **i** = 3 levels and conditions or irradiation (**J**) at **j** = 4 levels on maze learning in rats. He draws 24 animals randomly from a supply of each genetic strain and apportions each strain sample randomly and equally to the four conditions, so that his $3 \times 4 = 12$ cells each contain a maze score for each of $n_c = 6$ animals. He expects a medium ES for **I** and a large ES for **J** and following the operational definitions of Section 8.2.3, sets $f_I = .25$ and $f_J = .40$. Note that these values are standardized by the within cell populations and each of the main effects is independent of the other. (The question of the **I** × **J** interaction is considered in the next section under Case 3.) What is the power of these two main effect **F** tests at the **a** = .05 criterion?

For the test on the equality of the mean maze scores for the 3 strains (**I**), each mean is taken over $jn_c = 4(6) = 24$ animals. Thus, the specifications are:

$$a = .05, \quad u = i − 1 = 2, \quad f = .25, \quad n = 24.$$

Table 8.3.13 (**a** = .05, **u** = 2) at row **n** = 24 and column **f** = .25 indicates power of .45. (The degree of overestimation is slight: The tabulated value is based on $(u + 1)(n − 1) = 3(23) = 69$ denominator **df**, while the problem will have $ij(n_c − 1) = 60$. Also see footnote 2.) The chance of detecting a medium effect in strain differences under these specifications is not quite one in two.

For the test on the equality of means of the 4 irradiation conditions (**J**), each mean is taken over $in_c = 3(6) = 18$ animals. The specifications for the test on this main effect are

$$a = .05, \quad u = j − 1 = 3, \quad f = .40, \quad n = 18.$$

In Table 8.3.14, **a** = .05 and **u** = 3, at row **n** = 18, and column **f** = .40, he finds power = .80. (Again, this is a slight overestimate, the tabled value being based on $4(17) = 68$ denominator **df** with the correct value for the problem being 60.) The power value for the test on irradiation conditions

(**J**), given the large effect anticipated, is distinctly better than for strains (**I**); a probability of rejecting the null hypothesis of .80 means .80/.20 or four-to-one odds for rejection, under these conditions.

8.6   An experiment in developmental social psychology is designed to study the effect of sex of experimenter (**S** at **s** = 2 levels), age of subject (**A** at **a** = 3 levels), instruction conditions (**C**, at **c** = 4), and their interactions (which are considered in the next section) on the persuasibility of elementary school boys. A total **N** of 120 subjects is assigned randomly (within age groups and equally) to the $2 \times 3 \times 4 = 24$ cells of the design; thus, there are 5 cases in each cell. Expectations from theory and previous research lead the experimenter to posit, for each effect, the following ES for the three effects: $f_S = .10, f_A = .25$, and $f_C = .40$. (Note that these **f** values imply *partial* η^2, respectively, of .01, .06, and .14.) Using as a significance criterion **a** = .05, what is the power of each of the main effects **F** tests?

Note that this is a $2 \times 3 \times 4$ fixed factorial design, and that although we will not here consider the power testing of the four interaction effects (**S** × **A**, **S** × **C**, **A** × **C**, and **S** × **A** × **C**), they are part of the model (see Illustrative Example 8.7 in Section 8.3.4). The correct **df** for the denominator (within cell mean square) of all the **F** tests is thus $24(5 - 1) = 96$.

In testing the **S** effect, each of the two means for male and female experimenter is determined on $N/2 = 60$ observations. Thus, the specifications are

$$\mathbf{a} = .05, \quad \mathbf{u} = 2 - 1 = 1, \quad \mathbf{f} = .10, \quad \mathbf{n} = 60.$$

Table 8.3.12 for **a** = .05 and **u** = 1, at row **n** = 60, and column **f** = .10, indicates that power = .19. Although this value is based on $(\mathbf{u} + 1)(\mathbf{n} - 1) = 2(59) = 118$ denominator **df** instead of 96, the degree of overestimation is small. In any case, the probability of detecting **f** = .10 (a small effect) is poor.

Each of the three age groups means is determined on $N/3 = 40$ observations. The specifications for the determination of the power of the **F** test on the **A** main effect are

$$\mathbf{a} = .05, \quad \mathbf{u} = 3 - 1 = 2, \quad \mathbf{f} = .25, \quad \mathbf{n} = 40.$$

In Table 8.3.13 (**a** = .05 and **u** = 2), at row **n** = 40 and column **f** = .25, power = .68. This, too, is a slight overestimate (the table value presupposing denominator **df** of $3(39) = 117$, instead of the correct 96). Note that **f** = .25 defines a medium effect.

Finally, each of the 4 means of the test of **C** is based on $N/4 = 30$ cases. The specifications:

$$\mathbf{a} = .05, \quad \mathbf{u} = 4 - 1 = 3, \quad \mathbf{f} = .40, \quad \mathbf{n} = 30.$$

Table 8.3.14 at row **n** = 30, column **f** = .40 yields power of .96 (again a slight overestimate, since it is based on 4(29) = 116 denominator **df**). Under these conditions, the **b** (Type II) error (1 − power) is about the same as the **a** error, but note that a large effect has been posited.

In summary, and using the slightly overestimated tabled values, the experimenter has a poor (.19) expectation of detecting the small **S** effect, a moderately good (.68 or odds of 2:1) chance of detecting the **A** effect, and an excellent (.96) chance of finding a significant **C** effect, assuming his alternate hypotheses (i.e., his **f** values), **a** = .05, and **N** = 120. As an exercise, the reader may determine that changing the specifications to 6 cases per cell (**N** = 144), and leaving the other specifications unchanged, the tabled power values become .22 for **S**, .77 for **A**, and .97 for **C**. Note the inconsequential improvement this 20% increase in the size of the experiment has for the **S** and **C** effects, although bringing **A** from odds of 2:1 to odds of 3:1 might be worthwhile. Reaching significant power for **S** seems hopeless, but we have repeatedly seen that very large samples are required to obtain good power to detect small effects.

Example 8.7 in the next section provides power values for other specifications of **a** and **f** for this example and compares them with the power of interaction effects.

8.3.4   CASE 3: TESTS OF INTERACTIONS. A detailed exposition of interaction effects in experimental design is beyond the scope of this handbook; the reader is referred to one of the standard treatments (e.g., McNemar, 1962; Hays, 1963; Winer, 1962; Edwards, 1960). We assume throughout equal **n** in the cells of the factorial.

For our present purposes, we note that an **R** × **C** interaction can be understood in the following ways:

1. Differences in effects between two levels of **R**, say R_i and R_k (i, k = 1, 2, 3, . . . , r; i < k) with regard to differences in pairs of **C**, say $C_j − C_p$ (j, p = 1, 2, 3, . . . , c; j < p). More simply, a contribution to an **R** × **C** interaction would be a difference between two levels of **R** with regard to a difference between two levels of **C**. Thus, if in the population, the sex difference (males minus females) in conditioning to sound (C_j) is algebraically larger than the sex difference in conditioning to electric shock (C_p), a sex by conditioning stimulus (**R** × **C**) interaction would be said to exist. A first-order interaction (**R** × **C**) is equivalent to differences between differences; a second-order interaction (**R** × **C** × **H**) equivalent to differences between differences of differences; etc. (see example 8.8 below).

2. Equivalently, a first-order interaction (**R** × **C**) can be thought of as a residual effect after the separate main effects of **R** and **C** have been taken out or allowed for. Thus, after any systematic (averaged over

stimulus) sex difference in conditioning is allowed for, and any systematic (averaged over sex) difference in conditioning stimulus is also allowed for, if there remains any variation in the sex-stimulus cells, a sex by conditioning stimulus ($R \times C$) interaction would be said to exist. A second-order interaction ($R \times C \times H$) would be said to exist if there was residual variation after the R, C, H, $R \times C$, $R \times H$, and $C \times H$ effects were removed, etc.

3. A third equivalent conception of an $R \times C$ interaction implied by either of the above is simply that the effect of R varies from one level of C to another (and conversely). Thus, a nonzero sex by conditioning stimulus interaction means (and is meant by): The effect of a given stimulus (relative to others) varies between sexes or depends upon which sex is under consideration. This, in turn, means that there is a *joint* effect of sex and stimulus over and above any separate (main) effect of the two variables.

To index the size of an interaction, we use **f** defined in a way which is a generalization of the basic definition set forth in formula (8.2.1) and (8.2.2). First we return to the second conception of an $R \times C$ interaction above, where we spoke of a "residual effect" after the main effects of R and C have been taken out. Consider the cell defined by the ith level of R and the jth level of C, the ijth cell of the table, which contains in all **rc** cells. That cell's population mean is m_{ij}. Its value depends on (a) the main effect of R_i, i.e., $m_{i.} - m$, the departure of the population mean of level i of R, (b) the main effect of C_j, i.e., $m_{.j} - m$, the departure of the population mean of level j of C, (c) the value of m, and (d) the *interaction effect* for that cell, x_{ij}, the quantity in which we are particularly interested. Simple algebra leads to the following definition of x_{ij} in terms of the cell mean (m_{ij}), the main effect means $m_{i.}$, $m_{.j}$), and the total population mean (m):

(8.3.4) $$x_{ij} = m_{ij} - m_{i.} - m_{.j} + m.$$

When a cell has $x_{ij} = 0$, it has no interaction effect, i.e., its mean is accounted for by the R_i and C_j main effects and the total population mean. When all the **rc** cells have **x** values of zero, the $R \times C$ interaction is zero. Thus, the degree of *variability* of the **x** values about their (necessarily) zero mean is indicative of the size of the $R \times C$ interaction.

One cannot, however, compute their standard deviation as one does for a main effect (formula (8.2.2)]. The **x** values are constructed in such a way that they sum to zero in every row and column of the $R \times C$ table. This constraint on the degrees of freedom makes the appropriate divisor of the sum of the squares of **x** not **rc**, the number of **x** values (i.e., the number of cells), but the interaction $df + 1$. Thus, the (raw) variability measure of interaction effect analogous to σ_m of formula (8.2.2) is

$$(8.3.5) \qquad \sigma_x = \sqrt{\frac{\sum_1^{rc} x^2_{ij}}{(r-1)(c-1)+1}} \, ,$$

i.e., the square root of the sum over all cells of the squared **x** values divided by the interaction $df + 1$. This is, in fact, consistent with a generalization of formula (8.2.2) for σ_m, which can be read as the square root of the sum of the squared effects of a factor divided by that factor's $df + 1$, since the **k** of the denominator equals $u + 1$.

To obtain a standardized ES measure of interaction, we proceed as before to divide by σ, the within-cell population standard deviation, to obtain **f**:

$$(8.3.6) \qquad f = \frac{\sigma_x}{\sigma} \, .$$

The **f** for an interaction of formula (8.3.6) can be interpreted in the same way as throughout this chapter, as a measure of variability of (interaction) effects, whose mean is zero, standardized by the common within (cell) population standard deviation. Because it is the same measure, it can be understood:

1. in the framework which relates it to η and the proportion of variance of Section 8.2.2, as modified in terms of partial η for Case 2 in Section 8.3.3; or

2. By using the operational definitions of small, medium, and large **f** values of Section 8.2.3 (even though the discussion in these sections was particularized in terms of the variability of means, rather than of interaction effects); or

3. By writing the alternate-hypothetical cell means and computing the **x** values and σ_x and **f** by formulas (8.3.4)–(8.3.6). (This latter procedure is illustrated in example 8.8 below.)

For the sake of simplicity of exposition, the above discussion has been of **f** for a two-way (first-order) interaction. The generalization of **f** for higher-order interactions is fairly straightforward. For example, given a three-way interaction, $R \times C \times H$, with **R** at **r** levels, **C** at **c** levels, and **H** at **h** levels, there are now **rch** cells. Consider the cell defined by the **i**th level of **R**, the **j**th level of **C**, and the **k**th level of **H**. Its interaction effect is

$$x_{ijk} = m_{ijk} - m_i - m_j - m_k - x_{ij} - x_{ik} - x_{jk} + 2m,$$

where the x_{ij}, x_{ik}, and x_{jk} are the two-way interaction effects as defined in formula (8.3.4). Analogously to formula (8.3.5), the variability measure is

(8.3.7)
$$\sigma_x = \sqrt{\dfrac{\displaystyle\sum_{1=ijk}^{rch} x^2}{(r-1)(c-1)(h-1)+1}},$$

i.e., under the radical, the sum of the squared interaction effects over all **rch** cells, divided by the three-way interaction **df** + 1. Formula (8.3.6) then gives **f** for the three-way interaction.

In using the tables of this chapter for power analysis of interactions, the **n** for table entry is the sample size *in each cell* of the interaction in question. This is quite straightforward in an **R** × **C** design. In an **R** × **C** × **H** design, with **n** cases in each of the **rch** cells, the *triple* interaction **R** × **C** × **H** is a function of means based on **n** cases each, but the three two-way interactions are each functions of means where the third factor is "collapsed," and are thus based on more than **n** cases. For example, in an **R** × **C** × **H** of 3 × 4 × 5 levels with 6 cases in each of the 60 cells, the **n**'s to be used in the table for interactions are: $n_{R \times C} = 6(5) = 30$, $n_{R \times H} = 6(4) = 24$, $n_{C \times H} = 6(3) = 18$, but $n_{R \times C \times H} = 6$.

The degrees of freedom, **u**, are those for the interaction, $(r-1)(c-1)$ for a two-way interaction, $(r-1)(c-1)(h-1)$ for a triple interaction, etc.

As already noted, since the tables were computed on the premise of one-way tests (Cases 0 and 1), other uses do not lead to exact power values because the denominator **df** used in the computation of the tables values differs from the actual denominator **df** of the **F** test. We saw in main effect **F** tests in factorial design that the power values read from the tables are overestimated, although usually only slightly so. In contrast, tabled values for interaction tests are *under*estimated, again usually only slightly so. The reason for this is that the tabled values were computed for denominator **df** of $(u+1)(n-1)$. When used for an interaction test, the actual denominator **df** is actually larger: for example, in an **R** × **C** factorial at **r** and **c** levels, the actual denominator **df** is **rc** $(n-1)$, while the tabled value is for denominator **df** of $(u+1)(n-1)$, which, for the interaction **u** of $(r-1)(c-1)$, equals $[(r-1)(c-1)+1](n-1)$, a necessarily smaller value than $rc(n-1)$ when **r**, **c** are each at least 2. For example, in a 3 × 4 factorial with 8 cases per cell, the interaction **df** is $u = (3-1)(4-1) = 6$, and the actual denominator **df** is $(3)(4)(8-1) = 84$. When looked up in one of the three power tables for $u = 6$ at $n = 8$, the tabled power value is based on $(6+1)(8-1) = 49$**df**. Thus, there are actually more error **df** than were used to compute the tabled value. However, the degree of underestimation of power is inconsequential when $(u+1)(n-1)$ is large (say 40 or 50). Even when this quantity is small, the underestimation remains trivial when the number of cells is small (say no greater than 9).

Although generally overlooked by behavioral scientists, the power of tests of interactions in a factorial design is distinctly lower than that of the main effects for constant **f** and **a**. The reason for this lies in the fact that the **n** which governs the power of an **R** × **C** interaction test is the *cell* **n**, while the **n** for testing a main effect is a multiple of the cell **n** which depends on the number of levels of the other main effect(s), i.e., the number of observations on which the mean of each level of the main effect is found. Although **u**, the **df** for the numerator of the **F** test may be larger for the interaction (it cannot be smaller) than for the main effect, this does not compensate for the greater instability of the cell means. Further, this relative weakness of interaction tests progresses sharply with higher orders. This point will be illustrated in the examples.

In summary, power tests of fixed interaction effects proceed as follows: **u** is the **df** for the interaction and, together with the significance criterion **a**, determines the relevant power table. The table is applied to the ES posited in the form of **f**, which is set by using one or more of the methods detailed above, and **n**, the sample size of the relevant cells. The power read from the table is a (usually slightly) underestimated value. Linear interpolation between **f** values and between **u** values (tables) is adequate for most purposes.

Illustrative Examples

8.7 Reconsider the experiment described in example 8.6, an inquiry in developmental social psychology in which the factors were sex of experimenter (**S** at **s** = 2 levels), age of subject (**A** at **a** = 2 levels), and instruction conditions (**C** at **c** = 4 levels), i.e., a 2 × 3 × 4 factorial design, and the dependent variable a measure of persuasibility. There are **n** = 5 subjects in each of the 24 cells of the design, a total **N** of 120, and the **df** for within cells is 24(5 − 1) = 96. For convenience, we restate the specifications and resulting tabled power value for each of the main effect **F** tests:

> **S**:   **a** = .05,   **u** = 1,   **f** = .10,   **n** = 60;   power = .19.
> **A**:   **a** = .05,   **u** = 2,   **f** = .25,   **n** = 40;   power = .68.
> **C**:   **a** = .05,   **u** = 3,   **f** = .40,   **n** = 30;   power = .96.

Assume there is a particular interest in the sex of experimenter by age of subject (**S** × **A**) interaction, which is posited to be of medium size, i.e., **f** = .25, and the same significance criterion, **a** = .05, is to be used. Note that this interaction is based on a two-way table of means which results when the 4 levels of **C** are collapsed, leaving 2 × 3 = 6 cells. Thus, each of these cell means is based on $n_{S \times C} = N/6 = 20$. The **df** for this interaction is $u = (2-1)(3-1) = 2$. The specifications for the power of the **F** test of this interaction are thus

$$a = .05, \quad u = 2, \quad f = .25, \quad n_{S \times C} = 20.$$

In Table 8.3.13 ($a = .05$, $u = 2$) with row $n = 20$ and column $f = .25$, a power of .38 is found. This value is a slight underestimate because it is based on $(u+1)(n-1) = (2+1)(20-1) = 57$ denominator **df**, while the actual **df** for the denominator (within cells) is 96.

Power is poor here, despite the medium ES posited and a total **N** of 120, and, as was pointed out above, relatively poor power is the inevitable fate for tests of interactions. By way of contrast, note that the test of the **A** main effect, which was also for $f = .25$, $u = 2$, and $a = .05$, had a tabled power value of .68. The difference is that the operative **n** for the test of **A** was 40, while here it is 20.

The situation is even worse for the other two two-way interactions, **S** × **C** and **A** × **C**. Maintaining $f = .25$ for the sake of comparability, the specifications and resulting tabled power values are:

S × **C**: $a = .05$, $u = 3$, $f = .25$, $n_{S \times C} = 15$;

power (Table 8.3.14) = .32.

A × **C**: $a = .05$, $u = 6$, $f = .25$, $n_{A \times C} = 10$;

power (Tables 8.3.17) = .27.

This process reaches a crescendo of infirmity when we come to consider the power of the **F** test of the triple interaction, **S** × **A** × **C**. For the same specifications

$$a = .05, \quad u = (2-1)(3-1)(4-1) = 6, \quad f = .25, \quad n_{S \times A \times C} = 5,$$

power read from row $n = 5$, column $f = .25$ of Table 8.3.17 ($a = .05$, $u = 6$) is .13. Here, however, the underestimation of power is no longer trivial, since there are 24 cells and the denominator **df** for the tabled value, $(u+1)(n-1) = (6+1)(5-1) = 28$. This value is distinctly less than the 40–50 required when there are many cells to discount the underestimation of power as trivial. Even so, the underestimation is by no more than .05, and the power of the **F** test of this triple interaction is poor, indeed.

The relative weakness of tests of interactions is obviously a serious problem in research whose major purpose is the detection of interaction effects. The most obvious solution, increasing **n** per relevant cells, may be possible in some instances, but in many others would result in demands for experiments of a magnitude far beyond the resources of the experimenter. Another possibility worth considering is the reduction of the number of levels on one or more factors, thereby reducing the number of cells and increasing the **n** per relevant cell. Finally, in an effort to avoid doing **F** tests on interactions which are of low power and hence yield ambiguous negative results, one should consider setting less stringent significance criteria for interaction tests, e.g., **a** = .10 instead of .05. It may well be worth a larger Type I error risk to bring Type II error down to a tolerable level. The above stratagems should all be considered when the detection of interactions is important, and may, of course, be used in combination.

To help the reader get a feel for power of interaction tests as a function of **f**, **a**, and relevant cell **n**, tabled power values for all the interactions and main effects for this experiment are given below for the conventional **f** values for small, medium, and large ES, at **a** = ,01, .05, and .10. In addition, we give under **n** the effective **n** per relevant mean used in the table and under **df** the denominator **df** on which the tabled power values are based, which can be compared with the actual denominator **df** of 96. Since this example is not unrepresentative of factorial design applications in behavioral science, its careful study may prove rewarding. Recapitulating its structure, it is a three-way fixed factorial design, **S** × **A** × **C** (2 × 3 × 4) with 5 observations in each of its 24 cells.

Effect/a	f = .10			f = .25			f = .40			n	df
	.01	.05	.10	.01	.05	.10	.01	.05	.10		
S	06	19	30	56	79	87	96	99	*	60	118
A	05	15	25	44	68	79	92	98	99	40	117
C	04	13	22	36	61	73	88	96	98	30	116
S × A	02	09	17	17	38	52	55	78	87	20	57
S × C	02	08	16	13	32	45	46	71	82	15	56
A × C	02	08	14	10	27	40	40	66	74	10	63
S × A × C	01	06	12	04	13	23	12	31	45	5	28

* Power > .995.

8.8 A psychologist designs an experiment in which he will study the effects of age (**R**) at **r** = 2 levels, nature of contingency of reinforcement (**C**) at **c** = 4 levels, and their interaction (**R** × **C**) on a dependent learning variable. There are to be 12 subjects in each of the **rc** = 8 cells, and **a** = .05 throughout.

We will use this example to illustrate the direct specification of the alternate hypothesis and hence the ES. Assume that the area has been well studied and the psychologist has a "strong" theory, so that he can estimate the within-cell population standard deviation $\sigma = 8$, and further, he can state as an alternative to the overall null hypothesis specific hypothetical values for each of the eight cell's population means, the m_{ij}. The latter then imply the **R** means ($m_i.$), the **C** means ($m_{.j}$), and the grand mean **m**. They are as follows:

	C_1	C_2	C_3	C_4	$m_i.$
R_1	41	34	30	27	33
R_2	33	24	22	29	27
$m_{.j}$	37	29	26	28	$30 = m$

These values, in raw form, comprise his ES for the effects of **R**, **C**, and **R** × **C**. Their conversion to **f** values for the main effects is quite straightforward. Applying formula (8.2.2) for **R** and **C**,

$$\sigma_{m_R} = \sqrt{\frac{(33-30)^2 + (27-30)^2}{2}} = \sqrt{9} = 3.00,$$

and

$$\sigma_{m_C} = \sqrt{\frac{(37-30)^2 + (29-30)^2 + (26-30)^2 + (28-30)^2}{4}} = \sqrt{17.5} = 4.18.$$

When these are each standardized by dividing by the within-population $\sigma = 8$ [formula (8.2.1)], he finds

$$f_R = 3.00/8 = .38$$

and

$$f_C = 4.18/8 = .52.$$

For the **R** × **C** interaction ES, he finds the interaction effects for each cell using formula (8.3.4)

$$x_{ij} = m_{ij} - m_i. - m_{.j} + m.$$

Thus,

$$x_{11} = 41 - 33 - 37 + 30 = +1$$

$$x_{12} = 34 - 33 - 29 + 30 = +2$$

$$\vdots \quad \vdots \quad \vdots \quad \vdots \quad \vdots \quad \vdots$$

$$x_{24} = 29 - 27 - 28 + 30 = +4$$

These x_{ij} values for the 2×4 tables of means are

	C_1	C_2	C_3	C_4
R_1	+1	+2	+1	−4
R_2	−1	−2	−1	+4

Note that they are so defined that they must sum to zero in every row and column; these constraints are what result in the **df** for the $R \times C$ interaction being $u = (r − 1)(c − 1)$; in this case, $u = 3$.

Applying formula (8.3.7) to these values,

$$\sigma_x = \sqrt{\frac{\sum x^2_{ij}}{(r − 1)(c − 1) + 1}} = \sqrt{\frac{(+1)^2 + (+2)^2 + (+1)^2 + \cdots + (+4)^2}{3 + 1}}$$

$$= \sqrt{\frac{44}{4}} = 3.32.$$

Standardizing to find **f** [formula (8.3.6)],

$$f_{R \times C} = \sigma_x / \sigma = 3.32/8 = .42.$$

Thus, his alternative-hypothetical cell population means, together with an estimate of σ, have provided an **f** for the $R \times C$ effect (as well as for the main effects).

One of the ways in which to understand interactions, described in the introduction to this section, was as differences among differences. This is readily illustrated for this problem. Return to the cell means and consider such quantities as $m_{1j} − m_{2j}$, i.e., the difference (with sign) between the means of A_1 and A_2 for each level of C. They are, respectively, $(41 − 33 =) +8$, $(34 − 24 =) +10$, $+8$, and $−2$. Were these four values $(+8, +10, +8,$ and $−2)$ all equal, there would be zero interaction. Calling these values D_j and their mean $\bar{D}$ (here $+6$) for simplicity, σ_x can be found for a $2 \times c$ table by

(8.3.8)

$$\sigma_x = \sqrt{\frac{\sum_{j=1}^{c} (D_j − \bar{D})^2}{2c}} = \sqrt{\frac{(+8 − 6)^2 + (+10 − 6)^2 + (+8 − 6)^2 + (−2 − 6)^2}{2(4)}}$$

$$= \sqrt{\frac{88}{8}} = 3.32,$$

as before.

Returning to the determination of the power of the test on the $\mathbf{R} \times \mathbf{C}$ interaction, we summarize the specifications for this test:

$$\mathbf{a} = .05, \qquad \mathbf{u} = (\mathbf{r} - 1)(\mathbf{c} - 1) = 3, \qquad \mathbf{f}_{\mathbf{R} \times \mathbf{C}} = .42, \qquad \mathbf{n} = 12.$$

In Table 8.3.14 (for $\mathbf{a} = .05$, $\mathbf{u} = 3$) at row $\mathbf{n} = 12$, we find power at $\mathbf{f} = .40$ to be .60 and at $\mathbf{f} = .50$, .81. Linear interpolation for $\mathbf{f} = .42$ gives the approximate power value of .64. (We dutifully note that this value is an underestimate, since it is for denominator $\mathbf{df}$ of $(\mathbf{u} + 1)(\mathbf{n} - 1) = (4)(11) = 44$, while the problem's denominator $\mathbf{df}$ will be $\mathbf{rc}(\mathbf{n} - 1) = 88$, but the degree of underestimation is small.)

The power of the $\mathbf{R} \times \mathbf{C}$ interaction $\mathbf{F}$ test is about .64, while for the main effects:

$\mathbf{R}$: $\mathbf{a} = .05$, $\mathbf{u} = \mathbf{r} - 1 = 1$, $\mathbf{f}_{\mathbf{R}} = .38$, $\mathbf{n} = 48$,   power $= .95$,

$\mathbf{C}$: $\mathbf{a} = .05$, $\mathbf{u} = \mathbf{c} - 1 = 3$, $\mathbf{f}_{\mathbf{C}} = .52$, $\mathbf{n} = 24$,   power $= .99$.

We note again the relative infirmity of the interaction test.

8.3.5   THE ANALYSIS OF COVARIANCE. With a simple conceptual adjustment of frame of reference, all the previous material in this chapter can be applied to power analysis in the analysis of covariance.

In the analysis of covariance, each member of the population has, in addition to a value $\mathbf{Y}$ (the variable of interest or dependent variable) a value on another variable, $\mathbf{X}$, called the concomitant or adjusting variable, or covariate. A covariance design is a procedure for statistically controlling for $\mathbf{X}$ by means of a regression adjustment so that one can study $\mathbf{Y}$, freed of that portion of its variance linearly associated with $\mathbf{X}$. In addition to the assumptions of the analysis of variance, the method of covariance adjustment also assumes that the regression coefficients in the separate populations are equal. Detailed discussion of the analysis of covariance is beyond the scope of this treatment; the reader is referred to one of the standard texts: McNemar (1962), Blalock (1960), Walker & Lev (1953), Winer (1962).

Instead of analyzing $\mathbf{Y}$, the analysis of covariance analyzes $\mathbf{Y}'$, a regression-adjusted or statistically controlled value, which is

$$(8.3.9) \qquad \mathbf{Y}' = \mathbf{Y} - \mathbf{b}(\mathbf{X} - \overline{\mathbf{X}}),$$

where $\mathbf{b}$ is the (common) regression coefficient of $\mathbf{Y}$ on $\mathbf{X}$ in each of the populations and $\overline{\mathbf{X}}$ is the grand population mean of the concomitant variable. $\mathbf{Y}'$ is also called a residual, since it is the departure of the $\mathbf{Y}$ value from the $\mathbf{Y}\mathbf{X}$ regression line common to the various populations.

The analysis of covariance is essentially the analysis of variance of the $\mathbf{Y}'$ measures. Given this, if one reinterprets the preceding material in this chapter as referring to means and variances of the adjusted or residual $\mathbf{Y}'$ values, it is all applicable to the analysis of covariance.

For example, the basic formula for **f** (8.2.1) is σ_m/σ. For covariance analysis, σ_m is the standard deviation of the **k** population's *adjusted* means of **Y'**, that is, **m'**, and σ is the (common) standard deviation of the **Y'** values within the populations. The **d** measure of Section 8.2.1 is the difference between the largest and smallest of the **k** *adjusted* means divided by the within-population standard deviation of the **Y'** values. The use and interpretation of η^2 as a proportion of variance and η as a correlation ratio now refers to **Y'**, the dependent variable **Y** freed from that portion of its variance linearly associated with **X**. And so on.

An academic point: In the analysis of covariance, the denominator **df** is reduced by one (due to the estimation of the regression coefficient **b**). This discrepancy from the denominator **df** on which the tabled power values are based is of no practical consequence whatever in usual applications, say when $(u + 1)(n - 1)$ is as large as 15 or 20.

The analysis of covariance can proceed with multiple adjusting variates $\mathbf{X_i}$ ($i = 1, 2, \ldots, p$) as readily, in principle, as with one. The adjustment proceeds by multiple linear regression, so that

$$(8.3.10) \quad \mathbf{Y'} = \mathbf{Y} - \mathbf{b_1}(\mathbf{X_1} - \bar{\mathbf{X}}_1) - \mathbf{b_2}(\mathbf{X_2} - \bar{\mathbf{X}}_2) - \cdots - \mathbf{b_p}(\mathbf{X_p} - \bar{\mathbf{X}}_p).$$

Whether **Y'** comes about from one or several adjusting variables, it remains conceptually the same. The loss in denominator **df** is now **p** instead of 1, but unless **p** is large and **N** is small (say less than 40), the resulting overestimation of the tabled power values is not material.

The procedural emphasis should not be permitted to obscure the fact that the analysis of covariance designs when appropriately used yield greater power, in general, than analogous analysis of variance designs. This is fundamentally because the within-population σ of the *adjusted* **Y'** variable will be smaller than σ of the unadjusted **Y** variable. Specifically, where **r** is the population coefficient between **X** and **Y**, $\sigma_y' = \sigma_y\sqrt{1 - r^2}$. Since σ is the denominator of **f** [formula (8.2.1)] and since the numerator undergoes no such systematic change (it may, indeed, increase), the *effective* **f** in an analysis of covariance will be larger than **f** in the analysis of variance of **Y**. This is true, of course, only for the proper use of the analysis of covariance, for discussion of which the reader is referred to the references cited above.

No illustrative examples are offered here because all of the eight examples which precede can be reconsidered in a covariance framework by merely assuming for each the existence of one or more relevant covariates. Each problem then proceeds with adjusted (**Y'**) values in place of the unadjusted (**Y**) values in which they are couched.

8.4 SAMPLE SIZE TABLES

The sample size tables for this section are given on pages 374–382; the text follows on page 383.

Table 8.4.1

n to detect f by F test at a = .01
for u = 1, 2, 3, 4

u = 1
f

Power	.05	.10	.15	.20	.25	.30	.35	.40	.50	.60	.70	.80
.10	336	85	39	22	15	11	9	7	5	4	4	3
.50	1329	333	149	85	55	39	29	22	15	11	9	7
.70	1924	482	215	122	79	55	41	32	21	15	12	9
.80	2338	586	259	148	95	67	49	38	25	18	14	11
.90	2978	746	332	188	120	84	62	48	31	22	17	13
.95	3564	892	398	224	144	101	74	57	37	26	20	16
.99	4808	1203	536	302	194	136	100	77	50	35	26	21

u = 2
f

Power	.05	.10	.15	.20	.25	.30	.35	.40	.50	.60	.70	.80
.10	307	79	36	21	14	10	8	6	5	4	3	3
.50	1093	275	123	70	45	32	24	19	13	9	7	6
.70	1543	387	173	98	63	44	33	26	17	12	10	8
.80	1851	464	207	117	76	53	39	30	20	14	11	9
.90	2325	582	260	147	95	66	49	38	25	18	14	11
.95	2756	690	308	174	112	78	58	45	29	21	16	12
.99	3658	916	408	230	148	103	76	59	38	27	20	16

u = 3
f

Power	.05	.10	.15	.20	.25	.30	.35	.40	.50	.60	.70	.80
.10	278	71	32	19	13	9	7	6	4	3	3	2
.50	933	234	105	59	38	27	20	16	11	8	6	5
.70	1299	326	146	83	53	37	28	22	14	10	8	7
.80	1548	388	175	98	63	44	33	25	17	12	9	8
.90	1927	483	215	122	78	55	41	31	21	15	11	9
.95	2270	568	253	143	92	64	48	37	24	17	13	10
.99	2986	747	333	188	121	84	62	48	31	22	17	13

u = 4
f

Power	.05	.10	.15	.20	.25	.30	.35	.40	.50	.60	.70	.80
.10	253	64	29	17	12	8	7	5	4	3	3	2
.50	820	206	92	52	34	24	18	14	10	7	6	5
.70	1128	283	127	72	46	33	24	19	13	9	7	6
.80	1341	336	150	85	55	38	29	22	15	11	8	7
.90	1661	416	186	105	68	47	35	27	18	13	10	8
.95	1948	488	218	123	79	55	41	32	21	15	11	9
.99	2546	640	286	160	103	76	53	41	27	19	14	11

Table 8.4.2

n to detect f by F test at a = .01
for u = 5, 6, 8, 10

| | | | | | u = 5 f | | | | | | |
Power	.05	.10	.15	.20	.25	.30	.35	.40	.50	.60	.70	.80
.10	233	59	27	16	11	8	6	5	4	3	2	2
.50	737	185	82	47	30	22	16	13	9	6	5	4
.70	1009	253	113	64	41	29	22	17	11	8	6	5
.80	1193	299	134	76	49	34	26	20	13	10	7	6
.90	1469	368	164	93	60	42	31	24	16	12	9	7
.95	1719	431	192	109	70	49	36	28	18	13	10	8
.99	2235	560	249	141	91	63	47	36	24	17	13	10

| | | | | | u = 6 f | | | | | | |
Power	.05	.10	.15	.20	.25	.30	.35	.40	.50	.60	.70	.80
.10	218	55	25	15	10	7	6	5	3	3	2	2
.50	673	169	76	43	28	20	15	12	8	6	5	4
.70	917	230	103	58	38	27	20	15	10	8	6	5
.80	1080	271	121	68	44	31	23	18	12	9	7	6
.90	1326	332	148	84	54	38	28	22	14	10	8	6
.95	1547	388	173	98	63	44	33	25	17	12	9	7
.99	2003	502	224	126	81	57	42	33	21	15	11	9

| | | | | | u = 8 f | | | | | | |
Power	.05	.10	.15	.20	.25	.30	.35	.40	.50	.60	.70	.80
.10	194	49	23	13	9	6	5	4	3	3	2	2
.50	580	146	65	37	24	17	13	10	7	5	4	3
.70	785	197	88	50	32	23	17	13	9	7	5	4
.80	918	230	103	58	38	27	20	15	10	8	6	5
.90	1122	281	126	71	46	32	24	19	12	9	7	6
.95	1303	327	146	83	53	37	28	22	14	10	8	6
.99	1676	420	187	106	68	48	36	27	18	13	10	8

| | | | | | u = 10 f | | | | | | |
Power	.05	.10	.15	.20	.25	.30	.35	.40	.50	.60	.70	.80
.10	176	45	21	12	8	6	5	4	3	2	2	2
.50	515	129	58	33	21	15	12	9	6	5	4	3
.70	691	173	78	44	29	20	15	12	8	6	5	4
.80	810	203	91	51	33	23	18	14	9	7	5	4
.90	982	246	110	62	40	28	21	16	11	8	6	5
.95	1138	285	127	72	47	33	24	19	12	9	7	6
.99	1456	365	163	92	60	42	31	24	16	11	9	7

Table 8.4.3

n to detect f by F test at a = .01
for u = 12, 15, 24

					u = 12							
					f							
Power	.05	.10	.15	.20	.25	.30	.35	.40	.50	.60	.70	.80
.10	162	41	19	11	8	5	4	4	3	2	2	2
.50	467	117	53	30	20	14	10	8	6	4	3	3
.70	623	157	70	40	26	18	14	11	7	5	4	3
.80	726	182	82	46	30	21	16	12	8	6	5	4
.90	881	221	99	56	36	25	19	15	10	7	6	5
.95	1017	255	114	65	42	29	22	17	11	8	6	5
.99	1297	325	145	83	53	37	28	21	14	10	8	6

					u = 15							
					f							
Power	.05	.10	.15	.20	.25	.30	.35	.40	.50	.60	.70	.80
.10	147	37	17	10	7	5	4	3	2	2	2	--
.50	413	104	47	27	17	12	9	7	5	4	3	3
.70	548	138	62	35	23	16	12	10	6	5	4	3
.80	632	159	71	41	26	19	14	11	7	5	4	4
.90	769	193	86	49	32	22	17	13	9	6	5	4
.95	885	222	99	56	36	26	19	15	10	7	6	4
.99	1125	282	126	72	46	32	24	19	12	9	7	5

					u = 24							
					f							
Power	.05	.10	.15	.20	.25	.30	.35	.40	.50	.60	.70	.80
.10	118	30	14	8	6	4	3	3	2	2	--	--
.50	318	80	36	21	14	10	7	6	4	3	3	2
.70	417	105	47	27	17	12	9	7	5	4	3	3
.80	485	121	55	31	20	15	11	8	6	4	3	3
.90	578	145	65	37	24	17	13	10	7	5	4	3
.95	662	166	74	42	27	19	14	11	8	6	4	4
.99	831	209	92	53	34	24	18	14	9	7	5	4

Table 8.4.4

n to detect f by F test at a = .05
for u = 1, 2, 3, 4

u = 1
f

Power	.05	.10	.15	.20	.25	.30	.35	.40	.50	.60	.70	.80
.10	84	22	10	6	5	4	3	3	2	--	--	--
.50	769	193	86	49	32	22	17	13	9	7	5	4
.70	1235	310	138	78	50	35	26	20	13	10	7	6
.80	1571	393	175	99	64	45	33	26	17	12	9	7
.90	2102	526	234	132	85	59	44	34	22	16	12	9
.95	2600	651	290	163	105	73	54	42	27	19	14	11
.99	3675	920	409	231	148	103	76	58	38	27	20	15

u = 2
f

Power	.05	.10	.15	.20	.25	.30	.35	.40	.50	.60	.70	.80
.10	84	22	10	6	5	4	3	3	2	--	--	--
.50	662	166	74	42	27	19	15	11	8	6	5	4
.70	1028	258	115	65	42	29	22	17	11	8	6	5
.80	1286	322	144	81	52	36	27	21	14	10	8	6
.90	1682	421	188	106	68	48	35	27	18	13	10	8
.95	2060	515	230	130	83	58	43	33	22	15	12	9
.99	2855	714	318	179	115	80	59	46	29	21	16	12

u = 3
f

Power	.05	.10	.15	.20	.25	.30	.35	.40	.50	.60	.70	.80
.10	79	21	10	6	4	3	3	2	2	--	--	--
.50	577	145	65	37	24	16	13	10	7	5	4	3
.70	881	221	99	56	36	25	19	15	10	7	6	5
.80	1096	274	123	69	45	31	23	18	12	9	7	5
.90	1415	354	158	89	58	40	30	23	15	11	8	7
.95	1718	430	192	108	70	49	36	28	18	13	10	8
.99	2353	589	262	148	95	66	49	38	24	17	13	10

u = 4
f

Power	.05	.10	.15	.20	.25	.30	.35	.40	.50	.60	.70	.80
.10	74	19	9	6	4	3	2	2	--	--	--	--
.50	514	129	58	33	21	15	11	9	6	5	4	3
.70	776	195	87	49	32	22	17	13	9	6	5	4
.80	956	240	107	61	39	27	20	16	10	8	6	5
.90	1231	309	138	78	50	35	26	20	13	10	7	6
.95	1486	372	166	94	60	42	31	24	16	11	9	7
.99	2021	506	225	127	82	57	42	33	21	15	11	9

Table 8.4.5

n to detect f by F test at a = .05
for u = 5, 6, 8, 10

					u = 5							
					f							
Power	.05	.10	.15	.20	.25	.30	.35	.40	.50	.60	.70	.80
.10	69	18	9	5	4	3	2	2	--	--	--	--
.50	467	117	53	30	19	14	10	8	6	4	3	3
.70	698	175	78	44	29	20	15	12	8	6	5	4
.80	856	215	96	54	35	25	18	14	9	7	5	4
.90	1098	275	123	69	45	31	23	18	12	9	7	5
.95	1320	331	148	83	54	38	28	22	14	10	8	6
.99	1783	447	199	112	72	50	37	29	19	13	10	8

					u = 6							
					f							
Power	.05	.10	.15	.20	.25	.30	.35	.40	.50	.60	.70	.80
.10	66	17	8	5	4	3	2	2	--	--	--	--
.50	429	108	49	28	18	13	10	8	5	4	3	3
.70	638	160	72	41	26	18	14	11	7	5	4	4
.80	780	195	87	50	32	22	17	13	9	6	5	4
.90	995	250	112	63	41	29	21	16	11	8	6	5
.95	1192	299	133	75	49	34	25	20	13	9	7	6
.99	1604	402	179	101	65	46	34	26	17	12	9	7

					u = 8							
					f							
Power	.05	.10	.15	.20	.25	.30	.35	.40	.50	.60	.70	.80
.10	60	16	7	5	3	2	2	--	--	--	--	--
.50	374	94	42	24	16	11	8	7	5	4	3	2
.70	548	138	61	35	23	16	12	9	6	5	4	3
.80	669	168	75	42	27	19	14	11	8	6	4	4
.90	848	213	95	54	35	24	18	14	9	7	5	4
.95	1012	254	113	64	41	29	22	17	11	8	6	5
.99	1351	338	151	86	55	39	29	22	14	10	8	6

					u = 10							
					f							
Power	.05	.10	.15	.20	.25	.30	.35	.40	.50	.60	.70	.80
.10	55	14	7	4	3	2	2	--	--	--	--	--
.50	335	84	38	21	14	10	8	6	4	3	3	2
.70	488	123	55	31	20	14	11	8	6	4	3	3
.80	591	148	66	38	24	17	13	10	7	5	4	3
.90	747	187	84	48	31	22	16	13	8	6	5	4
.95	888	223	99	56	36	26	19	15	10	7	5	4
.99	1177	295	132	75	48	34	25	19	13	9	7	6

Table 8.4.6

n to detect f by F test at a = .05
for u = 12, 15, 24

| | u = 12 | | | | | | | | | | |
| | f | | | | | | | | | | |
Power	.05	.10	.15	.20	.25	.30	.35	.40	.50	.60	.70	.80
.10	51	13	7	4	3	2	2	--	--	--	--	--
.50	306	77	35	20	13	9	7	6	4	3	3	2
.70	443	111	50	28	18	13	10	8	5	4	3	3
.80	534	134	60	34	22	16	12	9	6	5	4	3
.90	673	169	75	43	28	20	15	11	8	6	4	4
.95	796	200	89	51	33	23	17	13	9	6	5	4
.99	1052	264	118	67	43	30	22	17	11	8	6	5

| | u = 15 | | | | | | | | | | |
| | f | | | | | | | | | | |
Power	.05	.10	.15	.20	.25	.30	.35	.40	.50	.60	.70	.80
.10	47	12	6	4	3	2	---	--	--	--	--	--
.50	272	69	31	18	12	8	6	5	4	3	2	2
.70	391	98	44	25	16	12	9	7	5	4	3	2
.80	471	118	53	30	20	14	10	8	6	4	3	3
.90	588	148	66	38	24	17	13	10	7	5	4	3
.95	697	175	78	44	29	20	15	12	8	6	4	4
.99	915	229	102	58	38	26	20	15	10	7	6	4

| | u = 24 | | | | | | | | | | |
| | f | | | | | | | | | | |
Power	.05	.10	.15	.20	.25	.30	.35	.40	.50	.60	.70	.80
.10	38	10	5	3	2	---	---	--	--	--	--	--
.50	213	54	24	14	9	7	5	4	3	2	2	--
.70	303	76	34	20	13	9	7	5	4	3	2	2
.80	363	91	41	23	15	11	8	6	4	3	3	2
.90	457	115	51	29	19	13	10	8	5	4	3	3
.95	525	132	59	34	22	15	11	9	6	4	4	3
.99	680	171	76	44	28	20	15	11	8	6	4	4

Table 8.4.7

n to detect f by F test at a = .10
for u = 1, 2, 3, 4

					$u = 1$							
					f							
Power	.05	.10	.15	.20	.25	.30	.35	.40	.50	.60	.70	.80
.50	542	136	61	35	22	16	12	9	6	5	4	3
.70	942	236	105	60	38	27	20	15	10	7	6	5
.80	1237	310	138	78	50	35	26	20	13	9	7	6
.90	1713	429	191	108	69	48	36	27	18	13	10	8
.95	2165	542	241	136	87	61	45	35	22	16	12	9
.99	3155	789	351	198	127	88	65	50	32	23	17	13

					$u = 2$							
					f							
Power	.05	.10	.15	.20	.25	.30	.35	.40	.50	.60	.70	.80
.50	475	119	53	30	20	14	11	8	6	4	3	3
.70	797	200	89	50	32	23	17	13	9	6	5	4
.80	1029	258	115	65	41	29	22	17	11	8	6	5
.90	1395	349	156	88	57	40	29	23	15	11	8	6
.95	1738	435	194	109	70	49	36	28	18	13	10	8
.99	2475	619	276	155	100	70	51	33	21	15	11	9

					$u = 3$							
					f							
Power	.05	.10	.15	.20	.25	.30	.35	.40	.50	.60	.70	.80
.50	419	105	47	27	18	12	9	7	5	4	3	3
.70	690	173	77	43	28	20	15	11	8	6	4	4
.80	883	221	99	56	36	25	19	15	10	7	5	4
.90	1180	296	132	74	48	34	25	19	13	9	7	5
.95	1458	365	163	92	59	41	30	24	15	11	8	7
.99	2051	513	229	129	83	58	43	33	21	15	11	9

					$u = 4$							
					f							
Power	.05	.10	.15	.20	.25	.30	.35	.40	.50	.60	.70	.80
.50	376	95	43	24	16	11	9	7	5	4	3	3
.70	612	154	68	38	25	18	13	10	7	5	4	3
.80	773	193	87	49	32	22	17	13	9	6	5	4
.90	1031	258	115	65	42	29	22	17	11	8	6	5
.95	1267	317	141	80	51	36	27	21	13	10	7	6
.99	1768	443	197	111	71	50	37	28	19	13	10	8

Table 8.4.8

n to detect f by F test at a = .10
for u = 5, 6, 8, 10

u = 5

Power	.05	.10	.15	.20	.25	.30	.35	.40	.50	.60	.70	.80
.50	343	86	39	22	14	10	8	6	4	3	3	2
.70	551	139	61	35	23	16	12	9	6	5	4	3
.80	693	174	77	44	28	20	15	12	8	6	4	4
.90	922	231	103.	58	37	26	20	15	10	7	6	4
.95	1128	283	126	71	46	32	24	18	12	9	7	5
.99	1564	392	175	98	63	44	33	25	16	12	9	7

u = 6

Power	.05	.10	.15	.20	.25	.30	.35	.40	.50	.60	.70	.80
.50	317	80	36	20	13	9	7	6	4	3	3	2
.70	506	127	57	32	21	15	11	9	6	4	3	3
.80	635	159	71	40	26	18	14	11	7	5	4	3
.90	838	210	94	53	34	24	18	14	9	7	5	4
.95	1022	256	114	65	42	29	22	17	11	8	6	5
.99	1408	353	157	89	57	40	30	23	15	11	8	6

u = 8

Power	.05	.10	.15	.20	.25	.30	.35	.40	.50	.60	.70	.80
.50	278	70	32	18	12	9	6	5	4	3	2	2
.70	436	110	49	28	18	13	10	8	5	4	3	3
.80	545	137	61	35	23	16	12	9	6	5	4	3
.90	717	180	80	46	29	21	15	12	8	6	4	4
.95	870	218	97	55	36	25	19	14	9	7	5	4
.99	1190	298	133	75	49	34	25	19	13	9	7	5

u = 10

Power	.05	.10	.15	.20	.25	.30	.35	.40	.50	.60	.70	.80
.50	250	63	28	16	11	8	6	5	3	3	2	2
.70	390	98	44	25	16	11	9	7	5	4	3	2
.80	482	121	54	31	20	14	11	8	6	4	3	3
.90	633	159	71	40	26	18	14	11	7	5	4	3
.95	765	192	86	49	31	22	16	13	8	6	5	4
.99	1040	261	116	66	42	30	22	17	11	8	6	5

Table 8.4.9

n to detect f by F test at a = .10
for u = 12, 15, 24

| | | | | | u = 12 | | | | | | | |
| | | | | | f | | | | | | | |
Power	.05	.10	.15	.20	.25	.30	.35	.40	.50	.60	.70	.80
.50	229	58	26	15	10	7	5	4	3	2	2	2
.70	355	89	40	23	15	11	8	6	4	3	3	2
.80	437	110	49	28	18	13	10	8	5	4	3	3
.90	571	143	64	36	24	17	12	10	6	5	4	3
.95	688	173	77	44	28	20	15	11	8	5	4	4
.99	931	233	104	59	38	27	20	15	10	7	5	4

| | | | | | u = 15 | | | | | | | |
| | | | | | f | | | | | | | |
Power	.05	.10	.15	.20	.25	.30	.35	.40	.50	.60	.70	.80
.50	205	52	23	13	9	6	5	4	3	2	2	2
.70	315	79	35	20	13	9	7	6	4	3	2	2
.80	386	97	43	25	16	12	9	7	5	4	3	2
.90	502	126	56	32	21	15	11	9	6	4	3	3
.95	603	151	68	38	25	17	13	10	7	5	4	3
.99	812	203	91	51	33	23	17	13	9	6	5	4

| | | | | | u = 24 | | | | | | | |
| | | | | | f | | | | | | | |
Power	.05	.10	.15	.20	.25	.30	.35	.40	.50	.60	.70	.80
.50	161	41	18	11	7	5	4	3	2	2	--	--
.70	246	62	27	16	10	7	6	5	3	2	2	2
.80	298	75	34	19	12	9	7	5	4	3	2	2
.90	382	96	43	25	16	11	8	7	5	3	3	2
.95	456	114	52	30	19	13	10	8	5	4	3	3
.99	607	152	68	39	25	17	13	10	7	5	4	3

The tables in this section list values for the significance criterion (**a**), the numerator degrees of freedom (**u**), the ES to be detected (**f**), and the *desired power*. The required size per sample, **n**, then may be determined. The chief use of these tables is in the planning of experiments where they provide a basis for decisions about sample size requirements.

The 33 tables are laid out generally four to a table number, by **a** levels and successively tabled **u** values within each **a** level. The subtable for the required **a**, **u** combination is found and **f** and desired power are located. The same provisions for **a**, **u**, and **f** are made as for the tables in Section 8.3, as follows:

1. Significance Criterion, **a**. Table sets are provided for nondirectional **a** of .01, .05, and .10, each set made up of tables for varying values of **u**.

2. Numerator Degrees of Freedom, **u**. For each **a** level, tables are provided in succession for the 11 values of **u** = 1 (1) 6 (2) 12, 15, 24. Since the number of means to be compared is **k** = **u** + 1, the tables can be used directly for sets of means numbering **k** = 2 (1) 7 (2) 13, 16, and 25, and for interactions whose **df** equal the above 11 values of **u**. For missing values of **u** (7, 9, 11, etc.), linear interpolation between tables will yield adequate approximations to the desired **n**.

3. Effect Size, **f**. **f** is defined and interpreted for equal **n** in Sections 8.2, and generalized for unequal **n** in Section 8.3.2 and for interactions in Section 8.3.4. As in the power tables, provision is made in the sample size tables for the 12 values: .05 (.05) .40 (.10) .80. Conventional levels have been proposed (Section 8.2.3), as follows: small ES: **f** = .10, medium ES: **f** = .25, and large ES: **f** = .40. (No values of **n** less than 2 are given, since there would then be no within-population variance estimate from the data.)

To find **n** for a value of **f** not tabled, substitute in

$$(8.4.1) \qquad\qquad n = \frac{n_{.05}}{400f^2} + 1,$$

where $n_{.05}$ is the necessary sample size for the given **a**, **u**, and desired power at **f** = .05 (read from the table), and **f** is the nontabled ES. Round to the nearest integer.

4. Desired Power. Provision is made for desired power values of .10 (except at **a** = .10 where it would be meaningless), .50, .70, .80, .90, .95, .99. See 2.4.1 for the rationale for selecting such values for tabling, and particularly for a discussion of the proposal that .80 serve as a convention for desired power in the absence of another basis for a choice.

8.4.1   CASE 0: **k** MEANS WITH EQUAL **n**. The sample size tables were designed for this, the simplest case. Find the subtable for the significance criterion (**a**) and numerator **df** (**k** − 1 = **u**) which obtain and locate **f** and desired power, to determine **n**, the necessary size per each sample mean. For nontabled **f**, use the tables to find $n_{.05}$ and substitute in formula (8.4.1).

Illustrative Examples

8.9   Reconsider the educational experiment on the differential effectiveness of **k** = 4 teaching methods to equal sized samples of **n** = 20 (example 8.1). Using **a** = .05 as the significance criterion, and **f** = .28, it was found that power was approximately .53. Now we recast this as a problem in experimental planning, where we wish to determine the sample size necessary to achieve a specified power value, say .80. Initially, to illustrate the simplicity of the use of the sample size tables for tabled values of **f**, we change his specification of **f** to .25, our operational definition of a medium ES. Summarizing, the conditions for determining **n** for this test are

$$\mathbf{a} = .05, \quad \mathbf{u} = \mathbf{k} - 1 = 3, \quad \mathbf{f} = .25, \quad \text{power} = .80.$$

In the third subtable of Table 8.4.4 (for **a** = .05, **u** = 3) with column **f** = .25, and row power = .80, we find that we need **n** = 45 cases in each of the 4 method groups. Thus, slightly scaling down his ES from .28 to .25, he needs 4(45) = 180 = **N** to have .80 probability of a significant result at **a** = .05.

Since his **f** was originally .28, we illustrate the determination of **n** for this nontabled value, leaving the other specifications unchanged:

$$\mathbf{a} = .05, \quad \mathbf{u} = 3, \quad \mathbf{f} = .28, \quad \text{power} = .80.$$

For nontabled **f**, we use formula (8.4.1). For $n_{.05}$, the sample size needed to detect **f** = .05 for **a** = .05, **u** = 3 with power = .80, we use the same subtable as above, the third subtable of Table 8.4.4 (for **a** = .05, **u** = 3) with column **f** = .05 and row power = .80 and find $n_{.05}$ = 1096. Substituting in formula (8.4.1),

$$\mathbf{n} = \frac{1096}{400(.28^2)} + 1 = \frac{1096}{31.36} + 1 = 35.9.$$

Thus, he would need 36 cases in each of his 4 groups to have power of .80 to detect **f** = .28 at **a** = .05. (This value of **n** is, as it should be, smaller than that which resulted when a smaller **f** of .25 was posited above.)

8.10   We reconsider the social psychiatric research of example 8.2, now as a problem in experimental planning. A pool of suitable in-patients is to be randomly assigned to **k** = 3 equal samples, and each subjected to a different microsocial system. Following this treatment, criterion measures will then be **F**-tested at **a** = .01. Temporarily, we revise the team's two proposed ES measures (the basis for which is described in example 8.2), **f** = .229 and .333, to a range of four tabled values: **f** = .20, .25, .30,. 35. It is desired that power be .90 and we seek the **n** required for each of these specifications, which, in summary, are

$$\mathbf{a} = .01, \qquad \mathbf{u} = \mathbf{k} - 1 = 2, \qquad \mathbf{f} = \begin{cases} .20 \\ .25 \\ .30 \\ .35 \end{cases}, \qquad \text{power} = .90.$$

We use the second subtable of Table 8.4.1 (for **a** = .01, **u** = 2) at row power = .90 and columns **f** = .20, .25, .30, and .35 and find the respective *per sample* **n**'s of 147, 95, 66, and 49. Thus, for these conditions, an **f** of .20 requires three times as large an experiment as an **f** of .35. Note that in terms of proportion of variance, the respective η^2 for these values are .0385 and .1091 (Table 8.2.2).

Having illustrated the direct table look-up afforded by tabled **f** values, we turn to the actual **f** values posited by the two factions on the research team in the original example, .229 and .333. These nontabled values require the use of formula (8.4.1). The specifications are

$$\mathbf{a} = .01, \qquad \mathbf{u} = 2, \qquad \mathbf{f} = \begin{cases} .229 \\ .333 \end{cases}, \qquad \text{power} = .90.$$

For $\mathbf{n}_{.05}$, the sample size needed to detect **f** = .05 for **a** = .01, **u** = 2, with power .90, we use the second subtable of Table 8.4.1 (for **a** = .01, **u** = 2) with column **f** = .05 and row power = .90 and find $\mathbf{n}_{.05}$ = 2325. Substituting it and **f** = .229 in formula (8.4.1),

$$\mathbf{n} = \frac{2325}{400(.229^2)} + 1 = 111.8,$$

and for **f** = .333,

$$\mathbf{n} = \frac{2325}{400(.333^2)} + 1 = 53.8.$$

Thus, if the "weak effect" faction (**f** = .229) is correct, samples of 112 cases are required, while if the "strong effect" faction (**f** = .333) is correct, only 54, less than half that number, are required per sample.

If they compromise by splitting the difference in **n** and use $(111 + 53)/2 =$

82 cases, we can solve formula (8.4.1) for **f**, the "detectable effect size," [3] for given **a**, desired power, and **n**:

$$(8.4.2) \qquad \mathbf{f} = \sqrt{\frac{\mathbf{n}_{.05}}{400(\mathbf{n}-1)}}$$

$$= \sqrt{\frac{2325}{400(81)}} = .268.$$

The interpretation of this result is that for an **F** test at **a** = .01 of three means each based on 82 cases to have power of .90, the population ES must be **f** = .268. Since the relationship involved is not linear, splitting the difference in **n** does not split the difference on **f**. The latter would be **f** = (.229 + .333)/2 = .281. If the latter was the basis for compromise, the experiment would demand, applying formula (8.4.1) to these specifications,

$$\mathbf{n} = \frac{2325}{400(.281^2)} + 1 = 74.6,$$

or 75 cases.

There is yet a third way of splitting the difference, i.e., between the .05 and .10 proportion of variance of criterion accounted for by experimental group membership, η^2. If the compromise is effected on this basis, $\eta^2 =$ (.05 + .10)/2 = .075. Then, from formula (8.2.22),

$$\mathbf{f} = \sqrt{\frac{.075}{1 - .075}} = .285.$$

Substituting this value of **f** with the **n**$_{.05}$ = 2325 for these conditions in formula (8.4.1),

$$\mathbf{n} = \frac{2325}{400(.285^2)} + 1 = 72.6,$$

or 73 cases, which hardly differs from the **n** demanded by averaging the **f**'s (75). This will generally be the case unless the two **f**'s are very widely separated.

8.4.2   CASE 2: **k** MEANS WITH UNEQUAL **n**. Sample size decisions for research planning in Case 2 offer no special problems. One must keep in mind

---

[3] The concept "detectable effect size" transcends its application here. It is useful in *post hoc* power analysis, particularly in the assessment of failures to reject the null hypothesis and in summarizing the results of a series of experiments bearing on the same issue. See Cohen (1965, p. 100).

that with unequal n_i, f is the standard deviation of the p_i-*weighted* standardized means, as described in Section 8.3.2. When the sample size tables are applied with the usual specifications, the n indicated in Case 2 is the *average* sample size of the k samples, i.e., $n = N/k$. Similarly, for nontabled f, the n found from formula (8.4.1) is the average sample size.

The unequal n_i case arises in research planning in various circumstances.

1. In political opinion, market research, or other surveys, where a total natural population is sampled and constitutent populations are of varying frequency, e.g., religious affiliations (as illustrated in Section 8.3.2), socioeconomic categories, etc. (See example 8.11 below.).

2. In experiments where one or more samples of fixed size are to be used, and the size of one or more samples is open to the determination of the experimenter. For example, scheduling problems may dictate that a control sample is to have 50 cases, but the sample sizes of two experimental groups can be determined using considerations of desired power.

3. In some experiments, it may be desired that a reference or control sample have larger n than the other k − 1 samples (Edwards, 1960, p. 152). (See example 8.12 below.)

In each of these circumstances, the average n which is read from the tables [or computed from formula (8.4.1)] is multiplied by k to yield the total N.

Illustrative Examples

8.11 To illustrate Case 1 in surveys of natural populations, return to example 8.3, where a political science class designs an opinion survey of college students on government centralism. A source of variance to be studied is the academic areas of respondents of which there are 6 (= k). The f for the anticipated unequal n_i is posited at .15, and a = .05. Now, instead of treating this as a completed or committed experiment (where total N was set at 300 and power then found to be .48), let us ask what N is required to attain power of .80. The specifications are

$$a = .05, \quad u = k - 1 = 5, \quad f = .15, \quad \text{power} = .80.$$

In the first subtable of Table 8.4.5 (for a = .05, u = 5) at column f = 15 and row power = .80, n = 96. This is the average size necessary for the 6 academic area samples. The quantity we need is the total sample size, N = 6(96) = 576.

Example 8.3 went on to consider the effect on power of a reduction of k from 6 to 3 more broadly defined academic areas. Paralleling this, we determine **N** needed for **k** = 3, keeping the other specifications unchanged:

$$\mathbf{a} = .05, \quad \mathbf{u} = \mathbf{k} - 1 = 2, \quad \mathbf{f} = .15, \quad \text{power} = .80.$$

From the second subtable of Table 8.4.4 (for **a** = .05, **u** = 2) for column **f** = .15, row power = .80, we find **n** = 144, so that **N** = 3(144) = 432. Note that going from 6 to 3 groups results here in a 25% reduction of the **N** demanded (from 576 to 432). Of course, we assumed **f** to remain the same, which would not necessarily be the case.

8.12 A psychophysiologist is planning an experiment in which he will study the effect of two drugs (A and B) on neural regeneration relative to a control (C). He plans that $\mathbf{n_A} = \mathbf{n_B}$ (which we call $\mathbf{n_E}$) but $\mathbf{n_C}$ is to be 40% larger, i.e., $\mathbf{n_C} = 1.4\mathbf{n_E}$. He posits that the three within-population-standardized mean differences will be $(\mathbf{m_A} - \mathbf{m}) = -.5$, $(\mathbf{m_B} - \mathbf{m}) = +.5$, and $(\mathbf{m_C} - \mathbf{m}) = 0$, that **a** = .05, and he wishes power to be .90. To determine the necessary sample size, he must first find the **f** implied by his alternate-hypothetical means. His total sample size is

$$\mathbf{N} = \mathbf{n_E} + \mathbf{n_E} + 1.4\mathbf{n_E} = 3.4\mathbf{n_E},$$

so

$$\mathbf{P_A} = \mathbf{P_B} = \frac{\mathbf{n_E}}{\mathbf{N}} = \frac{\mathbf{n_E}}{3.4\mathbf{n_E}} = .294$$

and

$$\mathbf{P_C} = \frac{1.4\mathbf{n_E}}{\mathbf{N}} = \frac{1.4\mathbf{n_E}}{3.4\mathbf{n_E}} = .412.$$

Combining formulas (8.3.1), (8.3.2), and (8.2.1),[4]

$$(8.4.3) \quad \mathbf{f} = \sqrt{\sum \mathbf{P_i} \left(\frac{\mathbf{m_i} - \mathbf{m}}{\sigma} \right)^2}$$

$$= \sqrt{.294(-.5^2) + .294(+.5^2) + .412(0^2)} = \sqrt{.1470} = .38.$$

Collecting the specifications:

$$\mathbf{a} = .05, \quad \mathbf{u} = \mathbf{k} - 1 = 2, \quad \mathbf{f} = .38, \quad \text{power} = .90.$$

[4] Although the means are equally spaced, we cannot use the **d** procedures of Section 8.2.1, which are predicated on equal **n**.

Since **f** is not tabled, we proceed to find the average **n** by formula (8.4.1), which calls for $n_{.05}$, the **n** required for these specifications of **a, u,** and power when **f** = .05. In the second subtable of Table 8.4.4, **a** = .05 and **u** = 2, row power = .90, and **f** = .05, $n_{.05}$ = 1682. Applying formula (8.4.1),

$$n = \frac{1682}{400(.38^2)} + 1 = 30.1.$$

But this **n** is for Case 1, the *average* **n** per sample. The total **N** = 3(30.1) = 90.3. The sample sizes are unequal portions of this, as specified: The sample size of groups A and B are each .294(90.3) = 27 and of group C is .412(90.3) = 37. Thus, with sample sizes respectively for A, B, and C of 27, 27, and 37, he will have a .90 probability that his **F** test on the 3 sample means will meet the .05 significance criterion, given that **f** = .38.

8.4.3   CASE 2: FIXED MAIN EFFECTS IN FACTORIAL AND COMPLEX DESIGNS. The Case 2 use of the sample size tables covers fixed main effects in factorial and other analysis of variance designs where sources of variance (main effects, interactions) other than the one under scrutiny exist. The chief considerations here, beyond those of Cases 0 and 1, are the (usually slight) overestimation of power and the interpretation of η and η^2 as partial values. The reader is referred to Section 8.3.3 for the details.

The complement of slight overestimation of power in the power tables is slight underestimation of **n** in Tables 8.4. For sample size estimation under typical circumstances, increasing the value of **n** found in the table (or computed from formula (8.4.1)] by one will more than compensate for the underestimation. The reader is referred to Section 8.3.3 for the exceptions (e.g., many cells with **N** not large, unreplicated Latin and Graeco-Latin Square designs).

The procedure for using the tables to determine **n** is essentially the same as for Case 0 (or for unequal **n,** as for Case 1). For tabled **f,** one applies the appropriate subtable for the specified **a** and **u** with **f** and the desired power and finds **n.** For nontabled **f,** one uses the appropriate table to find $n_{.05}$, and substitutes $n_{.05}$ and **f** in formula (8.4.1) to find **n.** In either case, **n** is the number of cases *per relevant mean* to be compared.

Illustrative Examples

8.13   In example 8.5, a factorial design (**I** × **J**) experiment in behavioral genetics was described: genetic strain (**i** = 3) by irradiation condition (**j** = 4), with maze learning as the dependent variable. The experimenter posits f_I (for strains) = .25 and f_J (for conditions) = .40, and sets **a** = .05 as significance criterion. Whereas Example 8.5 was presented as a *post hoc* determination of power for a specified sample size, we here will specify the power desired and determine the necessary sample sizes from the tables. With two or more factors in the same factorial experiment, the sample sizes necessary to meet the two or more sets of specifications will not, in general, agree. To illustrate: Assume that the **F** test for strains (**I**) is to have power specified at .70, so that the complete set of specifications is:

$$\mathbf{a} = .05, \quad \mathbf{u} = \mathbf{i} - 1 = 2, \quad \mathbf{f} = .25, \quad \text{power} = .70.$$

The second subtable of Table 8.4.4 (for **a** = .05, **u** = 2), at column **f** = .25 and row power = .70 gives **n** = 42. However, recall that this is the n_I, the sample size for each of the **i** = 3 strain means; thus the total **N** for the experiment is $\mathbf{i}n_I = 3(42) = 126$. Expressed in terms of sample size per *cell*, since there are **ij** = 12 cells, these specifications call for $\mathbf{n_c} = \mathbf{N}/\mathbf{ij} = 126/12 = 10.5$.

Consider now the effect due to irradiation conditions (**J**). Assume that this is the more important effect under study, and, accordingly, power is specified at .90, so that the conditions are

$$\mathbf{a} = .05, \quad \mathbf{u} = \mathbf{j} - 1 = 3, \quad \mathbf{f} = .40, \quad \text{power} = .90.$$

To find the sample size demanded for the **J** effect, we use the third subtable of Table 8.4.4 (for **a** = .05, **u** = 3) with column **f** = .40 and row power = .90 and find **n** = 23, the sample size per level of **J**, n_J. Since **j** = 4, this calls for a total $\mathbf{N} = \mathbf{j}n_J = 4(23) = 92$, or $\mathbf{n_c} = 92/12 = 7.7$ cases per cell.

A reconciliation of the $\mathbf{n_c}$ values of 10.5 and 7.7 is required. If the experimenter is prepared to settle for less than .70 power for the **I** effect test, he may accept the latter cell size specification, after rounding[5] to 8 per cell. This would yield **N** = 96, and $n_I = 32$, rather than 42 which is required for power = .70. To determine the power of the test on **I** with **n** = 32, enter the *power* Table 8.3.13 (for **a** = .05, **u** = 2) for column **f** = .25 and row **n** = 32, and read out power of .58. Or, at the other extreme, if he wishes that power for the **I** test not fall below .70 and accepts its cell $\mathbf{n_c}$ of 10.5 rounded up to 11, his power for the **J** test will be larger than the .90 specified. The 4 **J** means will each have $n_J = \mathbf{i}\mathbf{n_c} = 3(11) = 33$, and applying the power Table 8.3.14 (for **a** = .05, **u** = 3) with column **f** = .40 and row **n** = 33, we find power of .98.

He need not, of course, be constrained to the choice of the two extremes.

---

[5] Since these **n**'s are, as noted, underestimates, it is prudent to round fractional **n** values upward, whether or not the fraction exceeds .5.

For the specifications given above, reference to power Tables 8.3.13 and 8.3.14 gives power for the two tests for cell n_c varying from 8 to 11:

n_c	N	n_I	n_J	Power$_I$	Power$_J$
8	96	32	24	.58	.91
9	108	36	27	.63	.94
10	120	40	30	.68	.96
11	132	44	33	.75	.98

With such a table he can weigh for increasing **N** the increase in cost (time, resources, etc.) against the resulting power values for the two effects. Note, however, that no attention has been given to the test of the **I** × **J** interaction which is discussed in example 8.15 below.

8.14 Reconsider example 8.6, now as a problem in sample size determination to achieve specified power. The experiment is concerned with the effects on persuasibility in elementary school boys of sex of experimenter (**S**), age of subject (**A**), and instruction conditions (**C**), in respectively a 2 × 3 × 4 (= 24 cells) factorial design. The ES posited for the three effects are $f_S = .10$, $f_A = .25$, and $f_C = .40$ and the tests are to be performed at **a** = .05. Assume initially that power of .80 is desired for each of the three tests, subject to reconsideration and reconciliation of the differing **n**'s which will result.

Considering first the **S** effect, find the **n** demanded by the above specifications, which are

$$\mathbf{a} = .05, \quad \mathbf{u} = 2 - 1 = 1, \quad \mathbf{f} = .10, \quad \text{power} = .80.$$

In the first subtable of Table 8.4.4 for **a** = .05 and **u** = 1, with column **f** = .10, row power = .80, we find **n** = 394 for each of the two means! Thus, total **N** = 788, and sample size per cell 788/24 = 32.8. Although conceivable, it seems unlikely that an experiment of this size would be attempted. Note that **f** = .10 operationally defines a small ES, and we have seen in previous chapters that to have power of .80 to detect small ES requires very large sample sizes. This virtually restricts such attempts to large scale survey research of the type used in political polling and to sociological, market, and economic research.

Consider now the **n** demanded by the specifications for the age effect, which are

$$\mathbf{a} = .05, \quad \mathbf{u} = 3 - 1 = 2, \quad \mathbf{f} = .25, \quad \text{power} = .80.$$

In the second subtable of Table 8.4.4, for $a = .05$ and $u = 2$, with column $f = .25$, and row power $= .80$, we find $n = 52$ for each of the three age groups. Thus $N = 156$ and cell sample size $= 156/24 = 6.5$, or, rounded up, 7. This more modest n demand is primarily due to positing $f = .25$ (medium ES), and only quite secondarily to the increase in u.

Finally, we find n required for the test on C, as specified:

$$a = .05, \quad u = 4 - 1 = 3, \quad f = .40, \quad \text{power} = .80.$$

The third subtable of Table 8.4.4 (for $a = .05$, $u = 3$) at $f = .40$, power $= .80$, yields $n = 18$ for each of the four instruction condition means; thus $N = 72$ and cell sample size of $72/24 = 3$. This relatively small required N is primarily a consequence of positing $f = .40$, a large ES.

The three tests, of varying specifications, have led to varying N's of 788 for S, 156 for A, and 72 for C. The experimenter will probably have to sacrifice a powerful test of the S effect (at least using this design) since, even allowing $a = .10$, he would still require $N = 620$ for power of .80 (Table 8.4.7). Assuming no particular interest in the interactions, his effective choice is between the limits of $N = 72$ and 156, or cell n_c between 3 and 7. He may then set up a table (as in example 8.13) for the power which results for each test from their above specifications and each n_c, using the relevant power tables (8.3.13 and 8.3.14):

n_c	N	n_A	n_C	Power$_A$	Power$_C$
3	72	24	18	.45	.80
4	96	32	24	.58	.91
5	120	40	30	.68	.96
6	144	48	36	.77	.99
7	168	56	42	.83	$>.995$

Consideration of such a table will facilitate the sample size decision but note that it does not include the interactions.

8.4.4 CASE 3: TESTS OF INTERACTION. The reader is referred to Section 8.3.4 for a summary of the nature of interactions in fixed designs and the major considerations involved in their power analysis. We merely note here that just as the power tables understate power, so do the sample size tables in this section overstate the n, but the extent of these inaccuracies is typically slight. A much more serious problem, already stressed in Section 8.3.4, is that with all things equal, for a factorial design of any given N the power of tests on interaction is less, and usually much less, than the power of the tests on main effects. (This is most dramatically illustrated in example 8.7 below.) This is essentially because the effective sample size for an interaction is n_c, the number of observations on which the *cell* mean is based, while for a main effect it is in_c, where i is the number of cells over which data are cumulated for each main effect mean. Analogously, then, in experimental planning to determine the sample size necessary to attain adequate power for detecting interaction, the resulting **N** will typically be very large. Means of coping with this were described in Section 8.3.3.

The tables in this section are used for Case 3 as follows: The appropriate subtable for **a** (significance criterion) and **u** (interaction **df**) is used for **f** (defined and determined as described in Section 8.3.3) and the power desired. The **n** is then the sample size for the relevant cell of the interaction. It can then be multiplied by the number of cells to find **N**, the total sample size for the experiment. If **f** is not tabulated, we take recourse to formula (8.4.1) to find the cell **n**.

Illustrative Example

8.15   We return to example 8.8, which described a learning experiment of the effects of age (**R**) at $r = 2$ levels and contingency of reinforcement (**C**) at $c = 4$ levels on a learning variable. We assume that the $R \times C$ interaction is of primary interest. Although **f** for interaction can be specified by use of the proposed operational definition conventions in the same way as main effects (see Sections 8.3.4 and 8.2.3), in example 8.8, the **f** for the interaction was arrived at by specifying alternate-hypothetical cell means, and equaled .42. We recast the problem into one in which sample size is to be determined, given desired power and the other specifications. We also, initially, assume a *tabulated* **f** value for the interaction, i.e., $f = .40$ (a conventionally "large" effect). We will later use the interaction $f = .42$. We specify that the power desired for the test of the $R \times C$ interaction is .80, and that $a = .05$, as before. Summarizing, the specifications are

$$a = .05, \quad u = (r - 1)(c - 1) = 3, \quad f = .40, \quad \text{power} = .80.$$

In the third subtable of Table 8.4.4 (for $u = 3$, $a = .05$) with $f = .40$ and power $= .80$, we find $n = 18$. This is n_c, the *cell* sample size, and since there are $rc = 8$ cells, $N = 8(18) = 144$ cases required for the experiment to have an *a priori* probability of .80 of detecting an interaction **f** of .40 using $a = .05$ as the significance criterion.

If, instead, we posit the slightly larger $f = .42$ found as described in example 8.8, since this value is not tabled, we proceed by use of formula (8.4.1) to find the cell sample size. For the same specifications for **a** (.05), **u** (3), and power (.80), to find $n_{.05}$ we use the third subtable of Table 8.4.4

($a = .05$, $u = 3$) at row power $= .80$ and column $f = .05$; $n_{.05}$ is found to be 1096. Then, substituting it and $f = .42$ in formula (8.4.1), we find

$$n = \frac{1096}{400(.42^2)} + 1 = 16.5$$

or, rounded down,[6] 16 cases per cell, and therefore $N = 8(16) = 128$. The larger f, .42 rather than .40, results in a smaller N, 128 rather than 144.

If this N is beyond the experiment's resources, he might consider the possibility of setting the significance criterion for the interaction test at $a = .10$ rather than .05 (as discussed in example 8.7). This is, of course, always done *before* the experiment is run. The changed specifications are thus

$$a = .10, \qquad u = 3, \qquad f = .42, \qquad \text{power} = .90.$$

To find $n_{.05}$, using the third subtable of Table 8.4.7 (for $a = .10$, $u = 3$) with power $= .80$ and $f = .05$, yields 883. Substituting this and $f = .42$ in formula (8.4.1), we find

$$n = \frac{883}{400(.42^2)} + 1 = 13.5.$$

Rounding this value down to 13 cases per cell, these specifications, with the less stringent significance criterion for the interaction **F** test, call for a total $N = 8(13) = 104$ cases.

Using a less stringent significance criterion for the interaction test in no way constrains one's freedom in setting the criteria for the main effects, which, here, might well remain at $a = .05$, as posited in example 8.8. It was seen there that with 12 cases per cell, the .05 significance criterion for the f_R and f_C posited (.38 and .52, both relatively large) leads to power in the nineties for both main effect tests.

8.4.5   THE ANALYSIS OF COVARIANCE. As was discussed in the section on the use of the power tables in the analysis of covariance (8.3.5), no special procedural change takes place from analogous analysis of variance designs. What changes is the conception of the dependent variable, which becomes **Y′**, a regression-adjusted or statistically controlled value [defined in formula (8.3.9)], whose use may result in a larger ES than the use of the unadjusted **Y**. Population means, variances, ranges, etc., now merely refer to this adjusted variable in place of the unadjusted variable of the analysis of variance. For more detail, see Section 8.3.5.

---

[6] Since the **n**'s are slight overestimates, one can usefully adopt the practice of rounding fractional **n**'s downward, whether or not the fraction exceeds .5.

Thus, sample size estimation in the analysis of covariance proceeds in exactly the same way as in analogous analysis of variance designs.

8.5 THE USE OF THE TABLES FOR SIGNIFICANCE TESTING

8.5.1 INTRODUCTION. As is the case in most of the chapters in this handbook, provision for facilitating significance testing has been made in the power tables as a convenience to the reader. While power analysis is primarily relevant to experimental planning and has as an important parameter the alternative-hypothetical population ES, once the research data are collected, attention turns to the assessment of the null hypothesis in the light of the data. (See Section 1.5, and for some of the advantages of the corollary approach in **t** tests, Section 2.5.)

As was noted in previous sections, the tabled values when used for Cases 2 and 3 are approximations. Although the approximations are good ones (subject to the specified conditions), in significance testing, the F_c values would be understated in Case 2 and overstated in Case 3. Although the inaccuracies would typically be slight, it generally does not pay to use the tabled values of F_c for significance texting in Cases 2 and 3, since **F** tables are widely available in statistical textbooks and specialized collections (e.g., Owen, 1962). Accordingly, we do not discuss or exemplify the use of the F_c values in the power tables in this handbook for significance testing of fixed main effects or interactions (Cases 2 and 3).

For significance testing, the function of the data of interest to us in the Case 0 and 1 applications of this chapter is the **F** ratio for the relevant null hypothesis which is found in the sample, F_s.

In each power table (8.3) for a given significance criterion **a** and numerator **df**, **u**, the second column contains F_c, the minimum **F** necessary for significance at the **a** level for that **u**. The F_c values vary with **n**, the relevant sample size. Significance testing proceeds by simply comparing the computed F_s with the tabled F_c.

8.5.2 SIGNIFICANCE TESTING IN CASE 0: **k** MEANS WITH EQUAL **n**. Find the power table for the significance criterion (**a**) and numerator **df**, $u = k - 1$, which obtain. Enter with **n**, the size per sample mean, and read out F_c. If the computed F_s equals or exceeds the tabulated F_c, the null hypothesis is rejected.

Illustrative Examples

8.16 Assume that the educational experiment described in 8.1 has been performed: a comparison (at **a** = .05) of the differential effectiveness of

$k = 4$ teaching methods, for each of which there is a random sample of $n = 20$. Whatever the history of the planning of this experiment, including most particularly the anticipated ES ($f = .280$), what is *now* relevant is the **F** value (between groups mean square/within groups mean square) computed from the $4(20) = 80$ achievement scores found in the completed experiment, F_s. Assume F_s is found to equal 2.316. Thus, the specifications for the significance test are

$$a = .05, \quad u = k - 1 = 3, \quad n = 20, \quad F_s = 2.316.$$

To determine the significance status of the results, checking column F_c of Table 8.3.14 ($a = .05$, $u = 3$) for $n = 20$ gives $F_c = 2.725$. Since the computed F_s of 2.316 is smaller than the criterion value, the results are not significant at $a = .05$, i.e., the data do not warrant the conclusion that the population achievement means of the four teaching methods differ.

8.17   In example 8.2, a power analysis of an experiment in social psychiatry was described in which $k = 3$ equal samples of $n = 200$ each were subjected to different microsocial systems. Consider the experiment completed and the data analyzed. In planning the experiment, it was found that for the population ES values which were posited, at $a = .01$, power would be very large. This is, however, not relevant to the significance-testing procedure. Assume that the F_s is found to equal 4.912. What is the status of the null hypotheses on the three population means? The relevant specifications are

$$a = .01, \quad u = k - 1 = 2, \quad n = 200, \quad F_s = 4.912.$$

Table 8.3.2 (for $a = .01$ and $u = 2$) with row $n = 200$ yields $F_c = 4.642$. Since F_s exceeds this value, the null hypothesis is rejected, and it is concluded (at $a = .01$) that the three population means are not all equal. Note that one does *not* conclude that the population ES of the power specifications (in this case there were two values, $\eta^2 = .05$ and $.10$, or $f = .23$ and $.33$) necessarily obtains. In fact, the *sample* η^2 is $uF_s/[uF_s + (u + 1)(n - 1)] = .016$ and the best estimate of the population η^2 is $.013$ $(= \epsilon^2)$. See section 8.2.2 above and Cohen (1965, pp. 101–106 and ref.).

8.5.2   SIGNIFICANCE TESTING IN CASE 1: **k** MEANS WITH UNEQUAL **n**. When the sample **n**'s are not all equal, the significance testing procedure is as in Case 0 except that one enters the table with their arithmetic mean, i.e., **N/k** [formula (8.3.3)]. This will generally not yield a tabled value of **n**, but the **n** scale is such that on the rare occasions when it is necessary, linear interpolation between F_c values it quite adequate.

Illustrative Examples

8.18 Example 8.3 described an opinion poll on government centralism on a college campus in which there would be a comparison among means of **k** = 6 academic area groups of unequal size, with a total sample size of approximately 300. The **F** test is to be performed at **a** = .05. Assume that when the survey is concluded, the actual total **N** = 293, and **F$_s$** = 2.405. Since **N** = 293, the **n** needed for entry is **N**/**k** = 293/6 = 48.8. What is the status of the null hypothesis of equal population means, for these specifications, i.e.,

$$\mathbf{a} = .05, \quad \mathbf{u} = \mathbf{k} - 1 = 5, \quad \mathbf{n} = 48.8, \quad \mathbf{F_s} = 2.405.$$

In Table 8.3.16 (for **a** = .05, **u** = 5) see column **F$_c$**. There is no need for interpolation, since, using the conservative **n** of 48, **F$_c$** = 2.246, which is exceeded by **F$_s$** = 2.405. Therefore, the null hypothesis is rejected, and it can be concluded that the academic area population means on the centralism index are not all equal. (Note again the irrelevance to conclusions about the null hypothesis of the alternate-hypothetical ES of the power analysis described in example 8.3.)

8.19 In example 8.4, samples of varying **n** of psychiatric nurses from **k** = 12 hospitals were to be studied with regard to differences in mean scores on an attitude scale of Social Restrictiveness towards psychiatric patients. The total **N** = 326, so the average **n** per hospital is **N**/**k** = 27.2. The significance criterion is **a** = .05. When the data are analyzed, the **F$_s$** of the test of **H$_0$**: **m$_1$** = **m$_2$** = ... = **m$_{12}$** equals 3.467. The specifications for the significance test, thus, are

$$\mathbf{a} = .05, \quad \mathbf{u} = \mathbf{k} - 1 = 11, \quad \mathbf{n} = 27.2, \quad \mathbf{F_s} = 3.467.$$

There are no tables for **u** = 11. Although we can linearly interpolate between **F$_c$** values for **u** = 10 and **u** = 12 to find **F$_c$** for **u** = 11, it would only be necessary to do so if **F$_s$** fell between these two **F$_c$** values. The **F$_c$** value for the smaller **u** (here 10) will always be larger than that of the larger **u** (here 12). Thus, if **F$_s$** exceeds the **F$_c$** for **u** = 10, it must be significant, and if **F$_s$** is smaller than **F$_c$** for **u** = 12, it must be nonsignificant. Accordingly, we use Table 8.3.19 (for **a** = .05, **u** = 10) with row **n** = 27, and find **F$_c$** = 1.864. Since **F$_s$** = 3.467 is greater than this value, we conclude that the null hypothesis is rejected at **a** = .05. Again we call to the reader's attention that we do *not* conclude that the population ES used in the power analysis of example 8.4 necessarily obtains. That value was **f** = .25, hence (Table 8.2.2) the population η^2 posited was .0588. For the sample, η^2 is .1083 and ϵ^2, the best estimate of the population η^2, is .0771 (Section 8.2.2).

9

Technical Appendix: Computational Procedures

9.1 INTRODUCTION

Since this is a handbook intended for behavioral scientists, the computational procedures used to determine the power and sample size values of the tables were not given in the previous chapters so as not to interrupt the flow of the exposition of concepts and methods of application. Instead, this material is presented here for the interested reader. It may be used for computing power values or sample sizes in circumstances which are not covered by the tables provided.

All computed values were rounded to the *nearest* unit and are accurate within one or at most two units of the tabled value. Various computational checks were used, depending upon the function in question. For all tables, two additional checks were used: a monotonicity check throughout, and a check on consistency between power values and necessary sample size values where the latter fell within the range of the former and were independently determined. This check assures accuracy where it is most critical—when n is small.

Unless otherwise noted, where interpolation was necessary in tables which provided necessary computing values, linear interpolation was used because of the density of the argument relative to the needed accuracy.

9.2 t TEST FOR MEANS

9.2.1 POWER VALUES AND d_c. The approximation given by Dixon and Massey (1957, p. 253) was used for computing the power values in Tables

2.3.1–2.3.6. Expressing it in terms of **d**, solving for z_{1-b}, setting $n_1 = n_2 = n$ and **df** = 2(**n** − 1), gives (using the present notation):

(9.2.1)
$$z_{1-b} = \frac{d(n-1)\sqrt{2n}}{2(n-1) + 1.21(z_{1-a} - 1.06)} - z_{1-a}$$

where z_{1-b} = the percentile of the unit normal curve which gives power,

z_{1-a} = the percentile of the unit normal curve for the significance criterion—for one-tailed tests, $a = a_1$, and for two-tailed tests, $a = a_2/2$,

d = the standardized mean difference [formula (2.2.1)], and

n = the size of each sample.

This approximation was found to be quite accurate over the range of values of the tables when checked against available exact values. After all power values were computed, they were compared for the points made available by the computation of the **n** tables (2.4.1), and the few inconsistencies reconciled with the latter, which is an exact procedure (see Section 9.2.2).

The d_c values of the table, i.e., the sample **d** value necessary for significance, were found from the following relationship:

(9.2.2)
$$\delta = d\sqrt{\frac{n}{2}} = t_{1-a} + t_{1-b},$$

where t_{1-a} and t_{1-b} are percentile points for significance and power on the **t** distribution for **df** = 2(**n** − 1), and δ (delta) is the noncentrality parameter for noncentral **t**. As throughout, **a** in the subscript is a_1 or $a_2/2$. Since the d_c value occurs when power = .50, i.e., when $t_{1-b} = 0$, then

(9.2.3)
$$d_c = t_{1-a}\sqrt{\frac{2}{n}}.$$

The necessary t_{1-a} values were obtained from Owen (1962, Table 2.1).

9.2.3 SAMPLE SIZE VALUES. Owen (1965) provides tables for the noncentrality parameter of the **t** test, δ, as a function of degrees of freedom, **a**, and **b**. With equal sample sizes, each of **n**,

(9.2.4)
$$\delta = d\sqrt{\frac{n}{2}},$$

so that

(9.2.5)
$$n = \frac{2\delta^2}{d^2}.$$

The **df** for trial in Owen's tables was estimated from the power tables, and δ was found and substituted in formula (9.2.5) together with the **d** value for the column being computed in order to find **n**. When 2(**n** − 1) did not agree with the trial entry **df**, the table was reentered with new **df** = 2(**n** − 1), until agreement was found.

Owen's (1965) tables serve for all the **a** values in the subtables of Table 2.4.1 except $a_1 = .10$, and for all the desired power values except .25, $\frac{2}{3}$, .75, and .85. The **n** entries for these cases were found by the following procedure: Formula (9.2.1) was rewritten as

$$(9.2.6) \qquad \frac{z_{1-a} + z_{1-b}}{d} = \frac{(n-1)\sqrt{2n}}{2(n-1) + 1.21(z_{1-a} - 1.06)}.$$

The left-hand side was found for a given table entry, and the integral value of **n** determined which made the right-hand side as nearly equal to it as possible.

9.3 THE SIGNIFICANCE OF A PRODUCT MOMENT r

9.3.1 POWER VALUES AND r_c.

The **t** test for the significance of **r** proceeds from

$$(9.3.1) \qquad t = \frac{r\sqrt{df}}{\sqrt{1 - r^2}}$$

where **r** = the sample **r** and **df** = **n** − 2.

Solving formula (9.3.1) for **r**,

$$(9.3.2) \qquad r = \sqrt{\frac{t^2}{t^2 + df}}.$$

Criterion values for **t** at the requisite values for **a** and **df** = **n** − 2 were found from Owen (1962, Table 2.1) and applied in 9.3.2, yielding the r_c necessary for significance at **a** for the given **df**.

To find the power values, two procedures were used. For **n** = 8 (1) 25, 50, 100, 200, the tables provided by David (1938) were used. These tables give the frequency distribution of sample **r**'s for population **r** = .10 (.10) (.90) for the above **n**. The r_c value for each row of the Tables 3.3.1–3.3.6 was located in the appropriate column in David's tables and the probability integral (**b**, the Type II error rate) found by linear interpolation.[1] The complement of this value is the value entered in the power tables of Chapter 3.

---

[1] Except for **n** = 100, r_p = .40, where an error in printing seems to have occurred in which all values are displaced upward by one interval. For these values the arctanh transformation procedure was used (see below).

For **n** other than the above, power values were found by means of the arctanh **r** function, after several other approximations were checked and found inferior in their agreement with David. Graybill writes that the arctanh transformation "has the remarkable property of approximating the normal distribution even for fairly small **n** [1961, p. 209]." An even better approximation, recommended by Pearson and Hartly (1954, p. 29) was used, as well as their values for the transformation (Table 14):

$$(9.3.3) \qquad \mathbf{z}' = \text{arctanh } \mathbf{r} + \frac{\mathbf{r}}{2(\mathbf{n}-1)}.$$

This transformation was applied to both the ES $= \mathbf{r_p}$ (yielding $\mathbf{z_p}'$) and $\mathbf{r_c}$ (yielding $\mathbf{z_c}'$). Then, for each necessary table value, the percentile value for the unit normal curve which gives power, $\mathbf{z_{1-b}}$, was found from

$$(9.3.4) \qquad \mathbf{z_{1-b}} = (\mathbf{z_p}' - \mathbf{z_c}')\sqrt{\mathbf{n}-3}.$$

The resulting power values were found to agree with ± 1 unit as tabled with those found from David (1938), as described above.

9.3.2 SAMPLE SIZE VALUES. Two procedures were used here. For **n** up to 40 (and where possible up to 60), the already computed power tables were used to find **n** for the given power value (i.e., inversely). Since most of these values were obtained via the David (1938) exact distribution tables, they were both more easily and more accurately determined than by inversion of 9.3.4. The other values were found by substituting $\mathbf{z_{1-a}}/\sqrt{\mathbf{n}-3}$ for $\mathbf{z_c}'$ in formula (9.3.4), and solving for **n**:

$$(9.3.5) \qquad \mathbf{n} = \left(\frac{\mathbf{z_{1-b}} + \mathbf{z_{1-a}}}{\mathbf{z_p}'}\right)^2 + 3,$$

where $\mathbf{z_{1-b}}$ and $\mathbf{z_{1-a}}$ are, as before, the percentile values of the unit normal distribution for desired power and the **a** significance criterion (i.e., **a** in the subscript is $\mathbf{a_1}$ or $\mathbf{a_2}/2$).

9.4 DIFFERENCES BETWEEN CORRELATION COEFFICIENTS

9.4.1 POWER VALUES AND $\mathbf{q_c}$. The significance test of the difference between **r**'s is accomplished via the Fisher **z** transformation, i.e., $\mathbf{z} = \text{arctanh}$ **r**, and the ES is $\mathbf{q} = \mathbf{z_1} - \mathbf{z_2}$. Since the sample **q** is approximately normally distributed, power is given by

$$(9.4.1) \qquad \mathbf{x_{1-b}} = \mathbf{q}\sqrt{\frac{\mathbf{n}-3}{2}} - \mathbf{x_{1-a}},$$

where $\mathbf{x_{1-b}}$ and $\mathbf{x_{1-a}}$ are, respectively, the normal curve percentiles for power and significance criterion (**a** in the subscript is a_1 or $a_2/2$). (**x** is used in place of **z** to denote the normal curve deviate in order to avoid confusion of the latter with the Fisher **r** to **z** transformation.) Owen (1962) was the source of both the **z** transformation (Table 19.2) and normal curve values (Table 1.1).

For the q_c values necessary for significance, which are those for which power is .50, and therefore $x_{.50} = 0$, we substitute $x_{1-b} = 0$ in formula (9.4.1) and solve for q_c:

(9.4.2)
$$q_c = x_{1-a}\sqrt{\frac{2}{n-3}}.$$

9.4.2 SAMPLE SIZE VALUES. The **n** values for Table 4.4.1 were found by solving formula (9.4.1) for **n**:

(9.4.3)
$$n = 2\left(\frac{x_{1-a} + x_{1-b}}{q}\right)^2 + 3,$$

where **n** = the size of each sample yielding an **r**.

9.5 THE TEST THAT A PROPORTION IS .50 AND THE SIGN TEST

9.5.1 POWER VALUES AND **v**. Except for a few values (see below), all the power values of Tables 5.3 were found from the Harvard tables of the cumulative binomial probability distribution (1955). For each value of **n** of our standard set, the appropriate Harvard table for **P** = .50 was entered, and the value of **v** (where $v > n - v$) was found which came nearest to the given **a** value. Both **v**, the frequency needed for significance, and the "nearest" (exact) value of **a** are given in Tables 5.3.1–5.3.6. Then, the distributions for each of our standard values of **P** ($= .50 \pm g$) were entered with **v** to determine the power for each **g**, i.e., the proportion of samples which equal or exceed **v**.

The Harvard tables are unusually comprehensive, giving distributions for 62 values of **P** and 135 values of **n**, but it happens that none are given for **n** = 250, 350, and 450. For these values, power was found by means of the normal approximation:

(9.5.1)
$$z_{1-b} = \frac{nP - v + .5}{\sqrt{nP(1-P)}},$$

where the **v** necessary for significance at **a** ($= a_1$ or $a_2/2$) is

(9.5.2)
$$v = \frac{n + z_{1-a}\sqrt{n} + 1}{2},$$

rounding both **v** and power to the nearest value.

Formulas (9.5.1) and (9.5.2) can be used for nontabled values of **n, a**, and **g**. For **n** > 50, they agree closely with the exact value given by the Harvard tables.

9.5.2 SAMPLE SIZE VALUES. As noted in Section 5.4, **n** values less than or equal to 50 given in Table 5.4.1 are for **a** no greater than and power no less than the value stated for the subtable (rather than nearest values). These **n** values are those obtained from the Harvard tables, which give **n** = 1 (1) 50. For **n** > 50, formula (9.5.2) was substituted in formula (9.5.1) and the latter solved for **n**, giving

$$(9.5.3) \qquad n = \left[\frac{2z_{1-a}\sqrt{P(1-P)} + z_{1-b}}{2P - 1} \right]^2,$$

rounding to the *nearest* value. Formula (9.5.3) may be used to determine values of **n** for values of power, **a**, or **g** not given in Table 8.5.1.

9.6 DIFFERENCES BETWEEN PROPORTIONS

9.6.1 POWER VALUES AND h_c. The significance test of the difference between proportions is accomplished through the use of the arcsin transformation, i.e., $\phi = 2 \arcsin \sqrt{P}$, and the ES is $h = \phi_1 - \phi_2$. Since the sample **h** is approximately normally distributed, power is given by

$$(9.6.1) \qquad z_{1-b} = h\sqrt{\frac{n}{2}} - z_{1-a},$$

the **z** value being the normal curve percentiles for power and **a** level (**a** is a_1 or $a_2/2$).

Owen (1962, Table 9.9) was the source of the ϕ values for Table 6.2.1, and, as throughout, the normal curve values (his Table 1.1).

For h_c, the minimum sample difference in ϕ's necessary for significance, as before, set z_{1-b} equal to zero in (9.6.1), and solve for h_c:

$$(9.6.2) \qquad h_c = z_{1-a}\sqrt{\frac{2}{n}}.$$

9.6.2 SAMPLE SIZE VALUES. The **n** values for Table 6.4.1 were found by solving formula (9.6.1) for **n**:

$$(9.6.3) \qquad n = 2\left(\frac{z_{1-a} + z_{1-b}}{h} \right)^2$$

where **n** = the sample size for each sample.

9.7   CHI-SQUARE TESTS FOR GOODNESS OF FIT AND CONTINGENCY TABLES

The preparation of the tables for this chapter was greatly facilitated by Haynam, Govindarajulu, and Leone's "Tables of the cumulative non-central chi-square distribution" (1962). This definitive set of tables gives power as a function of the noncentrality parameter of noncentral chi square λ (lambda), **a**, and **u** (Haynam *et al.*, 1962, Table I) and λ as a function of **a**, power, and **u** (Haynam *et al.*, 1962, Table II). Many values of the arguments are presented, and it can readily be used to find power (Table I) and sample size (Table II) outside the limits of the tables provided in Chapter 7.

9.7.1 POWER VALUES. The relationship between λ, the noncentrality parameter, and **e**, the ES index, is simply

$$(9.7.1) \qquad\qquad \lambda = \mathbf{e}\mathbf{n},$$

where **n** = the total sample size.

Table I of Haynam *et al.* (1962) was used for **a**, **u**, and λ as found from (9.7.1), and power values were determined. Where interpolation for λ was necessary, it was linear. It is recommended that when power value differences between adjacent **e** values of our Tables 7.3 are large (e.g., greater than .10), and intermediate values of **e** are needed, rather than linearly interpolate between them, it is much preferable and quite simple to work from Table I of Haynam *et al.* (1962).

9.7.2 SAMPLE SIZE VALUES. Table II of Haynam *et al.* (1962) was used for the **n** tables (Tables 7.4.1–7.4.15). The requisite **a**, **u**, and desired power were found and λ was determined. Since, solving formula (9.7.1),

$$(9.7.2) \qquad\qquad \mathbf{n} = \frac{\lambda}{\mathbf{e}},$$

the tabulated λ was divided by the requisite **e**, and the resulting **n** found to the nearest integer. Due to the direct reciprocal relationship between **n** and **e**, formula (7.4.1) quite accurately gives **n** for nontabulated **e**, making unnecessary either interpolation for **e** in Table 7.4, or reference to Haynam *et al.* (1962) for the **a**, **u**, and power entries provided by Table 7.4.

9.8   **F** TEST ON MEANS AND THE ANALYSIS OF VARIANCE AND COVARIANCE

9.8.1 POWER AND $\mathbf{F}_c$ VALUES. The criterion values needed for significance, $\mathbf{F}_c$, were based on the (central) **F** table provided by Owen (1962) in his Table 4.1. It contains as argument all the numerator **df** ($=\mathbf{u}$) needed for our Tables 8.3. For **v** (denominator **df**), which for these tables is $(\mathbf{u} + 1)(\mathbf{n} - 1)$ Owen gives as argument 1 (1) 30, 40, 48, 60, 80, 120, ∞. Interpolation between these values was linear in the reciprocal of the required values.

The basic procedure used for computing the tabled power values was Laubscher's square root normal approximation of noncentral **F** (1960, Formula 6). In the present notation, this is

$$(9.8.1) \qquad z_{1-b} = \frac{\sqrt{2(u+\lambda) - \dfrac{u+2\lambda}{u+\lambda}} - \sqrt{(2v-1)\dfrac{uF_c}{v}}}{\sqrt{\dfrac{uF_c}{v} + \dfrac{u+2\lambda}{u+\lambda}}}$$

where the noncentrality parameter is

$$(9.8.2) \qquad \lambda = f^2 n(u+1),$$

and the denominator **df** is

$$(9.8.3) \qquad v = (u+1)(n-1).$$

The unit normal percentile value for power, z_{1-b}, gave excellent agreement with exact value determinations given in the literature (e.g., Laubscher, 1960; Lehmer, 1944; Tang, 1938) and computed from tables supplied by the National Bureau of Standards (NBS tables, see Section 9.8.2) except when **n** and **f** are small. Therefore, Laubscher's cube root normal approximation of noncentral **F** (1960, Formula 7) was also determined for all power values:

$$(9.8.4) \qquad z_{1-b} = \frac{1 - \dfrac{2(u+2\lambda)}{9(u+\lambda)^2} - \left(1 - \dfrac{2}{9v}\right)\left(\dfrac{uF_c}{u+\lambda}\right)^{1/3}}{\left[\left(\dfrac{2}{9v}\right)\left(\dfrac{uF_c}{u+\lambda}\right)^{2/3} + \dfrac{2(u+2\lambda)}{9(u+\lambda)^2}\right]^{1/2}}.$$

The cube root formula was used as a check and provided most of the power values for **n, f** small except for smoothing and reconciliation at available points with the **n** values computed from the NBS tables which are exact (see the following section).

9.8.2   SAMPLE SIZE VALUES. The sources used for computing the entries of the **n** tables (8.4.1–8.4.9) give ϕ as a function of **a**, power, **u**, and **v**.

$$(9.8.5) \qquad \phi = \frac{\lambda}{\sqrt{u+1}}$$

where λ = the noncentrality parameter of the noncentral **F** distribution. The relationship between **f** and ϕ is simply

$$(9.8.6) \qquad \phi = f\sqrt{n},$$

so that

(9.8.7) $$n = \left(\frac{\phi}{f}\right)^2$$

The sources for the ϕ values were:

1. An unpublished tabular computer print-out furnished by the National Bureau of Standards, "Tables of Power Points of Analysis of Variance Tests" (NBS tables).[2] These tables provide ϕ for varying **u** and **v** at **a** = .01, .05, .10, .20, and power = .10, .50, .90, .95, .99.

2. Lehmer (1944) provides ϕ values for varying **u** and **v** at **a** = .01, .05, and power = .70, .80.

In both sources, the necessary **u** values are tabled, and interpolation for **v** was linear in the reciprocal.

---

[2] In a cover letter accompanying the NBS tables it is stated that partial checking of the computed values revealed no errors exceeding two units in the last (third) decimal place of the ϕ values. The maximum error in **n** when formula (9.8.7) is applied is .0011n, i.e., slightly more than one-tenth of one percent, and therefore quite negligible.

References

Berelson, B., & Steiner, G. A. *Human behavior, an inventory of scientific findings.* New York: Harcourt, Brace & World, 1964.

Blalock, H. M., Jr. *Social statistics.* New York: McGraw-Hill, 1960.

Boneau, C. A. The effects of violations of assumptions underlying the **t** test. *Psychological Bulletin,* 1960, **57,** 49–64.

Boneau, C. A. A comparison of the power of the **U** and **t** tests. *Psychological Review,* 1962, **69,** 246–256.

Campbell, J. D. *Manic-depressive disease.* Philadelphia: Lippincott, 1953.

Cohen, J. The statistical power of abnormal-social psychological research: A review. *Journal of Abnormal and Social Psychology,* 1962, **65,** 145–153.

Cohen, J. Some statistical issues in psychological research. In B. B. Wolman (Ed.), *Handbook of clinical psychology.* New York: McGraw-Hill, 1965. Pp. 95–121.

Cohen, J. Multiple regression as a general data-analytic system. *Psychological Bulletin,* 1968, **70,** 426–443.

Cohen, J., & Struening, E. L. Opinions about mental illness: Mental hospital occupational profiles and profile clusters. *Psychological Reports,* 1963, **12,** 111–124.

Cohen, J., & Struening, E. L. Opinions about mental illness: Hospital social atmospheres and their relevance to effectiveness. *Journal of Consulting Psychology,* 1964, **28,** 291–298.

Cox, D. R. *Planning of experiments.* New York: Wiley, 1958.

Cronbach, L. J. *Essentials of psychological testing.* (2nd ed.) New York: McGraw-Hill, 1960.

Cureton, E. E. On correlation coefficients. *Psychometrika,* 1966, **31,** 605–607.

David, F. N. *Tables of the ordinates and probability integral of the distribution of the correlation coefficient in small samples.* Cambridge: University Press, 1938.

Dixon, W. F., & Massey, F. J., Jr. *Introduction to statistical analysis.* (2nd ed.) New York: McGraw-Hill, 1957.

Edwards, A. L. *Experimental design in psychological research.* (Rev. ed.) New York: Holt, Rinehart, & Winston, 1960.

Fisher, R. A. *The design of experiments.* New York: Hafner, 1949.

Fiske, D. W., & Jones, L. V. Sequential analysis in psychological research. *Psychological Bulletin,* 1954, **51**, 264–275.

Friedman, H. Magnitude of experimental effect and a table for its rapid estimation. *Psychological Bulletin,* 1968, **70**, 245–251.

Getzels, J. W., & Jackson, P. W. *Creativity and intelligence: Explorations with gifted students.* New York: Wiley, 1962.

Ghiselli, E. E. Dr. Ghiselli comments on Dr. Tupes note. *Personnel Psychology,* 1964, **17**, 61–63.

Graybill, F. A. *An introduction to linear statistical models.* Vol. 1. New York: McGraw-Hill, 1961.

Guenther, W. C. *Analysis of variance.* Englewood Cliffs, N.J.: Prentice-Hall, 1964.

Guilford, J. P. *Fundamental statistics in psychology and education.* (4th ed.) New York: McGraw-Hill, 1965.

Harrell, T. W., & Harrell, M. S. Army General Classification Test scores for civilian occupations. *Educational and Psychological Measurement,* 1945, **5**, 229–239.

Harvard University Computation Laboratory. *Tables of the cumulative binomial probability distribution.* Cambridge, Massachusetts: Harvard University Press, 1955.

Haynam, G. E., Govindarajulu, Z., & Leone, F. C. *Tables of the cumulative non-central chi-square distribution.* Cleveland: Case Institute of Technology Statistical Laboratory, 1962. (Case Statistical Laboratory, Publication No. 104.)

Hays, W. L. *Statistics for psychologists.* New York: Holt, Rinehart, & Winston, 1963.

Husén, T. *Psychological twin research.* Uppsala: Almquist & Wiksell, 1959.

Jensen, A. R. Review of the Maudsley Personality Inventory. In O. K. Buros (Ed.), *Sixth mental measurement yearbook.* Highland Park, N.J.: Gryphon, 1965.

Laubscher, N. F. Normalizing the noncentral t and F distributions. *Annals of Mathematical Statistics,* 1960, **31**, 1105–1112.

Lehmer, E. Inverse tables of probabilities of error of the second kind. *Annals of Mathematical Statistics,* 1944, **15**, 388–398.

MacKinnon, W. J. Compact table of twelve probability levels of the symmetric binomial cumulative distribution for sample sizes to 1,000. *Journal of the American Statistical Association,* 1959, **54**, 164–172.

MacKinnon, W. J. Concise table of three-place probabilities of the symmetric binomial cumulative distribution for sample sizes to 100. *Psychological Reports,* 1961, **10**, 291–300.

McNemar, Q. *Psychological statistics.* (3rd ed.) New York: Wiley, 1962.

National Bureau of Standards. *Tables of power points of analysis of variance tests,* 1963. Pre-publication copy, not completely checked.

The New Information Please Almanac for 1966. New York: Simon & Schuster, 1965.

Neyman, J., & Pearson, E. S. On the use and interpretation of certain test criteria for purposes of statistical inference. *Biometrika,* 1928, **20A**, 175–240, 263–294.

Neyman, J., & Pearson, E. S. On the problem of the most efficient tests of statistical hypotheses. *Transactions of the Royal Society of London, Series A,* 1933, **231**, 289–337.

Overall, J. E., & Dalal, S. N. Design of experiments to maximize power relative to cost. *Psychological Bulletin,* 1965, **64**, 339–350.

Owen, D. B. *Handbook of statistical tables.* Reading, Massachusetts: Addison–Wesley, 1962.

Owen, D. B. The power of Student's t-test. *Journal of the American Statistical Association,* 1965, **60**, 320–333.

Pearson, E. S., & Hartley, H. O. *Biometrika tables for statisticians.* Vol. I. Cambridge: University Press, 1964.

Peters, C. C., & VanVoorhis, W. R. *Statistical procedures and their mathematical bases.* New York: McGraw-Hill, 1940.

Scheffé, H. *The analysis of variance.* New York: Wiley, 1959.

Senders, V. L. *Measurement and statistics.* New York: Oxford University Press, 1958.

Siegel, S. *Nonparametric statistics for the behavioral sciences.* New York: McGraw-Hill, 1956.

Stephenson, W. *The study of behavior. Q-technique and its methodology.* Chicago, Illinois: University of Chicago Press, 1953.

Super, D. E. *Appraising vocational fitness.* New York: Harper & Row, 1949.

Tang, P. C. The power function of the analysis of variance tests with tables and illustrations of their use. *Statistical Research Memoirs,* 1938, **2**, 126–149.

Wald, A. *Sequential analysis.* New York: Wiley, 1947.

Walker, H., & Lev, J. *Statistical inference.* New York: Holt, Rinehart & Winston, 1953.

Wechsler, D. *The measurement and appraisal of adult intelligence.* (4th ed.) Baltimore: Williams & Wilkins, 1958.

Winer, B. J. *Statistical principles in experimental design.* New York: McGraw-Hill, 1962.

Index

Numbers in italics refer to the pages on which the complete references are listed.